P9-BJH-466

La Fouly

"Chatting About Mathematics and Life in a
Remote Swiss Alpine Village"

DISCARD

Silviu Guiasu

Department of Mathematics and Statistics
York University
Canada

Advanced Knowledge International 2005

Author

Professor Dr Silviu Guiasu
York University, Toronto
Department of Mathematics and Statistics
York University
4700 Keele Street, Ross Building
Toronto, Ontario M3J 1P3
Canada
Email: guiasus@pascal.math.yorku.ca

Publisher and Distributor

Advanced Knowledge International Pty Ltd
P O Box 228
Magill Adelaide SA 5072
AUSTRALIA
info@innoknowledge.com
http://www.innoknowledge.com

Copyright © Advanced Knowledge International Pty Ltd
2005

All rights reserved. This publication must not be reproduced in any form without the written permission of the publisher.

The Editor and the publisher can not assume any responsibilities related to the consequences of the use of this book.

ISBN 0-9752150-1-9

Printed in Australia

EMS
Lib.
QA
21
G 85
2005

PROLOGUE

Mathematics is a very special science. It is also little understood by the general public. Some people simply hate it. Some think that it is necessary but too abstract and difficult. Some consider mathematics to be useful only as a tool for other sciences and professions. Mathematicians are very often viewed as strange individuals, good at performing fast mental computations. It is a fact, however, that more and more people are using mathematics today or consider that mathematics is an important component of our culture and are willing to learn more about it. They are the potential readers of the following pages.

The main objective of this book is to discuss the content and development of different old and more recent chapters of mathematics and to present some details about the lives of important contributors to the development of mathematics. Without sacrificing rigour, the presentation has adopted an informal, conversational, and free style. It is rather a novel about mathematics and mathematicians.

The author believes that the content of the book will help many people understand that mathematics is a dynamic, vivid science and that the little known and small community of mathematicians has had many remarkable human beings and dramas inside it. The large majority of its pages contain no formulas. Those who really hate technical details, could very well skip them and focus only on the lives of some remarkable mathematicians and on the casual conversation between the two main characters of the book.

Dr. Lakhmi C. Jain, Professor of Knowledge-Based Engineering at the University of South Australia in Adelaide, with his well-known kindness, vision, and open-mindedness, immediately supported the idea of implementing such an ambitious but difficult project. The author is grateful to him and to the Advanced Knowledge International publisher for printing the book so fast and so well.

S.G.

York University, Toronto

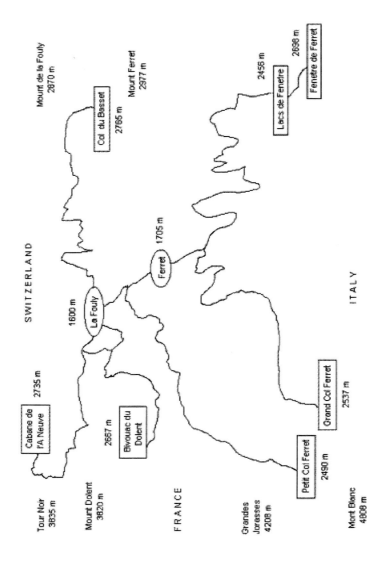

Hiking trails around the village La Fouly on Val Ferret in the Swiss Alps.

Contents

ARRIVAL

MIKE

My name is Mike. It isn't the name written on my official birth certificate but this is how I have been called since I was born and this is how all my friends are calling me. On the first day when I went to school and my official name was called up by my teacher, I didn't react, making a bad impression about my readiness to become a new pupil.

There are months and years in our lives when nothing really happens and, suddenly, a couple of days could be meaningful indeed, significantly changing our path and influencing our main decisions. It did happen to me one year after my high school graduation. I was 19 years old back then, confused and quite uncertain about what to do with my life. I had obtained very good results in school, without working too hard but, at the end of it, I didn't know what way to go and I decided to take one year off and make some money. For an entire year I worked in a Toronto restaurant, located in an area frequented mainly by business people, and I have to admit that, at the end of this period, my savings bank account didn't look bad at all for my standards. I spent almost nothing for food, and the rent for my modest room located in the basement of an old house was much lower than what some of my friends used to pay for similar rooms elsewhere in the city.

Sentimentally, I was involved with Linda and I focused on her all the pure romanticism only a teenager is capable of giving and experiencing. I liked everything about her and I was deeply happy just to see her, to smell her, to touch her, to talk to her, to listen to her, and spend some time with her. Having saved some money, I decided to take a trip to Europe during the summer time and Linda was excited about it. This would have been something new for both of us. Enthusiastically, we took a detailed map of Europe and we picked up Switzerland as our destination. Knowing some French, but no German or Italian, we decided to go somewhere in the canton Valais and we picked up the village La Fouly simply because it is located just in the mountains and its name is close to 'la folie'. In fact, that was meant to be our crazy summer.

Unfortunately, things didn't go the way they were supposed to. I don't want to talk about the details that are still painful for me. To make the long story short, Linda changed her mind and ultimately preferred to accompany a former boyfriend of hers, who had just bought a new fancy car, on a trip to Western Canada. My problem was that I didn't even know how to drive, and having no car seems to be a terrible handicap in dealing with people from my generation. My first reaction was to cancel the trip to Europe altogether but, in a moment of revolt against this world and fate in general, I decided, however, to go on with the initial plan and make it a soul searching voyage in the Swiss Alps.

A blue 747 Boeing jumbo jet plane of the KLM Dutch company took me from Toronto to Amsterdam in a little more than seven hours. Fortunately, the flight was uneventful, except that the plane was full and the members of a group of children, probably belonging to an organized trip, made a lot of noise, throwing the little white cushions at each other, some of them landing on my head, without any attempt from the part of the smiling flight attendants to temper them. The adults have no right these days to say something to the juniors of the new generation even when they behave like little devils. Luckily, they slowed down when the lights went out and the movie started.

It was early in the morning when the plane arrived at the big and modern Schiphol Airport in Amsterdam. I had one day and one night ahead of me to have a glimpse of the city. The airport is connected to the center of the city by a rapid train and the ride takes about 25 minutes. I arrived at the Central Station of the old Amsterdam very early in the morning. Not many people were around. A young man, looking confused and under time pressure, asked me directions in French about how to go to Utrecht by train. I put my knapsack and handbag down and I made one step closer to the rail timetable, giving him some explanations about the next available trains from Amsterdam to Utrecht, and he ran fast to catch the first one. In the meantime, like magic, my handbag containing my passport, the plane tickets, my only credit card, and more than half of my cash money disappeared, being artfully taken away perhaps by an accomplice of his, hidden behind one of the many thick columns of the Central Station. I couldn't do anything about and it took me a little time until I realized that I was really in a big trouble. After loosing Linda, now having been robbed in Amsterdam! A real nightmare.

What followed showed me that the evil is not omnipresent and that there are many good people around who are more than willing to help somebody in distress. And I did look distressed for sure. A kind policeman filled in an official statement about what happened with me and gave me indications about what to do. The KLM agency in Amsterdam issued new plane tickets, a new credit card was sent to me in 24 hours, and still having some cash money left in one of my pockets, I went to the Canadian consulate in Hague where I got a new passport on the next day. After a night spent in a hostel in Hague, where they allowed me to sleep free of charge, I returned to Amsterdam. With all my problems solved in such a record time, I became alive again. Suddenly, Amsterdam looked beautiful, with its maze of canals, hundreds of bridges, thousands of boats, ten thousands of rusty bicycles, a lot of old and coloured houses, friendly people, excellent pastries, tasty beer, and a catchy 'joie de vivre'.

GENEVA

The flight from Amsterdam to Geneva took about one hour and fifteen minutes. The landing was a little bumpy but nothing to be worried about. From the Geneva airport, relatively small but quite fancy, a direct train brought me to the Central Station, Gare de Cornavin, in Geneva city, in not more than 10 minutes.

It is said that Geneva is the smallest important city in Europe. Practically, its central part may be covered just by walking, which I really liked, because I lose my sense of orientation every time I take a bus and I feel vulnerable, physically and mainly financially, in a taxi cab. Although it has only about 400000 inhabitants, including its suburbs, Geneva appeared to me as being a very noisy city, at least in summer. As my modest hotel had no air conditioning, I had to leave the window open during the night but I could hardly sleep due to the permanent noise made by cars, motorcycles, ambulances, police cruisers, and peo-

ple talking loudly. Perhaps there are more quiet residence areas in the
city. Otherwise, I doubt that all those people working for some 200
international organizations housed in Geneva, including the Office of
the United Nations, and deprived of a normal night sleep, could make
intelligent decisions during the day.

The nicest part of the city is just around the western end of Lake
Léman, or Lake Geneva as it is also called, the largest of the lakes in the
Alps, crossed by the rapid and rather dark green waters of the big river
Rhône, continuing its flowing into France. Walking along the shore of
the lake I saw people of different nationalities and races, speaking all
sorts of different languages, but it was difficult to differentiate between
permanent residents, temporary residents, and tourists.

During the two days spent in Geneva, I tried to see as much as
possible and I even had enough energy and enthusiasm to scratch in
a small notebook some technical details worth to remember. Unfortunately, some pages from the beginning of the notebook have been
somehow lost. They contained precise data on the length, width, and
depth of Lake Léman, and about when exactly and how the speed of
sound in water had been measured there long ago. Therefore, I can
only say that the lake is very long (more than 70 kilometers), very wide
(the maximum width of approximately 14 kilometers) and very deep
(the maximum depth of approximately 300 meters) but these numbers
should be taken only as very rough approximations because my memory is not very good as far as numbers are concerned. I remember,
however, that the mighty vertical jet of water, or 'Jet d'Eau' how it is
called, the landmark of Geneva, located on the lake, just in front of the
little island Jean Jacques Rousseau, soars up to a height of 145 meters.

Fortunately, other pages of my notebook have remained intact and,
looking into them, I can remember other things seen there. On the
highest point of the old town there is the Cathedral of Saint-Pierre,
monumental as building but very austere inside, practically without
other decorations than those provided by lovely stained-glass windows
and a couple of grey statues. It has, however, an adjacent small chapel
which is a real jewel. In a coin of the Cathedral, I saw a poster with
important historical dates, stating that in Geneva, the city of refuge,
school education had become obligatory in 1536. In fact, in the 16th
century, when the works of Luther reached the city, in 1536 the Ref-

ormation and the Republic were proclaimed and Calvin was called to Geneva to build a 'Protestant Rome'. The University of Geneva was created in 1559, and the people of Geneva achieved political and religious independence in 1602, by preventing the Duc of Savoie from invading and annexing the city. Even in our times, December is a special month of celebrations and 17th century costume parades commemorate the battle which took place on the 11th of December 1602 between the Savoyards and the inhabitants of Geneva. Soon, the city of Calvin became the center of the Reformation. In the park facing the University of Geneva, called 'Parc des Bastions', there is the impressive Geneva's monument to the Reformation, containing the huge statues of the main reformists, in the following order, from right to left, facing them: István Bocskay, Thomas Cromwell, Roger Williams, John Knox, Théodore de Bèze, Jean Calvin, Guillaume Farel, Gaspard de Coligny, Guillaume le Taciturn, and Fred Guillaume le Grand Électeur, the middle four being the most important ones and much bigger dimensionally. Not far from that place, I noticed the bust of Henry Durant, the founder of the Red Cross. Only then I realized that the red cross on white background is just the complement of the Swiss flag which shows a white cross on red background.

On a wall of the University, I read the following text in French: 'We are told to stop AIDS instead of trying to stop the exhaust fumes made by cars. But we are dying from the exhaust fumes and not from AIDS.' The irony is that just on the day when I read this, and just from the park of the University, the International Rally of the Alps got its start. Created in 1932 by the Automobile Club of Marseille-Provence, the annual rally-marathon brings together old cars, at the beginning of July, in a six-day friendly competition. The departure of the numbered old cars is from the Reformation Wall of 'Parc des Bastions', going through Switzerland, Germany, and Italy, with consecutive overnight stops in the localities: Bürgenstock, Ischgl, Garmisch-Partenkirchen, Cortina d'Ampezzo, Madonna di Campiglio, and the finish in St.-Moritz. Among the 80 cars in competition, I couldn't detect two identical ones. According to the coloured catalogue, distributed free of charge, some of the cars, still in excellent technical shape, were as old as 1921, 1927, or 1929. The youngest one was 42 years old. Each car had a driver and an assistant passenger, generally the wife, husband, friend, or child of the driver. Many cars in the competition had no cover, exposing their occupants to the capricious Alpine weather. During more than two hours, it was really interesting to watch the departure of the cars, one-by-one, in a competition against time, accompanied by the ovations of the bystanders and the sounds of a Dixieland jazz band. I am sure that the inscription from the wall of the University about the exhaust fumes didn't refer specifically to the old cars of the nostalgic International Rally of the Alps, but I am also sure that the Rally itself didn't contribute to the improvement of the air quality in Geneva on that particular day.

The small hotel I stayed at was very modest, in an old building subject to a drastic process of consolidation and renovation, still too expensive for my expectations, but very clean and with a generous buffet breakfast included in the price of the room. For the other meal of the day, I bought something from a supermarket close at hand or I went to Pizza Hut in evening, which I really enjoyed more than ever before.

I took advantage of the 'admission free' days and I visited some museums. As it always happens, I saw many interesting things but now I can remember very few of them, which is quite depressing. From the Museum of Natural Sciences, I remember only the large fossils, the regional fauna, a live tortoise with two heads, a film with what happens inside a bird nest during the spring time, and a movie about two major land slips and rock falls that had happened in the Tätsch region, and what measures have been taken in order to protect the barrage at the Lake Viège and the security of the village Randa from a future similar catastrophe in that region.

The Art and History Museum was less tiring and quite pleasant to visit. I enjoyed the collection of weapons, some of the Greek and Roman art treasures, and a fine picture gallery. Each major French impressionist had one or two paintings displayed in a relatively small room. The big frames were reserved, however, for the portraits of representatives of the old local nobility, with or without horses to ride on. The most entertaining part was in the room devoted to the modern art. I remember a real car compressed into a compact rectangular bloc of metal, a vivid display of the real content of a table at the end of a lavish rustic meal, including the residues from dirty dishes, a fragment from a real Irish cobble stoned street, and a functioning seven-meter diabolic machine, containing a lot of wheels, transmission belts, and electronic circuits, at the end of which a simple brush was shining a banal shoe.

The Museum of the History of Science is very small but well located in the middle of one of the beautiful parks on the shore of Lake Léman. It contains mainly fine instruments, invented or made by local people along the years, with emphasis on the legendary Swiss precision and accuracy in designing delicate mechanisms.

After the unfortunate experience in Amsterdam, I became reluctant to talk to anybody. But I looked at people and I walked and walked, all day long. I spent some time looking at the tiny Russian Orthodox Church with nine golden domes like in fairy tales, at the Brunswick Monument built for Duke Karl II of Brunswick who, for reasons unknown to me, left his money to the city of Geneva, at the delicate statue of the Empress Elizabeth of Austria, assassinated there by an anarchist at the end of the 19th century, and at the original flower clock which did function according to the high Swiss watch making standards.

The best time I had was when I walked along the shore of the lake Léman, as far as I could, watching hundreds of little boats and dignified white swans floating on the water of the lake. I was even lucky enough to benefit of a clear weather and see, far away, looking to the south, the snowy vague contour of the Mont Blanc (4807 meters), the highest pick in the Alps, sitting there like a sleeping giant.

As a lot of international organizations have been based in Geneva, along the lake, I saw the Palace of the United Nations and the Wilson Palace, in which the old League of Nations met between 1925 and 1936. Finally, in the evening of 13th July, on the border of Lake Léman, a Grand Ball was organized, open to anybody. Not many people dared to dance, however, and more preferred just to sit and sip from a glass of beer. I enjoyed the old French style tunes and canzonets played by an old fashioned orchestra, where the accordion was the main instrument, and I spent almost an hour listening to the music and looking at the water of the lake while the dark of the night settled in. But, as Linda sneaked again into my thoughts, I left.

LA FOULY

Time has come to speed up the move towards the final destination of my trip. On a sunny Monday, early in the morning, I took a train from Geneva to Martigny. It is said that the trains in Switzerland function like a perfect Swiss clock. It seems to be so, indeed. They leave on time, they arrive on time, and, as far as I could see, there are always empty seats. The only problem is that they take very short stops in stations and you have to be very quick in getting on or off. The short ride was quite pleasant. For about one hour, the railroad followed the north side of the Lake Geneva, passing through many narrow towns like Lausanne, Vevey, and Montreux. On the right side, the long lake and, on the left side, high hills with vineyards. Close to Montreux, which by the way is well-known for the jazz festivals organized there every summer, I saw the small but romantic Chillon Castle, built on the lake, which is said to have inspired Mary Shelley when she wrote her horror novel Frankenstein. After Montreux, the lake remained behind and the mountains showed up, taller to the south side. Half an hour later, the train arrived in Martigny, a small town, with a little castle, like a fortress, on a hill and an 'amphithéâtre gallo-romain' as landmarks visible from the train. Martigny is important because you can take there narrow mountain trains to go either to Chamonix, at the base of Mont Blanc in France, or to the picturesque valleys Val d'Entremont and Val Ferret in the Swiss canton of Valais.

In Martigny, I had very little time to look around because the narrow but very modern and comfortable two-coach St.-Bernard Express train to Orsières was already waiting to depart. I do regret that I had no time to take a picture of the electric train on narrow rails having a huge St.-Bernard dog, with a small barrel with cognac hanging around his neck, drawn on the exterior of each coach, on a vividly coloured background. There were very few passengers on the train and no time to ask questions. The train started climbing slowly but firmly along a fast torrent coming from the mountains. There is one railroad from Martigny to Sembrancher, which is an essential ramification point. People who want to go to Le Châble, from where they can access Val de Bagnes, and go by bus either to Fionnay and Mauvoisin (2100 meters), or to the fancy resort Verbier, have to switch to another St.-Bernard express train waiting there. Alternatively, some trains from Martigny go directly to Le Châble, in which case people who want to go to Orsières and eventually access by bus either Val Ferret up to Praz-de-Fort, La Fouly, and Ferret, or Val d'Entremont up to Liddes and Bourg-St.-Pierre, or the elegant resort Champex-Lac, have to switch trains in Sembrancher. All in all, on a beautiful sunny and fresh day, the trip from Martigny to Orsières lasted only about 25 minutes.

Orsières is neither a town nor a village. Something in between or rather a collection of several villages making up what is called in the region as a 'bourg'. Perhaps, long ago, there were bears around because its name resembles the equivalent French word 'ours'. But this is only my own speculation. Anyway, in Orsières I had to wait half an hour before taking the St.-Bernard Express bus to La Fouly. There are eight buses from Orsières Gare to La Fouly, between 6:52 and 18:10, and from La Fouly to Orsières Gare, between 7:23 and 18:44. The one-way trip lasts only about 25 minutes. The bus station was just at the train station. Orsières seemed unusually quiet, with almost nobody around. Close by was a bakery and I bought a fresh little bread, just taken from the oven, having a divine flavour. Waiting for the bus to come, I enjoyed my bread and looked at the wooden poster from the station containing some details about Orsières. What I remember is only the fact that, long ago, Val Ferret was used by the pilgrims from the Northern Europe for crossing the Alps on their way to Rome and other religious sites. In 972, l'abbé de Cluny, Saint Mayeul, on his way back from Italy, was captured, together with his escort, by brigands in Orsières, and later freed after a huge ransom was paid. But nobody kidnapped me and I boarded the small but coquet bus with only four other passengers. The narrow but well-paved road mounted to south, or to be more precise, to south-south-west, in a smooth serpentine on Val Ferret, along the torrent La Drance de Ferret, with taller and taller mountains rising up on both sides of the valley. Passing through the village Praz-de-Fort, after about 25 minutes, the bus stopped in front of the post office of the village La Fouly, where I was the only passenger getting off, whereas the bus continued its way, for a couple of more minutes, until reaching its final destination in the hamlet Ferret, at the end of the valley with the same name.

The first impression was stunning. The mountains were very close on both sides of the valley. The western range looked high, rocky, rugged, and snowy. Wooden houses, with overwhelmingly red flowers at the windows, were scattered on the much milder and green eastern side of the valley. Facing the post office, on the other side of the narrow main road, was Edelweiss, a three-star hotel, built in the style of a beautiful alpine lodge, having as background a huge glacier hanging from a range of spikes making the transition between two impressive white peaks.

As nobody was around, I entered the hotel and I asked a very young waitress about the location of the camping site. Following her instructions, it was very easy to reach it. I went south, along the road, until the end of the village, which took only five minutes, I turned right, and crossing a bridge over a torrent, I was just in the middle of the 'Camping Des Glaciers'. I couldn't imagine a better place for a camping. A large meadow, a little inclined, mounting towards west with a smooth slope, among big trees and bushes, facing the steep glacier from which two streams were rapidly flowing down to join La Drance de Ferret.

In a coin of the camping, I found a small building containing an office, showers, and a garbage room. In front of it was a board with different announcements. I paid the camping tax for a week and I looked for a proper place to install my small compact tent for two people. Around, there were all sorts of large, family tents and many cars, scattered on a large area, some on the open meadow, some under tall fir trees, and some between bushes, but all obviously trying to have some kind of privacy. Looking around, I couldn't detect two identical tents and I was proud that my own proved to be unique as far as I could see. Installing the tent was quite pleasant and it didn't take me much time to do it. The place chosen by me wasn't far from one of the streams coming down from the glacier, on the flat top of a hillock. The closest tent was about 15 meters away from mine and belonged to a family of four that seemed to be rather of a relatively quiet type.

Once installed, I prepared a quick early lunch consisting of a soup, four slices of Hungarian winter salami, orange juice, two biscuits, and an apple. After cleaning around, I changed my clothes, put on my mountain boots, closed the tent, and took my little knapsack containing a bottle of drinking water, some dark chocolate, an electric flashlight, and a waterproof vest, deciding to move around for getting to know something about the close surroundings.

Getting out of the camping area, I went south, along a narrow valley that seemed to be quite deserted. On the right side of it, as I advanced towards south, I was impressed by a kilometer long, and about 80 meters tall, perfectly vertical cut in the bordering mountain, like having the rock freshly sliced by some powerful giant. Above the long cut was a very steep green portion with the same kind of rocks as those from the bottom of the valley, and above the green portion appeared visible the menacing margins of a new glacier that couldn't be seen from the village or from the camping. The valley was full of boulders and the unmarked path was interrupted by two skew moraines still easy to climb. On the left side, a rapid stream was running down towards La Fouly, now left behind. After passing the second moraine, it became clear that the rapid stream came from the big glacier above the long vertical cut, disappearing inside a 20 meters long chimney, dug by the water in the hard rock of the mountain, and reappearing, a little down, at the end of the chimney, as a beautiful cascade, about 30 meters long, from which the waters of the generated stream were busy going down between the big boulders, to join the torrent Drance de Ferret in the village La Fouly.

JOHN

I like cascades, but who doesn't? They have something monumental in them. I went closer to this one, looked up, and listened to the noise made by the falling mass of water. I could feel a cool air and drops of cold water sprayed on my chicks and hands, coming from the falling water. And suddenly, on the other side of the stream, I saw an older man standing, like frozen, on a big rock and staring at the running water of the stream. Slender, tall, with long grey hair and trimmed beard, he wore a Gore-Tex green equipment, consisting of a short coat and waterproof pants, and had two red mountain sticks made from light metal in his hands. Around his neck he had a black string holding a pair of sunglasses, hanging on his chest, and a white string holding an outdoor hat of the same colour, like those worn by explorers in Sahara desert but with wider margins, hanging on his back, ready to be used if needed. He was the first human being met during my 30-minute trip since I have left the village, slowly mounting along this isolated valley. I waved my hand. As waken from his inner thoughts, he looked at me, waved back, and, after a couple of minutes, jumping from boulder to boulder, he crossed the torrent, with an unusual ease for his age, joining me at the base of the cascade.

 –"Hello, how are you? It is very relaxing, at least for me, to watch a water stream running fast. It brings motion in a static environment. I could stay and watch it for hours. It changes all the time still remaining the same. Looking at the red maple leaf stuck to your knapsack, you must be a Canadian. Are you? My name is John. I spent two full years in Canada and I had a good time there. How are you and how have you decided to come in such a remote place?"

This was John and this was his direct, friendly way of talking. The difference in age just disappeared. He treated me like being his equal and I felt good about this. What impressed me most, except his way of talking, were his eyes: deep, warm, and with a kind of sadness in them. I introduced myself and I explained the reasons and the events that brought me to La Fouly. Then, I asked him about his own reasons for coming here.

 –"Well, it's a long story. In fact, I am here now for the seventh time. I always came with my wife but this time she couldn't come. Something came up in the last moment and she couldn't make the trip. In fact she introduced me to the mountains, or the mountains to me, how you want to take it, long, very long ago, when we were only students. She likes the mountains and, every time when we end a vacation, she is very very depressed."

 –"It seems that you miss her this time."

 –"As a matter-of-fact, I do. Alone, I am tempted to be lazy, lingering around, as I am doing today. She always introduced some kind of discipline and didn't allow a good day, like the one we are having today, to be wasted without hiking somewhere. This is a good thinking because in the mountains the weather could change rapidly and we can do nothing about. Every good day must be taken as a gift from God, or Nature, no matter how you like to put it."

–"I came here by pure chance. But how did you discover this place? Or, to state it differently, why do you come so often just to this particular village? Looking on the map, Switzerland has so many mountains to choose from. In my case, it just happened due to the funny name of the village. But it seems that the choice looks promising."

–"In fact, we spent sixteen summer vacations in Switzerland. First time, we bought a Swiss pass for foreigners, allowing us to take any train, boat, or bus, in any number, on any day of an interval of fifteen consecutive days. We kept Zürich as our fixed point, spending the nights in a hotel there, and every day, without any luggage, we went somewhere, to different destinations, spent there a couple of good hours, looking around and walking as much as we could, returning to Zürich at the end of the day. That was an excellent opportunity to cover the country quite well. It was tiring to spend so much time on so many trains but we could locate a lot of nice places, worth of coming to for longer stays in future trips. We were mainly interested in going to the end of remote valleys but we also visited briefly important cities and towns like Geneva, Bern, Fribourg, Neuchâtel, Lucerne, and Lugano. That vacation devoted to a thorough, global exploration of Switzerland paid off. For a couple of good years we kept going in two different places, spending one week in each and hiking around. We quickly learned that the best solution, for us at least, was to choose a village, at the end of a valley, and therefore the closest to the mountains, as fixed point. There is always a good hotel in any such village where you can stay and where you get a clean, quiet room, an indispensable shower, an excellent breakfast, and a copious dinner. This is the so called half-boarding or demi-pension kind of hotel reservation we always made, and which is what the hotels seem to prefer. Remarkably enough, except the incomparable scenery, the hotels in such villages offer much more and cost much less than the similar hotels in big cities like Zürich, Geneva, or Bern.

Anyway, from such a remote village, there are generally about five main hiking trails to try. Counting on five good or only acceptable days out of seven, the respective trails could be normally covered. Weather permitting, after a healthy buffet breakfast, we started our daily hiking around 8:30 in the morning, with very light knapsacks, taking for lunch only water or fruit juice, small breads, two small cheese triangles for each of us, and a couple of simple biscuits. A village at the end of such a valley is already located at a relatively high altitude, somewhere between 1600 and 2000 meters. Therefore, during the daily hiking, it is possible to climb without many problems, depending of course on the level of difficulty of the respective trail, up to about 2600 meters, and sometimes even higher. The trails in the Swiss Alps, accessible from such a last village on a mounting valley, follow a relatively common pattern. First, you go up, continuously, until you reach the end of the trail, which could be a glacier, a saddle point, a smaller peak, a hut, a cabin, or a refuge, generally in a beautiful setting. There you take a break and have a modest lunch. Afterwards, you descend, also continuously, more often than not, following the same path. Obviously, you cannot reach the top of the big, snowy picks. Some daredevils, well equipped, climb some abrupt rocky walls or glaciers as well, but I am not one of them. Therefore, I am talking about regular hikers. Whereas some famous peaks in the Alps, like Mont Blanc, about 4810 meters tall, in France, not far from here, or Matterhorn, 4478 meters high, also in the canton Valais, have been conquered by many mountaineers along the years, the first time in 1786 and 1865, respectively, it is amazing to think, however, that there are tall but less famous peaks where nobody ever put his feet on.

But, going back to what can be done from a a remote village at the end of a mounting valley, there are about five good hiking paths, generally going up to a hut or a refuge, at the border of a glacier. Some of these paths are shorter or easier and some are longer or more difficult. Often, a hiking trail could be divided into three parts. The first part is easy, often accessible even to cars, and leads to some kind of restaurant. The second part is only for people but the path is relatively wide and goes to a spacious lodge, or cabane in French, in a nice location, often near a lake or a stream. Here you can still find food or even spend the night. The third part is generally arduous, with a narrow path having sometimes chains or cables to make climbing and descending safer in more exposed portions, and ends at a refuge or hut belonging to the

Swiss Alpine Club, abbreviated on maps as SAC hut, located at the end or at the margin of a glacier. The final hut, refuge, or cabin, may be used only as an ultimate shelter, having few facilities, if any. Normally, the climbing ends there. At least for me.

More adventurous and experienced people, well equipped, continue the trip, crossing glaciers and passing on a different side of the mountain. I prefer to descend from the final hut along the same path I used to climb on, maybe with some minor deviations, because, sometimes, from up there, it is easier to see some other variants of going downhill. As a matter-of-fact, for myself, I always divide the climbing part of the daily hiking trip in four parts and every time when I descend, I am amazed by how much I was able to climb on the way up.

Therefore, as I said before, counting on five good days out of seven, as far as the weather is concerned, the program of each day follows the same pattern: A good breakfast in the morning, then going up somewhere, according to the choice made on the previous evening, taking a very light knapsack with water or soft drinks and very little food, a short stop at the end of the climbing, the descent, a shower at the hotel, a copious dinner at the restaurant of the hotel, a short walk in the dark after dinner, plans for the next day, followed by a deep sleep."

–"Not bad at all. Are you not afraid of possible dangers, like falling, meeting wild animals, or getting lost?"

–"If the weather is good and you are cautious, closely following the path, there are no real dangers. No animal here attacks hikers. There are no bears and no wolves. Or, it is better to say that there were no wolves around for a very long period of time. Recently, there have been some rumours going on about some kind of 'beast', resembling a huge wolf, who has made visible himself in the region, attacking and killing sheep, even 25 during one single night. I don't know whether or not this story is true. What I know is that lately you can see dogs guarding sheep and cows up in the mountains. No such dogs could be seen before. Anyway, it is not like in the Canadian Rocky Mountains where big animals are not afraid of humans and some of them, like bears or even elks, could be aggressive and attack people, especially if they are provoked. By the way, not far from Jasper, in Alberta, for the first time in my life, I saw a big bear in wilderness, at a very close distance. Fortunately, he or she was busy looking for something under a fallen tree and didn't pay any attention to us. That was really scary."

– "I believe you. In Canada we have plenty of animals everywhere. Not long ago, when I was invited for dinner to the cottage of one of my friends, before living, the host went outside ahead of us, with a big stick in his hand, to check whether there was no black bear around the house. According to him, some bears roamed around every night in summer. Even in Toronto, the raccoons are frequent visitors. I have a very special relationship with a beautiful red little squirrel who comes everyday, even several times on the same day, to take nuts from me. I am not sure that I do the right thing, because feeding wild animals is not always a good idea. Anyway, I offer the squirrel five regular nuts and one big Brazilian nut. Without any exception, the squirrel always chooses the big one first and hides it somewhere in a big pine tree. Are there animals in European mountains?"

– "Yes, there are bears and wolves, but I never saw any during my walking and hiking trips in the mountains. They sometimes attack sheep, cows, or horses, mainly in the mountains. Packs of wolves could be dangerous for people during the winter time. But I don't ski and I go in the mountains only in summer. In some countries the mountains are not very high, they don't exceed 2500 meters, and generally are not covered by snow in summer. They are, however, beautiful. There are rocks, lakes, caves, many climbing paths of different degrees of difficulty, plenty of forests, but, unfortunately, not enough cottages, lodges, and refuges. In many such places you can have the satisfaction of reaching the top of a mountain. This is not possible in Switzerland, where the glaciers, the snow, and the high altitude prevent you from reaching the summit. I was surprised also to see that the paths are better marked in Carpathian mountains, for instance, with different geometric signs, like strips, disks, triangles, of different colours. In Switzerland, almost all paths are marked by a red strip. When several different paths meet, intersecting together, it becomes a problem to find out which one should be yours. This happens mainly when at such an intersection point there are no arrows to give details about each possible direction to follow."

–"In Switzerland, what places have you chosen for your vacations as fixed points for hiking around?"

–"Many, in fact. In some places we went only once but, in other places, several times. We spent seven-day stays in Kandersteg, Lauterbrunen, Engelberg, Silvaplana, Saas Fe, Zermatt, Zinal, Arolla, Fionnay, Bourg St.-Pierre, and La Fouly. Each of these places, and the corresponding surrounding area, of course, is different and just great. If somebody asked me to recommend only one of them, I would choose Zermatt, without any doubt. It may be reached by a clog train from Brig. In order to protect it from pollution, the cars are not allowed there and they have to be left behind in Täsch. Zermatt is still considered to be a village but it has a tremendous number of hotels, shops, boutiques, restaurants, all sorts of entertainment, and a lot of houses and villas. For giving a taint of old mountain village, every morning, a troop of sheep with little bells around their necks, and supervised by two authentic shepherds, parade on the main road, annoying the shopkeepers who have to sprinkle and clean quickly what the members of the troop leave behind. The village is very popular with tourists that make its narrow streets very crowded indeed, especially in evening. It is, however, my first recommendation to somebody coming to Switzerland for the first time because it is a very picturesque Swiss village, with many old wooden houses, surrounded by 21 peaks exceeding 4000 meters, which, except their beauty, also create there a favourable and more stable micro-climate. The range of mountains there includes Monte Rosa, a giant, with a peak of about 4638 meters, the highest mountain in Switzerland, and, especially, Matterhorn, the most beautiful mountain imaginable, a white pyramid of about 4478 meters high, whose picture is the landmark of the Swiss Alps, that could be seen on many Swiss chocolate boxes, and whose summit may be seen even from the train station. There are many exciting trails around. Being a famous resort, it is also a very expensive place to stay at."

–"If this village Zermatt is your recommendation number one, why did you come to La Fouly the seventh time?"

–"As a matter-of-fact, we spent three vacations in Zermatt, and three vacations in Arolla, which, at an altitude of 2006 meters itself, is the highest village we have stayed in, from which it is not so difficult to go up to 3000 meters during the daily hiking trips. But, however, the place that has fitted best to our tastes is La Fouly. As you have noticed, La Fouly is situated almost at the end of the Ferret Valley, or Val Ferret, how it is called here, at an altitude of 1600 meters. It is a wild alpine setting. It is also a staging post on the Mont Blanc Tour, which is abbreviated here, on many indicators, as TMB. Tourists, of very different nationalities, normally come form Italy, through the Grand Col Ferret and spend a night here, very often at the Edelweiss Hotel. Their luggage is carried by horses. I get always depressed when I see how much stuff is put on these horses when they leave in the morning. When such a group arrives, the dining room of the hotel is changed correspondingly. Tables are joined together to allow the tourists to eat together and talk, all at the same time. They show a great appetite and are quite noisy. On the next morning, it is better to come early for the buffet breakfast because they leave nothing behind before leaving to another destination of the tour.

From La Fouly, one can see the beautiful snowy peaks of Mont Dolent, just above your camping site, Tour Noir, and Les Aiguilles Rouges. As entertainment, it is a good place for mountain biking, jogging, and even para-gliding, but not many people are doing this. There is even a tennis court, in a very good condition, at the Edelweiss Hotel, but I never saw anybody playing. There are no night clubs, discotheques, or bars, and this is what makes it so special in this age of electronic noise and senseless frolic. La Fouly kept civilization and crowds at bay, stopped the passage of time, and remained a pure village, in the good, old sense of the word.

This doesn't mean that La Fouly is an empty place. Except the beautiful small wooden villas spread around, some of them being available for rent, there are three hotel restaurants, namely Hôtel Edelweiss, by far the most exquisite one, where we use to stay every time we come here, Hôtel Des Glaciers, and Grand Hôtel du Val Ferret, a coffee-house, called Café Restaurant de la Fouly, a gift shop, a Sports shop with clothes and tourist equipment, a small post office, a small hidden chapel, an office for hiring guides, a tourist office where they post daily the precious local weather forecast, and a small but absolutely excellent self-service food shop called Supermarché. There is even a chair lift going up to Alpage de la Fouly, at an altitude of 2122 meters, on the eastern, milder side of the village, which functions during the first 15 minutes of each hour, between 8:00 and 16:15, every day in July and August. Can you hope for more in a small village at the end of a wild valley in the Alps? What makes La Fouly attractive is hiking along the many trails of different degrees of difficulty, in a beautiful, unpolluted, and quiet alpine environment where you can hear your own thoughts and really feel yourself becoming a little part of Nature. This is something rarer and rarer to experience these days even in Switzerland."

–"What does 'alpage' really mean?"

–"Alpage means an alpine pasture, which often has a wooden shepherd hut and a sheepfold or enclosure for cows on it."

–"I didn't expect to have all these glaciers so close to the village itself. And I don't have a detailed map of the region to know the names of the mountains around."

–"Well, I can tell you. But let us go back to the village first because I want to show you other nice places in its close vicinity."

We looked again at the narrow cascade and we followed down the approximate path descending slowly towards the village. On our left-hand side, at the base of the vertical cut in the mountain, John showed me a bronze plaque fixed on the rock, in memory of four young people, two engineers and two jurists, between 24 and 31 years old, who died there on January 3, 1939, due to an avalanche which fell down along the Combe des Fonds.

Arriving in the village, John took me to a board, on the main road, where a detailed map of the region was posted, and pointing to the mountains surrounding us and looking on the map for identifying the corresponding altitudes, explained the local geography to me:

–"If you look to the western side of Val Ferret, where the highest picks are close to 4000 meters, moving from the left-hand side to the right-hand side, the points of interest are: Grand Col Ferret (2537 meters), Petit Col Ferret (2490 meters), Mount Dolent (3820 meters), with the bivouac Dolent (2667 meters), Mount Tour Noir (3835 meters), the most impressive here, located just in front of your camping site, and Grand-Darrey (3040 meters), where the hut Cabane de l'A Neuve (2735 meters), which cannot be seen from here, is built on a big rock like a citadel. Looking to the eastern side of Val Ferret, where the tops of the range are below 3000 meters, moving again from the left-hand side to the right-hand side, the highest picks are Mount de la Fouly (2870 meters), which I really don't know how it could be accessed, Col du Basset (2765 meters), Mount Ferret (2977 meters), I also know nothing remarkable about, Les Lacs de Fenêtre (2456 meters), Fenêtre de Ferret (2698 meters), and far away, the Col du Grand St-Bernard (2469 meters)."

– "Why is my camping called the Camping of Glaciers because I can see only one glacier in front of it, looking west?"

– "There are cases when several glaciers join together, giving the impression that there is only one. From here, we can see the Glacier de l'A Neuve, under the summit Tour Noir. There is, however, another glacier, which cannot be seen from here, located on the northern face of Mount Dolent. These two big glaciers are joined in their lower part. There are two very rapid torrents, called Reuse de l'A Neuve and Reuse de l'Amône, respectively, look here on the map, that go into the bigger torrent La Drance de Ferret which flows north, descending along Val Ferret. Your camping is located under the glacier, just in between the two narrower torrents."

– "All the names seem to be French around here."

– "Basically yes, but some words and names belong to the local dialect and cannot be found in a French dictionary. For instance, I don't really know what 'reuse' means. I guess only that it is a local word for the French 'ruisseau', which means 'stream', but I am not sure."

−"There are so many letters 'A' in the names around. What could that mean?"

−"I asked the same question to somebody from the region and the explanation I got is that 'A', 'Au', or 'Ar' are abbreviations for an old form of alpem, or mountain pasture."

−"You seem to know very well all the names of all the peaks in the Alps."

−"Don't make me laugh, please! Just the opposite is true. My wife is desperate about my inability to learn the names of mountains, valleys, lakes, and rivers. I always use to say that all the names have been given by human beings and have no specific value. Nature has created marvelous beauties without any names attached. Even if I am a very slow learner, after so many visits here, however, I finally can manage in dealing with the main names of the local geography. But I should suggest to you, if you are not tired, to make a short tour around your camping area, along a west semicircle of radius one kilometer, or maybe a little less, centered at the Edelweiss Hotel."

I wasn't tired at all and we started our short trip on the semicircle proposed by John. We crossed a bridge over La Drance de Ferret and followed a curved unpaved road, soon transformed into a narrow but well maintained path, going closer towards the western range of mountains, leaving the village behind and the camping area to the right. John looked carefully around, examining several trees as he was searching for something.

−"I am very surprised indeed," he said. "There used to be about nine numbered posts along this path, called 'Sur les traces du loup', with pictures and commentaries meant for tourists of all ages about a strange beast who apparently showed up in the region. The posts described the mystery of the beast of Val Ferret, alerting people about a wild animal, apparently a huge wolf, or maybe more wolves, terrorizing the high mountain pastures at an altitude of 2500 meters. It was said that, during the summer of 1995, the 'strangling beast' had killed more than 117 sheep, 27 of them in only one night. Between 1947, when the last wolf had been shot in Valais, and 1995, no such animal was seen in the region Entremont-Ferret. The newly arrived predator attacked only during the night, covering a vast territory in Val d'Entremont and Val Ferret, passing through Combe de l'A. Some people believed that the beast perhaps had come from Italy, where there are about 500-1000 protected wolves."

–"Why have disappeared all these unusual and intriguing posts?"

–"This is what I am asking myself. Who knows? Perhaps somebody thought that they could scare the tourists and especially the campers. Or, no traces have been noticed in the recent years, or maybe the beast itself decided to remove any mention of its frightening visits in the region! Leaving any joke aside, however, I can say that something has changed in the last years around here. Not long ago, many flocks and herds were up in the mountains unattended. During hiking trips, it was common to meet cows or sheep without any supervisor or guardian around. Not now. There are shepherds and mainly dogs everywhere."

–"This is not good news because I am afraid of dogs."

–"Who isn't? But let us hope that they are intelligent enough to make a distinction between peaceful tourists and thieves or predators."

During our walk, we met an indicator pointing to west-south and mentioning the Refuge Dolent. John explained me that it is a small, red, compact cabin fixed on a rock at the margin of the Dolent glacier, meant for those interested in glacier or mountain wall climbing, not for the regular tourists whose aim is hiking on safe trails.

–"We can climb a little until we reach the portion above the Combe des Fonds, but without going farther."

And this is what we did. The narrow and sometimes muddy path mounted abruptly, in a short serpentine, through weeds and high trees grown on rocks, until we reached the base of a sequence of absolutely vertical metallic stairs. We carefully climbed the stairs, about 15 meters high and, at the end of them, we stopped at the beginning of a very inclined meadow without any trees or bushes.

−"It is quite difficult to go up there because the narrow path, going under the glacier and above the abrupt vertical cut of the Combe des Fonds seen by you in the morning, is quite open, very exposed and, consequently, not safe at all. In fact, the risk of an avalanche during the springtime, or falling boulders in summer, is not negligible and perhaps this is the reason why the valley we were on today is not marked and, therefore, not recommended for hiking. Anyway, there is nobody up there at the Refuge. The mountaineers are asked to keep the place clean and to bring down any garbage. They are also warned that there is no fuel available for lighting a fire."

−"I have noticed that it is very clean all over around the village."

−"Yes, indeed so. In fact, during the hiking, the tourists are expected to leave no garbage on the trails or up there, when they stop for lunch. The hikers generally bring down the residues, especially cans and bottles, and deposit them in the big garbage bins of the village. Once, during a hiking from Zermatt to Gornergrat, which faces Monte Rosa, my wife and I have met several students, hired on summer jobs to collect the remained litter on that trail, very popular with the tourists in the months of July and August. 'Keep our mountains clean,' seems to be an imperative here."

It was a little more difficult to descend the metallic stairs than to climb them, but I tried not to look downwards. Once we returned to the indicator from which we started our short climbing towards the Refuge Dolent, we resumed the walk along the semicircle surrounding the camping area. The most interesting was the crossing of the Reuse de l'A Neuve on a wooden bridge. The torrent, impossible to be crossed by feet, was coming with a high speed through big white boulders, rushing down, noisily and foamily, from the Glacier de l'A Neuve, above us. Continuing our walk, we closed the semicircle, returning to the village without crossing the second torrent, Reuse de l'Amône, at the right-hand side of the camping area, looking to the west. Both torrents coming from the Glacier de l'A Neuve join La Drance de Ferret, whose water is caught in an accumulation basin, at the end of La Fouly, from where it is allowed to continue its descent to Orsières but only after using a part of its energy for producing electricity.

It was the right time to have lunch. We sat down on the bank of La Drance de Ferret, cooling the soft drinks, safely blocked by an improvised little barrage of rocks, in the cold water of the river, and eating what we had in our knapsacks. It wasn't much to eat but everything tasted so good outdoors. While eating, John asked me:

–"What are your plans for the next days?"

–"Well, to be frank with you, I didn't make up my mind about. At the camping site, I saw an announcement about guided tours called something like 'The shepherds's path' and 'Crossing the high mountain pastures', going through different places around. I am thinking about taking them but I want to ask about the cost first."

–"Just forget about it! Such tours are not for you but for older and unexperienced people who can bring even children with them. The tours just visit several places, nicely located, it is true, at a medium altitude, where the milk from sheep or cows is processed and where it is possible to spend some time and sample the produce of the local dairy. But you can use your time here much better. If you want, we can go together on some trails around in the next couple of days."

–"It would be fine with me, but do you think that I could cope with the difficulties of hiking at high altitude? I don't want to be a burden for you."

–"Don't be silly. You look fit and I am no longer young to run up and down the slopes. We can manage, don't worry. So, it is settled. Tomorrow, if the weather is good, we'll go to the Col Grand Ferret. It is a long trail but without major hiking difficulties. But now, as our lunch was quite light, we can still go to the opposite, eastern side of La Fouly. I want to show you a strange place, not far from here."

–"Is it dangerous to walk in the surrounding mountains?"

–"No, if you are cautious and the weather is good. Obviously, the glaciers could be dangerous but I don't cross them, except some small ones that have no water coming out from them. In fact there are two kinds of glaciers. A dry glacier has no snow covering. They are grey or blue and the crevasses are clearly visible. A wet glacier still has white snow on it and some crevasses could be hidden under a thin layer of snow. They are dangerous because some of them could be very deep and, very often, down below there is a stream of water. Crossing a glacier can be done only together with a group of people, generally very early in the morning, when it is still cold enough, and requires adequate equipment consisting of special alpine hobnails attached to the boots and solid ropes. As I said, I don't cross big glaciers, but I like to be close to them and spend time looking at them. In the month of July or August avalanches are rare and very local, but stones falling along or below steep slopes could be sometimes a problem."

The little wooden houses, cottage style, of the village La Fouly climb on the relatively gentle slopes of the eastern side of Val Ferret. There are about 200 of them, all oriented towards the northern side of the valley, facing the Glacier de l'A Neuve in between the almost identically high peaks Tour Noir, to the right, as we look west, and Mont Dolent, to its left. Due to the slope, no house is shading the other houses, allowing them a full view of the beautiful range of the rugged mountains from the western side of Val Ferret. At the windows, omnipresent red flowers, perhaps pelargoniums, bring a delightful uniformity to the coquettish houses. On a paved and inclined secondary road, perpendicular to the main road, made to access the houses of the village, we went up to the end of the little village. At the end of the road, and of the ski-lift mounting in parallel with the road, we followed a narrow path, entering a forest with some very tall fir trees. Stopping for a while behind one of them, John looked up and told me:

–"Lately, I have become more and more impressed by trees. The animals can move looking for food and a safer place to live but a tree has to survive in the same place for hundreds of years. It seems to be a very childish remark but I really didn't give much thought about it before. I do believe that in Europe, at least, we don't take enough care of trees as we ought to."

–"I don't think that there is such a problem in Canada. At least not yet. Very often trees grow up unexpectedly in a back yard without even be planted. Especially maples in Ontario. Many trees, however, are cut down when a new mall or new houses are built. The builders don't seem to make serious efforts to keep some nice trees and integrate them in the new construction site as I read that they do in some Scandinavian countries."

After a slow ascent through the forest, to our right-hand side we met a moraine, on the other side of which, a narrow stream was coming from a strange and wooded short but wild valley, abruptly descending from a mountain with dark, breakable, and frail rocks. A very strange place indeed.

–"It is quite surprising that such a weird place could be found so close to the village," said John. "As you can see, there is nobody around and not many come here because, look, there are plenty of unpicked wild strawberries everywhere. Let us sit down and enjoy the scenery. Looking south, the rugged side of the mountain, at the end of this short but very inclined valley, can be seen only from here. It looks so wild. I don't know whether the 'strangling beast' ever came here but if it did, it definitely came through this valley or still resides somewhere around here."

For about twenty minutes nobody said anything, both of us just looking around and breathing deeply, everyone with his own thoughts. It was so calm. Fortunately, no beast came out from the forest of the rugged valley to spoil our moments of silence. Then, for the first time, I was the one to start a dialogue:

–"What do you do, I mean, when the vacation is over?"

–"I am a university professor of mathematics in Manchester. For ten years, at the beginning of my career, I worked in a research institute and, in the last 30 years, I taught mathematics in different universities."

–"What kind of mathematics have you taught?"

–"Well, different courses, but mainly applied mathematics, like information theory, coding theory, probability theory, mathematical statistics, statistical mechanics, and, in the last twenty years, operations research, which is a kind of applied optimization. I am very close to the official retirement but I don't want to think too much about it. Life has to be taken as it is. I use to say that life is not so short to panic about but not so long to waste its good moments. I just want to enjoy every day of my life, as it comes around, and sometimes I succeed in doing just that. Unfortunately, sometimes I don't. But I don't want to be boring either, talking about me or about mathematics."

–"Oh, just the contrary. I have to confess that I am at a crossroads in my own life. I am positive about going to university and getting an academic education and I also know that mathematics has been the only subject I felt comfortable with. I don't know, however, whether to become a professional mathematician or go for engineering or management science, the last two being somewhat safer for future jobs as far as the salary and availability are concerned. This is why I should be indebted to you if you could tell me, as much as possible, about mathematics and mathematicians. But I am afraid that I am asking too much. In fact you are on vacation and perhaps want to forget about mathematics for a while."

-"Don't be so formal, Mike! We'll have enough time in the next days to talk about many different things. As you must know, teachers talk a lot and I am not an exception. 'Déformation professionnelle', how people in Valais would say. For me, it will be a real challenge to talk about mathematics without using a chalk and blackboard or a pencil and paper. In order to make mathematics more human, perhaps the best strategy would be to talk about great mathematicians and what they did, as far as I know. But, my God," he said looking at his watch, "it is already six o'clock. Look what I am suggesting to you. I noticed that you had a very light lunch and, as I kept you busy all day, you had no time to go to the Supermarket and buy something consistent to eat. Please, allow me to invite you to have dinner with me this evening at Edelweiss hotel. As I have a table reserved for me, it will be easy to bring you as my guest. Dinner is to be served at seven o'clock sharp. Don't forget, we are in Switzerland and the local people are obsessed with precise time. It would be a pleasure for me to have dinner together and we could continue our talk. I generally don't like to be too pushy but now, exceptionally, I don't accept no as an answer."

I mumbled some kind of excuses but I wasn't very convincing. At the same time, I was really very hungry and in no disposition to prepare my own dinner without buying first something from the Supermarket, supposed to close at seven o'clock. Consequently, rather ungraciously, I accepted the kind invitation. We went down to the village, John to the hotel, I to my tent to get rid of the knapsack, wash my hands, and take a pullover for evening and lighter shoes. At five minutes to seven, I entered the restaurant of Edelweiss hotel. It had two rooms: one, more popular, as a kind of bar, and another, a bigger one, very elegant, but still warm, cozy, as the interior of a stylish mountain cottage, where John was waiting for me. He had a reserved table indeed, just at a large window facing the Glacier de l'A Neuve to the west. Closer to the hotel was La Drance de Ferret, after which I could see a good part of the camping site between the torrent and the range of western mountains. The glacier, in particular, seemed to be so close; I had the impression that I could touch the white sleeping giant.

–"As we came here so many times, they always give us a table and a room facing the western side of the valley, with the Glacier de l'A Neuve just watching us. And we watch it."

Then, something magic happened. At seven o'clock sharp, the sun disappeared behind Les Aiguilles Rouges that connect the summits of Tour Noir and Mount Dolent and, as Nature was switching off the daily light, suddenly, evening's twilight came down on La Fouly.

The four-course dinner was just fabulous: entré (melon and dry, smoked ham); a light soup, or 'potage' how they call it there; the main dish, or 'la pièce de résistence', how the very young waiter called it (roasting pork sprayed with black pepper sauce, mashed potato, and minced leek); and ice-cream as dessert. I enjoyed dinner very much but I pointed out to John that eating like that everyday I could easily become obese.

−"Let's check. Tell me your height in centimeters."

−"170."

−"If we subtract 150 from it, it makes 20. Dividing by 4, for males, or by 2 for females, in your case we get 5. Subtract from your height in centimeters the number 100, which makes 70, and finally subtract from it the number 5, previously obtained. We obtain your ideal weight 65 kilograms. If your actual weight exceeds the ideal weight by 20%, you are obese indeed. What is your weight?"

−"61 kilograms."

−"So, you have no reason to worry about obesity right now."

For drinking, I was offered a choice between beer or wine. John suggested to try a small glass of relatively light, crispy wine Fendant from the region, but he was quick in adding:.

−"Only one glass, for each of us, because tomorrow morning we have to be in perfect shape."

While sipping our chilly wine Fendant, after the main dish, John took a postcard from his pocket and showed it to me. It contained the coloured picture of a beautiful snowy mountain from Valais and, at the left-hand corner of its bottom, the following text was printed in calligraphic letters:

Supplique du Valaisan:

> Seigneur, donne-moi …
> La santé pour longtemps,
> De l'amour tout le temps,
> Des impôts modérément,
> Du travail pas trop souvent,
> Du Fendant éternellement!

I put the postcard on the table and, happy to prove my knowledge of French, I said:

– "Which in my free translation, which destroys the rhyme, would be:

> Valaisan's petition:
>
> My God, please give me …
> Good health for a long time,
> Love all the time,
> Taxes moderately,
> Work not very often,
> Wine Fendant eternally!"

– "Bravo, well done, but let me put in some naive rhymes as well," said John, "and state it like:

> Valaisan's prayer:
>
> My God, please give me …
> Good health for a long time,
> Love just all the time,
> Work only from time to time,
> Taxes quite in moderation,
> Wine Fendant on daily basis!".

That evening, the restaurant wasn't full and there was no implicit pressure on us to leave. Also, there was enough time allowed between the four courses of the dinner. Therefore, I was quite anxious to resume our discussion started in the afternoon and told John:

–"In North America, at least, people talk a lot about famous names in hockey, baseball, basketball, golf, or movie industry. Almost nothing about scientists, in general, and mathematicians, in special."

–"Not only in North America. The same is true in Europe except that soccer has to be added to the list. But even in universities, the few scientists who are explicitly mentioned in different disciplines are only names without any human traits added to them. Once, I was teaching in a large lecture hall when an unexpected power outage occurred. As there were no windows there, the dark was absolute and, as I generally write on the blackboard everything, I had to stop lecturing. Waiting for the electric power to restore, I started talking to my students in the dark room. It was an interesting experience and they proved to be very nice and cooperative. Having nothing better to do, I decided to discuss topics from the history of mathematics. I was really stunned to see how little they knew about. In a class of 58 undergraduate fourth year students and 11 graduate students enrolled in my operations research class, very few had heard about big names in mathematics and almost nobody knew anything about their lives. I have to confess that talking about the unusual lives of some great mathematicians in that atmosphere of complicity between professor and students, generated by the darkness from the lecture hall, made that day really memorable. And not only for me, as I would hear later from friends of my students."

–"Have you ever taught a course on history of mathematics?"

–"As a matter-of-fact, I didn't. Once, the idea crossed my mind but I realized that I wasn't able to do that. Simply because whatever you read about the great contributors to the development of mathematics cannot be 100% trusted. Essential details could remain unknown for ever and some of the stuff which is available could be simply unreliable. There is also the tendency of presenting the great scientists as being angels. Some were, some weren't, but how could we know the absolute truth about how they really were and about what they did in their lives? Sometimes the truth could be easily distorted for the sake of a good story.

It seems to be a little easier to evaluate their scientific contribution. For those who lived long ago, we can better appreciate and rate the importance of their achievements to the progress of different disciplines of mathematics. But in such cases, sometimes important documents are missing, being lost or undiscovered, and many disputes about priority remain unsolved or are settled down in a debatable way. With modern mathematics, it is even more difficult to distinguish between what is really important and what is not. With so many contributions, so many journals, so many conferences, and so many books, it is very difficult to dominate what is being done today in mathematics and to get a perspective about where to go from now on. Fashion does exist even in mathematics and often there are groups of people who decide what is important and what is not, influencing what kind of mathematics should be published in certain major journals or whom to give prestigious awards or scientific honours. Mathematicians are human beings after all and, as I have said, some are angels but some are not. At the same time, every great man has his own foibles. But, in talking or writing about great mathematicians from the past, I always prefer to take what was positive and what they achieved in their lifetime.

The great advantage in mathematics, however, is that we can prove. A correct proof could be checked by other mathematicians. Some of them could simplify the proof or give a more elegant equivalent of it. A proof could be wrong or incomplete but, sooner or later, it could be rejected or fixed by other people. I find very refreshing to know that if a teacher proves a standard theorem and makes a mistake in it, good students, retracing the steps of the proof home, using a piece of paper and a pencil, could discover the error and correct it by themselves. Somebody once said that any scientific domain becomes mature only when it uses some kind of mathematical approach in dealing with its own problems because only in mathematics we can prove. It seems to detect here the arrogance of a mathematician. Maybe, but at the same time we have to admit that if a certain surprising new experimental result is announced in a certain discipline, like chemistry or nuclear physics, for instance, more often than not, we cannot perform the respective experiment ourselves and we have to wait until another well-equipped laboratory can afford to do it and eventually confirm or infirm the respective result."

–"Perhaps the entire history has been plagued by lack of absolute objectivity. Different people relate different events in different ways. We like the legends, however, even if we don't believe everything they say, and we love some heroes even if we doubt that they had really been as they were described. I always liked Napoleon and the Beatles, for instance."

–"Yes, perhaps I should be more romantic and less critical. I remember that, when I was a little kid, I heard somebody saying that in Spain, there was a famous soccer goalkeeper Zamora, who never got any goal in his net and used to bring a revolver with him every time he played, ready to commit suicide when he would be finally defeated. Amazingly enough, I did believe that the story was true and I wanted to be as good as Zamora in our soccer games taking place in the back yard of my elementary school. Now, I am more of a skeptic, like a historian who, long ago, got a six-year sentence and was imprisoned in the London Tower. He was allowed to write in his seclusion and was working on describing the events of a certain period from the tumultuous history of England. One day, he looked out the window and saw a mock battle between two 'armies' of children going on beyond the walls of the prison. After a very short while, a friend of his came to visit him and started by telling about the fight between the children witnessed by him too, a couple of minutes before. Puzzled, the historian realized that the same battle has been seen under completely different angles by him and by his trusted friend. Consequently, he decided to give up writing about historic events.

A similar feeling makes me incapable of teaching a full course about history of mathematics. But you are right. We need heroes, we need models to admire, imitate, and follow. This is why sometimes, when I write on the blackboard the name of an important mathematician, I prefer to take a short break and say something about him and his life. Once, at the end of an academic year, a Japanese student frankly told me that she had enjoyed the short history stories more than all the other topics taught by me. I cannot say that I was very happy about it. Still, this encouraged me to continue telling my students details about the lives of major contributors to the development of different chapters of the course I was teaching. Unfortunately, there isn't much time available for doing this when we have so many technical topics to cover and the academic year is so short. Anyway, talking informally and occasionally about history of mathematics is very pleasant but teaching a rigorous, formal course dedicated only to this subject is something I wouldn't dare to do."

It was almost nine o'clock when I reached my tent. The night was pleasant; dry and neither warm nor cold, but rather on the cool side. The sky was full of shining, blinking stars. Everything seemed so vivid, without the pollution and artificial lights enveloping the big cities. A couple of fires set by campers sent around a wooden smoke which, outdoors, didn't smell bad at all. This also gave you some kind of assurance that you were not alone in a forest, below a huge glacier, in the middle of the night. It is the paradox of wanting privacy but feeling more comfortable knowing that some humans are, nevertheless, not so far away. The implicit solidarity of the campers!

In spite of the many events of the day, I wasn't tired at all. I arranged my stuff for the night-time and I went to take a shower. Coming back to my tent, I hanged up my powerful flashlight, set to maximum intensity, took my notebook, and started writing down what I saw and heard during the busy day. I decided to keep a strict track of everything that is going to happen during the next days, describing first the brief technical details of the daily hiking, followed by a gist of what I found out or learned from the discussions with John on the respective day. But I also decided to go to sleep not later than eleven o'clock every night. It's a promise to myself!

The cold of the night and a total silence descended on the vast camping site. I was happy to get into my warm and tight sleeping bag and the last thought on my mind was that the idea of coming to La Fouly wasn't so bad after all.

FIRST DAY

GRAND COL FERRET

When I opened my tent on Tuesday morning, a cloudless, blue sky and the sun, reaching only the snowy upper part of Tour Noir and Mount Dolent at this early hour, announced a very promising day for hiking. As John had suggested to meet at 9:15 in front of Edelweiss Hotel for going to the Grand Col Ferret, I had enough time to do some invigorating physical exercises, wash myself, dress, go to the Supermarket, which in fact is a small food shop that, however, has everything somebody really needs and opens at 8:00, shop for food, have a good breakfast in my tent, and prepare my equipment and light knapsack. How many things can be done when distances are short! In Toronto, I need one hour to go downtown from my house, taking a bus and the subway.

At 9:15 sharp, John came out of the hotel and we started our first hiking trip from La Fouly.

−"I hope that you could sleep well because last night was quite chilly. Look at the top of the western mountains; they are powdered with fresh snow."

−"I had no problem. My sleeping bag is light but very good, filled with penguin hair, and the tent may be tightly closed. Canadians are outdoors people and there are some excellent shops for buying hiking equipment."

Close to the hotel, on the signpost for tourists, I read: Ferret 45 min, La Peule 2h, Grand Col Ferret 3h 30 min. Adopting John's strategy, the trail from La Fouly to the Grand Col Ferret could be split in four parts, or stages.

Stage 1. From La Fouly (1600 meters), we went south and, a little later, south-south-east, on the main paved road, with the torrent La Drance de Ferret to our right-hand side, flowing down in opposite direction to ours. After about 20 minutes, the Glacier of Mont Dolent could be much better seen. John also showed me the Refuge Dolent, called Bivouac du Dolent, as a small red box at the margin of the Glacier, and also La Cabane de l'A Neuve, barely visible, as a very remote small cottage on the top of a tall huge rock. Both of them cannot be seen from La Fouly. Frankly speaking, being so far away up there, I couldn't have noticed them without being shown to me by John who knew their location from his previous trips.

After about half an hour, we arrived at the tiny village, or rather hamlet, Ferret (1705 m). It has a small hotel, a restaurant, and a couple of houses. At the entrance to the village, there is a very small and austere 300-year old chapel of Notre-Dame-des-Neiges, facing the glaciers from the western side of Val Ferret. Close by is a forest of larches and steep slopes. The paved road continued, for about 20 more minutes, through a forest with high trees, offering a welcome shade after the sunny road from La Fouly to Ferret, and ended at the high mountain pasture, or 'alpage', called Les Ars (1755 m). That was the end of Stage 1 and there was a bifurcation there: an unpaved road goes south-south-east and later turns east, towards Lacs de Fenêtre, and another unpaved road goes south towards the Grand Col Ferret.

Stage 2. From Les Ars, we descended a little, towards south, and crossed La Drance de Ferret on a wooden, large bridge, heading west, and then south again, by mounting in serpentine on an unpaved, narrow road, but good enough to be used by a single small and solid car. Some fir trees and bushes were on both sides of the road. Val Ferret, suddenly turns west-west-south, leaving a relatively short ramification of it to continue towards south, its original orientation. Until almost to the end of our trip, Val Ferret would remain to our left-hand side, becoming deeper and deeper as we continued to ascend on its abrupt side. The road, in a large serpentine, continued its relatively smooth ascent until we reached an open and large plateau, on which, at the end of the road, after a big turn to north, there was another 'alpage', La Peule, or Peuvaz, using the local dialect, at an altitude of 2071 meters. From Les Ars, we needed about an hour to arrive at La Peule. We took a short break. There were there some tourists, of different ages, and speaking different languages, some of them sitting at some simple, wooden tables, sampling some dairy products prepared by the owners of the 'alpage'. There were some electrical machines around, for processing milk, perhaps. I liked the Swiss flag, waved by the light wind, just in front of La Peule, and the fact that the kennel of an ugly dog was surrounded by a safe fence. On the arrow of the signpost for tourists we read: Grand Col Ferret 1h 30 min.

Stage 3. As the unpaved road ended at the 'alpage' La Peule, we followed a large and well-maintained path, marked with a red strip from time to time, abruptly mounting west and south-west, in a tedious, brutal serpentine with many short turns, on the mountain behind the 'alpage'. That proved to be the most arduous portion of the trail.

–"I always use to say that, after learning how to ignite a fire, the wheel and the serpentine have been the greatest inventions of humanity," said John jokingly.

Except the grass, there was no vegetation there, except the omnipresent wild flowers, of course, but even them were rarer than before. Anyway, no trees, and no bushes. After the difficult portion of the ascent, the path turned to the west-west-south and, still climbing, became almost linear for a long, long time. On our left, the valley became deeper and, on the other side of it, the mountain was bleak, without any traces of paths, but with long stripes of snow like the back of a zebra. The white stripes on the other side of the valley became longer and wider as we continued our smooth ascent. Soon, some patches of snow appeared on our side of the valley, as well.

–"The best month to come here is August and not July. And much depends on how much snow they had here in the previous winter," said John. "A couple of years ago, when they had in the winter an unusually abundant snow, reaching seven meters in La Fouly, as the local people there told us, we came here at the beginning of July, like now, and big portions of all the trails around, including the trail to the Grand Col Ferret, were still completely covered by snow. It was exciting and amusing but very tiring and, sometimes, even dangerous."

There were many tourists going to and coming from the Grand Col Ferret. In fact, John had told me that this trail was the most popular with tourists, being long but very safe and relatively easy. At one moment, we met a compact group of people, marching around a strong horse whose back was covered by a lot of special bags holding the belongings of the members of the group. Seeing my amazement, John was quick in explaining to me:

–"This is a group doing the Mont Blanc Tour, which on the indicators for tourists is abbreviated as TMB. They come now from Italy, climbing to the Grand Col Ferret, from La Vachey, and descend to La Fouly, where they spend one night at Edelweiss Hotel. Tonight, the restaurant will be crowded indeed. Normally, they put together several small tables, making up one long table at which they eat together, talking all of them simultaneously."

–"If this is Mont Blanc Tour, why do they come to Switzerland?"

–"The standard tour takes 11 days and passes through France, Italy, and Switzerland, moving from pass to pass, around Mont Blanc, which is the highest peak in the Alps, with an altitude of 4808 meters, if I remember well. During summer, there are two TMBs every week, one moving clockwise and the other one counter-clockwise. In La Fouly, they spend the Tuesday night and Wednesday night, respectively."

–"And what is the poor horse doing?"

–"He or she spends the night outdoors, on the narrow meadow behind Edelweiss Hotel, near the tennis court. Not so long ago, many portions of the path from La Fouly to the Grand Col Ferret were very narrow and really dangerous for horses carrying so many bags. The Mont Blanc Tour was in fact the main reason for enlarging the path, making it more accessible and much safer both for tourists and for horses."

Soon after meeting the TMB group, just in front of us appeared the white top of the impressive mountain Grandes Jorasses which became taller and taller as we moved closer in its direction. The recently melted snow made the path muddy on some portions of it. One hour has passed since we had started our ascent from La Peule.

Stage 4. Our path, almost linearly oriented towards west-west-south, suddenly turned south, crossing Val Ferret, which ended there, closing at the Grand Col Ferret. A narrow stream, coming perhaps from some glacier covered by patches of snow, offered a good place to stop and take a break. After crossing the stream, the path ascended vigorously, on snow on its last portion, towards the saddle offered by the Grand Col Ferret. On the top of it, there was no snow, and no hut or shelter either, but only a stone sign, with the letters 'S' towards north and 'I' towards south, marking the frontier between Switzerland and Italy, and a round table from copper, indicating the name, altitude, and direction to each of the main mountains around. I felt like dominating a large area all around me.

It was very cold up there, and John warned me that it was almost always windy on the top of every Col which makes the transition from one valley to another one, on the opposite side of a mountain. But the panorama was amazing. Looking south, behind we had the Swiss Val Ferret, and in front of us, looking down, was the Italian Val Ferret, descending somehow along a milder slope, and with no snow in sight. To the right we had a range of white glaciers and abrupt mountain peaks at very close distance, projected on the blue sky. Far to the left, the impressive large white silhouette of Mont Combin de Valsorey was in contrast with the dark Mont Velan, too steep for keeping snow on it. The duration of stage 4 was about 17 minutes. John seemed to be overwhelmed by the scenery, and thought necessary to give me a professorial speech:

–"The Grand Col Ferret (2537 meters) is on the border between Switzerland and Italy. It is said that it has been used as a passage in

Alps since Antiquity. I have been told by local people that this Col has been used since very long ago, frequently by smugglers. As you have seen, without taking any long break, but going in a moderate rhythm, the ascent took us around three hours and 15 minutes. At Grand Col Ferret, coming from La Fouly, the mounting Swiss Val Ferret descends into the Italian Val Ferret, down to Courmayeur. The snowy southern face of Mont Blanc's summit is partially obscured by the Grandes Jorasses and Aiguille du Geant, which, frankly speaking, look more impressive than what can be seen from the top of Mont Blanc itself, which is tall indeed but rather flat on the top. From the Grand Col Ferret, looking to Switzerland, you could see the Grand Combin with a distant view of the Rhône Valley. Looking north, it is possible to see a little from the Petit Col Ferret, and even to cross there from here. If the weather is good, we are going to go there tomorrow, directly from La Fouly. Now, we are looking at the impressive view of the Italian side of Mont Blanc."

I don't remember how long we stayed there but I do remember that it was quite difficult to decide to leave. The descent from the Grand Col Ferret to La Fouly was supposed to take two hours and 30 minutes, but we stopped several times, admiring the surroundings and talking. More exactly, incited by me, John did the talking and I was a more than willing listener. We took a very long break on the arduous slope above La Peule, from which the serpentine of the path descending from Lacs Fenêtre, on the other side of Val Ferret, was clearly visible, lighted by the late afternoon sun. Fewer and fewer tourists were around but, at some point, we met a group of youngsters on mountain bicycles, heading towards the Grand Col Ferret at such a late hour, more on foot than on bicycle, looking really bad, as being on the verge of having a heart attack. God be with them!

We talked a lot during our trip to the Grand Col Ferret, mainly on our way back. The calm afternoon and the beautiful surroundings offered an ideal background for discussing about all sorts of things. John showed no particular intention to talk about his profession or mathematics in general, but I was interested in getting as much as possible from his knowledge and experience as a professional mathematician.

As a result, the last part of the day was mainly devoted to chatting about mathematics. I asked a lot of questions, not all of them very intelligent, I have to admit, but John showed a tremendous patience in answering them in a friendly, almost collegial way. At some moments, he seemed to become very tuned up to the topics under discussion, allowing his thoughts to flow freely from his mind and even heart, looking somewhere very far, to a point located outside this world or, I am not sure about, belonging to the inside of his inside. Everything started with generalities about the contents and meaning of mathematics but switched to more specific topics about some big contributors to the development of mathematics, which I enjoyed most.

–"What kind of courses are to be taken by somebody who wants to get a degree in mathematics?"

–"Things could be different in different universities. Basically, however, there are some requirements that are taken into account everywhere. Much depends on what kind of mathematics the student wants to specialize in. Thus, some want to study mainly pure mathematics, some are interested in applied mathematics, and some intend to become statisticians. Often, a Bachelor degree in mathematics in any of these streams, which requires about four years, is enough to look for and hopefully get jobs in teaching, with a certificate in education which needs one extra year, or in different companies and governmental services. The major banks are more and more interested in hiring system analysts who are going to deal with the stock market and forecast. After graduation, good students go for a Master's degree and possibly a subsequent PhD degree in one of these streams, with the objective of doing research and looking for academic positions. There are also students who need a mathematical background and good grades for taking later courses in engineering, physics, chemistry, biology, sociology, and even in the medical school or dentistry."

–"Are there enough jobs for mathematicians?"

–"It is difficult to get the real picture of the job market for mathematicians. It could be very different in different countries. Apparently, there are always jobs for teaching mathematics in elementary or high schools everywhere because mathematics is an important discipline in any school. With jobs in different companies or banks, it much depends on the need which could heavily fluctuate. Any recommendation from an influential person could help. Candidates with a background in statistics, or applied mathematics, especially when they are familiar with how to use computer packages, are generally preferred by companies and any previous experience could help for getting the job. For research or academic positions the competition is much tougher. Here again, there are considerably more candidates for a position in pure mathematics and fewer in statistics or applied areas. Also, the personal qualities and the weak points of the candidate could play and do play an important role not only in getting the new job but also in keeping it later. Not many positions come with tenure and even when there is a tenure track position involved, normally it takes a couple of long years and many evaluations for finally earning the job security. As in any hierarchy, super-incompetent and super-competent people are equally vulnerable because they menace the internal stability. Some companies need routine work to be done promptly and accurately. They value a disciplined and conscientious personnel. Some other companies need new blood, encourage new ideas, and are willing to take risks involved by breaking the daily routine and exploring new venues. The personal luck cannot be ignored either. Catching the right train, being in the right place at the right time. I had mediocre students who got good jobs with a surprising ease and excellent students who had a hard and long time to find something suitable for them. Sometimes a better candidate is considered overqualified for the job and somebody else gets it. All this been said, the professional competence is still the main quality needed in the majority of cases."

−"You haven't told me what kind of courses ought to be taken in a standard mathematics program."

−"Right. Assuming a solid background from high school or a preparatory college, a student has to start by taking linear algebra, differential calculus, and integral calculus courses. They are prerequisites for any other courses in a mathematics program. A course on discrete mathematics with computer applications could help also. This would be the first level. At the next level, courses on set theory and logic, algebraic structures, multivariate calculus, differential equations, probability and statistics, numerical methods, and operations research would offer a solid basic preparation for a professional mathematician. The third level would involve more specialized courses, to choose from, on number theory, combinatorics, complex analysis, geometry, graph theory, partial differential equations, advanced algebra, actuarial mathematics, mathematical modeling, regression analysis, optimization, topology, functional analysis, risk theory, stochastic processes, time series analysis, statistical quality control, simulation, experimental design, computational mathematics, and advanced numerical methods, depending on the specific program the student is in. Nobody can take all these courses but I should say that the first two levels mentioned are more or less compulsory. Obviously, there are shortcuts for those who need a more superficial qualification. Thus, for those interested in getting just basic knowledge in statistics, for instance, they don't need advanced calculus at all and could take only linear algebra, discrete mathematics with computer applications, and introductory courses in statistics that use only the finite mathematics, without any theoretical proofs, and focus on data processing and on problem solving."

ALGEBRA

–"All I know about algebra is how to solve algebraic equations of second degree and manipulate operations between algebraic polynomials. But perhaps there is much more to it."

–"Classical algebra, a continuation of arithmetic, deals basically with solving numerically equations and systems of equations. It is one of the oldest domains in mathematics and its origins are lost in time, about 4000 years ago. Historians speak about Egyptian, Babylonian, Greek, Hindu, and Arabic algebras. The words 'algebra' and 'algorithm' have Arab origins. After so many years, it would be very difficult, if not impossible, at least for me, to accurately say who influenced whom, mainly if we take into account that the symbolic, formal algebra, as we are using it today, has been developed only in the 16th century, due to

François Viète (1540-1603). It is said that the ancient mathematicians were able to solve, using words, linear and even quadratic equations. A famous book is considered to have been *Arithmetica*, written by Diophantus about 2250 years ago, where integer and rational solutions of systems of equations in several variables were investigated.

The introduction of new types of numbers has influenced the development of algebra. Everybody felt comfortable with the set of positive integers, related to counting, and the rational numbers, or fractions, introduced by dividing line segments in equal parts, but some schools rejected either the negative numbers or the irrational numbers, like the square root of 2, for instance, which, according to the theorem of Pythagoras from Euclidean geometry, represents the length of the diagonal of a square with the sides equal to 1. The legend says that the Pythagorean mathematicians, strongly believing in the mystical significance of the integer and rational numbers in the harmonious architecture of the world, were very upset by the discovery of irrational numbers and swore to keep secret there existence.

Making a huge jump in time, we arrive to the European algebra. About 450 years ago, important new contributions were achieved when Italian mathematicians succeeded in solving cubic and quartic equations by radicals and François Viète, already mentioned, introduced the literal symbolism which made algebra look basically like it is presented in the textbooks of our days. Replacing numbers by letters was an important step for developing general algorithms for solving equations.

In the 17th century, Pierre de Fermat and René Descartes, independently developed the analytic geometry, a fusion between algebra and geometry, allowing our intuition to visualize the algebraic concepts by attaching points in plane and space to pairs or triplets of numbers, respectively, and lines, curves, planes, and surfaces to polynomials in one or several variables. Also, the concept of number has been extended by accepting square roots from negative numbers, called improperly imaginary numbers. They had to be introduced for allowing any quadratic equation to have two solutions, like the simple equation $x^2 + 1 = 0$, for instance, whose solutions are $\sqrt{-1}$, denoted by the universal symbol i and $-\sqrt{-1}$ or $-i$. Remarkably enough, the complex numbers $a + bi$, where a and b are real numbers, called the real part and the imaginary part of the complex number $a + bi$, respectively, are just sufficient to solve any algebraic equation. Every real number a may be viewed as being a complex number $a + bi$ whose imaginary part b is equal to zero."

–"Therefore, how many kinds of numbers are used today and why are they needed?"

–"As I have said, the positive integers, or natural numbers, were introduced for counting objects. Adding natural numbers we get always natural numbers. But subtracting a natural number from another natural number, we sometimes get a natural number, like when we subtract 3 from 6, but sometimes we don't, like when we want to subtract 5 from 4, for instance. In order to make subtraction between natural numbers possible, we have to introduce negative integers. The multiplication between integers is always an integer but dividing an integer by another integer we sometimes get an integer, like dividing 6 by -2, but sometimes we don't, like when we divide 7 by 3, for instance. In order to make the division between integers always possible, we have to introduce the fractions, or rational numbers, like 7/3. Each rational number may be written as a decimal number that has either a finite number of decimals, like $7/5 = 1.4$, or an infinite number of decimals, where a group of such decimals is repeated indefinitely, like $7/3 = 2.33333 \ldots$. The numbers that are represented using infinitely many decimals, but are not rational numbers, are called, improperly, irrational numbers. They are much more numerous than the rational numbers. The rational and irrational numbers, taken together, form the set of real numbers, which is identified with the set of points of a horizontal line called the real line. Some of the real numbers could be solutions of some algebraic equations with integer coefficients, and are called algebraic numbers. Some real numbers cannot be solutions, or roots, of any algebraic equation with integer coefficients in which case they are called transcendental numbers. The most famous transcendental numbers are the irrational numbers $\pi = 3.14 \ldots$, known from the formula πr^2 which gives the area of a circle with radius r, and $e = 2.71828 \ldots$, very important in number theory and calculus. Further on, as I said before, if we want to solve any algebraic equation with integer coefficients, we have to introduce the complex numbers $a + bi$

which, due to Carl Friedrich Gauss, may be represented as points (a, b) in the complex plane, with the real part a on the horizontal real axis and the imaginary part b on the vertical imaginary axis."

–"What is it known about solving algebraic equations because, as I said before, I know how to solve only quadratic equations whose general form is $ax^2 + bx + c = 0$?"

–"Closer to our times, the fundamental theorem of algebra has been proved, stating that any polynomial of degree n in one variable, which is something like $a_0x^n + a_1x^{n-1} + \ldots + a_{n-1}x + a_n$, where x is the variable and the coefficients $a_0, \ldots, a_n$ are rational numbers, has just n roots, where a root of a polynomial is a value of the variable for which the respective polynomial is equal to zero, and these roots are either real or complex numbers. When a polynomial of degree n is equal to zero, we get an algebraic equation of degree n. The polynomial is quadratic, or cubic, or quartic, or quintic if the degree n of the polynomial is 2, 3, 4, or 5, respectively. Finally, in a dramatic way, Niels Abel proved that a general quintic equation cannot be solved by radicals and Évariste Galois showed that a polynomial equation may be solved by radicals if and only if the group of permutations of its roots has a special structure called soluble. But talking about Abel and Galois requires a much longer time. They are two of the romantic mathematicians and, maybe, I will talk about them some other time. Anyway, as I said before, linear algebra is a 'must' for any mathematician, whatever his future specialization would be. It mainly deals with systems of linear equations or systems of linear inequalities, and teaches us how to manipulate vectors and matrices, a powerful and compact tool in coping with linearity."

–"Is solving equations the only objective of algebra today?"

–"No. In fact, when Galois used the concept of group of permutations he made the transition from the classical algebra to what is called modern algebra. Its main characteristic is generality and this is why modern algebra is also called abstract algebra. Following the model of Euclidean geometry, in the 19th century, British mathematicians introduced the axiomatic thinking in algebra and the general algebraic formalism. The concept of group, for instance, refers to any set of elements in which a single operation, called composition, is defined, associating a well defined element of the set to any pair of elements of the set, and satisfying some basic properties like associativity, which reduces the composition of any number of elements to successive compositions of pairs of elements, has a neutral element, which composed to any element leaves this element unchanged, and to any element there corresponds another element, called its inverse, such that by composing them we get the neutral element of the group."

–"I am getting lost here. Could you be more specific, please?"

–"A group G is a set of elements in which a composition law is defined, denoted either as the addition from elementary algebra, in the so-called additive groups, or as the multiplication from elementary algebra, in the so-called multiplicative groups. The composition of any pair (a, b) of elements of the group is another element of the group, denoted by $a + b$ in an additive group and ab in a multiplicative group.

The composition law of an additive group satisfies the following properties: 1) Associativity: $(a + b) + c = a + (b + c)$, for all elements a, b, c of the group; 2) There is a neutral element 0 such that: $0 + a = a$ for every element a of the group; 3) For every a of the group, different from 0, there is the inverse element $-a$ such that: $(-a) + a = 0$. The group is commutative, or Abelian, if $a + b = b + a$ for every elements a, b of the group.

The composition law of a multiplicative group satisfies the following properties: 1) Associativity: $(ab)c = a(bc)$, for all elements a, b, c of the group; 2) There is a neutral element 1 such that: $1a = a$ for every element a of the group; 3) For every a of the group, different from 0, there is the inverse element a^{-1} such that: $a^{-1}a = 1$. The group is commutative or Abelian if $ab = ba$ for every elements a, b of the group.

The group generated by the elements $a, b, \ldots$, called generators, is obtained by applying the corresponding composition law (addition, for an additive group, or multiplication, for a multiplicative group) to any finite number of these elements and their inverses. In a multiplicative group, the cyclic group generated by a single element a contains the elements 1, a, $a^2, \ldots, a^{n-1}$, such that $a^n = 1$, where n is the order of the cyclic group, and $a^2 = aa$, $a^3 = aaa$, etc.

You already know some particular groups yourself! Thus, the set of integers is a group, more exactly an additive group, when the composition refers to adding integers, in which case the neutral element is the number zero, and the inverse of a number n is obtained by changing its sign, which gives $-n$. Likewise, the set of distinct fractions is a group, more exactly a multiplicative group, with respect to the composition defined by multiplying fractions, in which case the neutral element is the number 1, and the inverse of a fraction m/n is just n/m."

—"Therefore the elements of a group are numbers and the composition law means performing operations between numbers like the addition and multiplication, respectively."

—"Not quite. There are many groups of transformations, which are not numbers. Thus, as I mentioned before, Évariste Galois first dealt with the group of permutations of the roots $x_1, \ldots, x_n$ of an algebraic equation. Such a permutation is obtained when the roots $x_1, x_2, \ldots, x_n$ are arranged in a different order, like $x_2, \ldots, x_n, x_1$, for instance. There are $1 \times 2 \times 3 \times \ldots \times n$, which is a huge number when n is large, called 'n factorial', such possible permutations of n distinct roots.

Following what Augustin-Louis Cauchy (1789-1857) did, if we have a set of four objects, denoted by $\{a, b, c, d\}$, then a particular permutation obtained when a, b, c, d are replaced by b, d, a, c, respectively, for instance, may be viewed as being a substitution represented as a transformation:

$$\begin{pmatrix} a & b & c & d \\ b & d & a & c \end{pmatrix} \quad \text{or, equivalently,} \quad \begin{pmatrix} b & d & a & c \\ d & c & b & a \end{pmatrix}$$

There are $4! = 1 \times 2 \times 3 \times 4 = 24$ possible permutations of the set $\{a, b, c, d\}$. These permutations, taken together, form a group of transformations. The composition of two permutations means to permute the elements of a permutation whose result is another permutation. The neutral transformation is to leave the order of the elements unchanged. The inverse of a permutation means to rearrange the order induced by that permutation back to the initial order which were in place before the application of the respective permutation.

By the way, the number of distinct permutations of the 26 letters of the English alphabet is the impressively very large number: 26! = 403 291 461 126 605 635 584 000 000."

–"This is unbelievable! I cannot even read it. And 26 is still a small number. What about 10 000!?"

–"Nobody can read it because we have no names for such huge numbers in the current language. Normally a trillion is the word of the largest number unit used in talking about financial transactions, for instance, or about a country's deficit. In fact, the factorial is the most rapidly increasing function we are dealing with. By the way, we were amazed when we learned that some primitive tribes used only six names for the numbers in counting, corresponding to: 'one', 'two', 'three', 'five', and 'more'. With respect to the names for the values of the factorial function, we are all at a very primitive level either."

–"I start to understand what a group means. It denotes an algebraic structure but its specific elements could be of a very different nature. Could you give another example of group?"

–"We can find groups in geometry, as well. Thus, the elements of the group could be the translations of a given rigid figure along a given direction. Here rigid means that all the points of the given figure are equally translated and the distances between them remain the same during these translations. Composing two translations is a new translation, obtained by performing the two given translations successively. The neutral translation is leaving the figure untranslated, and the inverse translation is obtained by performing the translation in the opposite direction by the same amount of displacement, such that applying a certain translation followed by its inverse translation is equivalent to keeping our figure unmoved in the initial position.

As well, we can talk about the group of rotations of a certain rigid figure with respect to a fixed center of rotations. The groups of symmetries play an essential role for a better understanding of the structure of atoms, nuclei, and elementary particles.

When general properties of a certain group structure are studied in an abstract way, the results obtained may be applied to every particular group of that type. Dealing with general groups, we ignore the unessential details found in any specific group and we focus only on the consequences induced by the general composition law and its axioms. Sometimes, we add new axioms to the initial general axioms and we obtain special groups with more specific properties. Thus, if the composition law of a group is commutative, which means that composing an element a with an element b is the same as composing b with a, the respective group is called Abelian, and has additional properties which don't hold in an arbitrary group. But, in order to avoid dealing with empty concepts, every time when we add new axioms we must be sure that such new structures do exist, or could exist, having no internal contradictions."

–"But, if we take the group of integers with respect to the addition, it makes no difference if we add 3 to 7 or 7 to 3."

–"Yes, because the respective group is commutative, or Abelian, but this doesn't happen in any group. Thus, in the second half of the 19th century, a British mathematician, Arthur Cayley (1821-1895), introduced the important algebra of matrices. A vector is a system of several numbers, called its components. These components may be arranged either in a row, which gives a row vector, or in a column, in which case it is called a column vector. A matrix is a tableau of numbers, with m rows and n columns, called $m \times n$ matrix. Therefore, such a matrix may be viewed as consisting of m row vectors with n components arranged in a column, or, equivalently, as n column vectors with m components arranged in a row. In fact, a row vector with n components may be viewed as being a $1 \times n$ matrix, whereas a column vector with m components may be viewed as being an $m \times 1$ matrix. Instead of dealing with individual numbers, we deal with entire rows, columns, or rectangular tables of numbers. Such a global approach provides a useful tool in coping with complexity. An $m \times n$ matrix and an $n \times r$ matrix may be multiplied by summing up, algebraically, the products between the components of each row from the first matrix with the corresponding components from each column of the second matrix. The result is a new $m \times r$ matrix. In particular, if we deal with 2×2 matrices, the sum and the product of two such matrices are defined by:

$$\begin{pmatrix} a & b \\ c & d \end{pmatrix} + \begin{pmatrix} e & f \\ g & h \end{pmatrix} = \begin{pmatrix} a+e & b+f \\ c+g & d+h \end{pmatrix};$$

$$\begin{pmatrix} a & b \\ c & d \end{pmatrix} \times \begin{pmatrix} e & f \\ g & h \end{pmatrix} = \begin{pmatrix} ae+bg & af+bh \\ ce+dg & cf+dh \end{pmatrix}.$$

The composition law given by the multiplication between matrices is not commutative, even when the multiplication is performed between matrices having the same number of rows and columns, called square matrices.

Matrices have many applications in applied mathematics, physics, and engineering. Instead of dealing with numbers we deal with tables of numbers taken together. In the algebra of square matrices $m \times m$, the neutral element with respect to the addition is the matrix having all entries equal to zero. Also, the neutral element with respect to the multiplication defined above is the matrix having the number 1 on the main diagonal and the number 0 in all other positions. The funny thing is that just the noncommutativity of the multiplication between matrices proved to play an important role in the matrix formulation of quantum mechanics by Werner Heisenberg in 1924."

–"What other structures, except groups, are studied in modern algebra?"

–"Oh, many many other structures. I am not competent to list them all here. Before mentioning some of them, let me say that modern mathematics is very abstract but there have been always particular models or entities who have inspired the introduction of a new abstract concept. In its original form, algebra dealt with mathematical operations on numbers considered from a formal point of view. The magnitudes have been denoted by letters on which operations are carried according to formal rules. Later the magnitudes have been replaced by the elements of an abstract set. Thus the properties of the addition of integers, have inspired the introduction of the abstract concept of group, as we have just discussed. But now, instead of taking only one composition law in a set, as we do in groups, we can take two such composition laws defined in the same set. The properties of the addition and multiplication of integers, taken together, have induced the definition of the abstract concept of ring. The properties of the addition and multiplication of real numbers, taken together, have induced the introduction of the concept of field. And so on.

Taking an abstract set endowed with some operations on it defines an algebraic structure. The advantage is that there are groups, rings, or fields whose elements are not necessarily numbers. For instance, if instead of one composition law between the pairs of an abstract set of elements we define two different composition laws, each with a well defined neutral element, with specific inverse elements assigned to each element with respect to each of these laws, and we connect the two composition laws using a distributive property, like $a(b + c) = ab + ac$, for instance, we obtain the important algebraic structure called field. Don't ask me why the name field was chosen because I have no idea and, anyway, it had to be called somehow."

– "Could you explain again what is the difference between a ring and a field?"

– "A set of elements is a field if there are two different composition laws, let me say law #1 and law #2, such that the respective set is a group with respect to each of these two laws and these two composition laws are connected such that, roughly speaking, if an element a is composed, according to law #2, with the result of the composition of the elements b and c, according to law #1, we obtain the same outcome as composing, according to law #1, the results of composing a and b and a and c, by using law #2. More often than not, the composition law #1 is represented by the sign '+', like the addition in arithmetic, and the group with respect to it is called additive group. Similarly, the composition law #2 is represented by the sign '·', which is sometimes even ignored, like the multiplication in algebra, and the group with respect to it is called multiplicative group. The set of rational numbers, or distinct fractions, and the set of real numbers, which is geometrically identified to the real line, are examples of fields with respect to the addition and multiplication taken as composition laws.

Therefore, dealing with a set in which two composition laws '+', addition, and '·', multiplication, are defined, a field is both an additive group and a multiplicative group. A ring is an additive group but not a multiplicative group. It has all the properties of a field except that not every element has an inverse with respect to the multiplication law.

The set of integer numbers, for instance, is an Abelian group with respect to the addition, but only a ring, and not a field, if we take the multiplication, as a second composition law, into account, because there is a neutral element, namely the number 1, but not an inverse of an integer with respect to the second composition law. Thus a ring is a poorer algebraic structure, therefore more general, than a field, but richer, therefore more specific, or particular, than the structure of group.

There are other algebraic structures bearing funny names like the ideal, for instance. When the elements of a ring are multiplied by a certain element of the ring, called generator, we obtain a subset of the respective ring called ideal. The set of even numbers is an ideal, generated by the integer 2, in the larger ring of all integers; it is a ring itself, included into the larger ring of all integers, and has the supplementary property that any even number remains even when it is multiplied not only by an even number but by any integer as well. This makes it a special kind of ring. Therefore, the set of even numbers is an ideal included into the larger ring of integer numbers, which is included into the larger field of rational numbers, which is included into the field of real numbers, which is included into the larger field of complex numbers.

Not every algebraic structure, however, has a funny name chosen for nobody knows what reasons. Thus, the abstract algebraic structure of vector space is an Abelian additive group of elements called vectors, for which an external multiplication with other elements called scalars is also defined, such that multiplying a vector by a scalar we get another vector. This structure was inspired by the vector calculus, so useful in mechanics, electrodynamics, or engineering. A vector in mechanics is a sophisticated entity, which has a direction, an orientation, and a length. Very often, it is represented as an arrow. We can add two vectors, by taking the diagonal vector of the parallelogram generated by the two vectors, and to each vector, there is an inverse vector which has the same direction, the same length, but opposite orientation. If a certain vector is given, we can multiply it by a real number, called scalar, and the result is a new vector which has the same direction, and the same orientation, if the scalar is positive, or opposite orientation, if the scalar is negative; its length is the length of the initial vector multiplied, arithmetically, by the absolute value of the scalar. The absolute value of 5 is 5 and the absolute value of -5 is also 5. More often than not, the absolute value of a number a is denoted by $|a|$, and it is equal to a, if a is positive, and to $-a$, if a is negative.

The structure of vector space is an important concept where algebra, inspired by geometry, generalizes concepts from the two-dimensional Euclidean space, which is our plane, and the three-dimensional Euclidean space, which is our regular space we live in, to abstract n-dimensional spaces which cannot be geometrically visualized but in which we can still talk about vector's length and direction, as well as about angles and orthogonality between vectors with n components. Thus, in an n-dimensional vector space, a vector $\mathbf{u}$ has n components, which are real numbers, $\mathbf{u} = (a_1, \ldots, a_n)$. It may be viewed as being a row vector, if its components are arranged in a horizontal row, or a column vector, if its components are arranged in a vertical column. If $\mathbf{v} = (b_1, \ldots, b_n)$ is another vector, then the sum of them is a new vector $\mathbf{u} + \mathbf{v} = (a_1 + b_1, \ldots, a_n + b_n)$, the multiplication with a scalar α is the vector $\alpha \mathbf{u} = (\alpha a_1, \ldots, \alpha a_n)$, and the scalar product between $\mathbf{u}$ and $\mathbf{v}$ is a number, $\mathbf{u} \cdot \mathbf{v} = a_1 b_1 + \ldots + a_n b_n$. The scalar product allows us to calculate the length, called also norm, of a vector $\mathbf{u}$, as being $\|\mathbf{u}\| = \sqrt{\mathbf{u} \cdot \mathbf{u}}$, and the cosine of the angle θ between two vectors $\mathbf{u}$ and $\mathbf{v}$, given by $\cos\theta = \mathbf{u} \cdot \mathbf{v}/(\|\mathbf{u}\| . \|\mathbf{v}\|)$. The vectors are orthogonal if their scalar product is equal to zero, in which case Pythagoras's theorem $\|\mathbf{u} + \mathbf{v}\|^2 = \|\mathbf{u}\|^2 + \|\mathbf{v}\|^2$ holds in such an n-dimensional space. Algebra allows us to operate formally in abstract spaces where our intuition doesn't help us much."

– "Who did invent vector spaces?"

– "The word 'invent' is not much used in mathematics. It is more suitable in engineering, where somebody invents a certain technical device. I don't know who exactly introduced and studied the algebraic structure of abstract vector space, but one name that should certainly be mentioned is Hermann Grassmann (1809-1877), who, by the way, began studying theology before teaching mathematics in Berlin.

Anyway, defining different kinds of algebraic structures is only one of the objectives of modern algebra. Another objective is to deal with correspondences between the same or different types of algebraic structures that allow to represent a certain algebraic structure in terms of other algebraic structures. A simple example is provided, for instance, by an application from a group G to another group L such that to each element of G it corresponds a distinct element of L and to each element of L it corresponds a distinct element of G, such that the internal composition laws (the abstract addition and multiplication) from G correspond to the internal composition laws (the abstract addition and multiplication) from L. Such an application is called isomorphism and the groups G and L are said to be isomorphic if there is an isomorphism between them. Even if the two groups G and L could be very different, if they are isomorphic, they may be considered as having identical abstract algebraic structures. In such a case G may be represented by L and vice versa.

Personally, I have always found algebra to be a very useful part of mathematics, that has to be studied, but I also find it too abstract for my tastes if you remain inside it during all your mathematical life and don't apply its results for solving problems in other chapters of mathematics, physics, or engineering. This doesn't mean that you cannot see very happy pure algebraists, isolated in their ivory algebraic tower. But I am afraid that I have annoyed you with too many details."

–"No, you didn't. Frankly speaking, you did not! It is true, however, that some stuff seems difficult sometimes. Anyway, please give me the pieces of paper on which you wrote down some formulas or mathematical symbols. I want to keep them."

–"I am really sorry. From now on I will try to avoid topics and details that are too technical from mathematical point of view. But please feel free to stop me when things become too elaborate or too boring."

SET THEORY AND CLASSIC LOGIC

–"You have mentioned the word set several and several times and not only when they were related to different kinds of numbers. You have also mentioned a set included into a larger set. Is 'set' a mathematical concept or the loose word used in the colloquial talking?"

–"Modern mathematics is based on set theory. A set is a very general concept and general concepts cannot be defined; they can only be explained using similar general concepts. In mathematics, a set is any collection of elements. We can talk about sets of numbers, sets of points, sets of geometric figures like sets of spheres or sets of triangles, sets of groups, etc. A set may be finite, like the set of positive integers smaller than 100, infinite but countable, like the set of all positive integers, or infinite and uncountable, like the set of real numbers.

Often, a set is associated with a certain property or a certain sentence. Thus, the sentence 'Being an even positive integer' defines a set of numbers. For the number 4, for instance, this proposition is true and therefore 4 belongs to the corresponding set. For 7, on the other hand, it is false, and 7 doesn't belong to the given set. Conversely, if a set A is given, the statement 'Belonging to A' is a sentence p which is true for the elements of A and false for the elements that don't belong to A. This is why we can talk either about a set A or, equivalently, about the corresponding sentence, or proposition, p.

If we deal only with the elements x of a total set Ω, let 1 and 0 denote the truth values 'true' and 'false', respectively, and $p(x)$ denotes the truth value of proposition p for the element x. The subset A of the total set Ω corresponding to proposition p is the set of elements x of Ω for which proposition p is true, which means $p(x) = 1$. The complementary set of A, denoted by $\overline{A}$, is the set of elements of Ω for which proposition p is false, which could be written $p(x) = 0$, where '=' stands for 'the truth value is'. The proposition associated to the complementary set $\overline{A}$ is 'non p', which is true when p is false and false when p is true. Two sets are equal if they contain the same elements. We borrow from algebra and arithmetic the sign '=' for equality between sets.

We can perform operations on sets which are very similar to the operations from the classic logic, which originated from the works of

Aristotle (384-322 BC). Thus given two sets A and B, their union $A \cup B$ is a new set consisting of the elements belonging to A or to B or to both of them. Their intersection $A \cap B$ is a new set consisting of elements that belong both to A and to B. A set without any element is called the empty set and is denoted by $\emptyset$. Two sets with empty intersection are called disjoint. If the elements of a set A belong also to a set B, we say that A is included in B or, equivalently, that B includes A as a subset, symbolically denoted by $A \subset B$.

We can see, from their definition, that the union, intersection, complementarity, and inclusion, between the subsets of a total set Ω correspond to the logical operators 'or' $\vee$, 'and' $\wedge$, 'non', and 'implies' $\Rightarrow$, between the corresponding propositions associated with the respective subsets. Two proposition p and q are equal, and we write $p = q$ if p is true if and only if q is true and p is false if and only if q is false. The implication between propositions satisfies two properties, called *modus ponens*, according to which if $p \Rightarrow q$ and p is true then q is also true, and *modus tollens*, according to which if $p \Rightarrow q$ and q is false, then p is also false.

Mathematicians and logicians use to denote abstract sets, or their associated propositions, like discs in a bigger rectangle, called universe. Two discs that don't intersect, for instance, represent disjoint sets. Using such geometric representations of sets, called Venn diagrams, after the logician John Venn, we can easily prove well-known laws from set theory and logic, like the law of double negation $\overline{\overline{A}} = A$, or non(non p) = p, and Augustus De Morgan's laws, according to which $\overline{A \cup B} = \overline{A} \cap \overline{B}$ and $\overline{A \cap B} = \overline{A} \cup \overline{B}$, or, equivalently, non$(p \vee q)$=(non p)$\wedge$(non q) and non$(p \wedge q)$=(non p)$\vee$(non q), where p and q are the propositions corresponding to the subsets A and B, respectively.

The parallel between subsets and propositions from classic logic could be pushed even father. If $\mathbf{1}$ denotes the proposition associated to the total set Ω, which means the proposition always true, and $\mathbf{0}$ denotes the proposition associated with the empty set $\emptyset$, or proposition always false, then: $A \cup \overline{A} = \Omega$, which is the so-called *tertium non datur*, or the principle of the excluded third, and $A \cap \overline{A} = \emptyset$, in the language of set theory or, equivalently, $p \vee$(non p)=$\mathbf{1}$ and $p \wedge$(non p)= $\mathbf{0}$, in the language of classic logic."

BOOLE

–"In general, we use propositions when we talk or write and logic, as far as I know, teaches us how to reason correctly. Does this mean that the mathematics of propositions, if there is such a mathematics, isn't given by the current algebra, as it was taught in school, but by the set theory?"

–"This is just so. George Boole (1815-1864) showed convincingly that the operations with sets do resemble the logic operations with sentences and not the operations from arithmetic. Thus $A \cup A = A$ and $A \cap A = A$, in set theory, or $p \vee p = p$ and $p \wedge p = p$, in logic, fundamentally differ from $3 + 3 = 6$ and $3 \times 3 = 9$, from arithmetic.

In fact Boole used the same operations $+$ and $\cdot$, like in arithmetics and algebra, but their significance was completely different. Thus, $+$ was used by him for 'union', or the logical operator 'or', and $\cdot$ for 'intersection', or the logical operator 'and'. If 0, 1, and $\overline{x}$ denote 'false', 'true', and 'non x', respectively, then the so called Boolean algebra uses rules that don't exist in arithmetic and standard algebra but that are similar to the operations on sets, like: $x + x = x$, $x \cdot x = x$, $x \cdot \overline{x} = 0$, $x + \overline{x} = 1$, $\overline{x + y} = \overline{x} \cdot \overline{y}$, or $\overline{x \cdot y} = \overline{x} + \overline{y}$, for instance.

This is a totally different kind of mathematics, rather symbolic or propositional than numerical. This explains why the algebra created by George Boole eventually proved to be essential in abstract probability theory, where the possible events form a so-called Boolean algebra, in computer science, and in some chapters of artificial intelligence like pattern-recognition, for instance."

–"What do you know about Boole's life?"

–"Very, very little. He was Irish and lived in the first half of the nineteenth century and had a short life. When he was 40 years old, he married Mary Everest, 23 years old, whose uncle Sir George Everest was Surveyor-General of India and had the world's highest mountain named after him. George Boole wrote poetry. In ten years of marriage they had five daughters. His health had never been robust. When he was only 49 years old, Boole died of an inflammation of the lungs, or pleuro-pneumonia, after walking about six kilometers in a pouring rain going to a lecture he delivered in wet clothes. I have seen a modern new Boole Library at the University College in Cork. He was a profoundly religious man. He regarded the human mind as the finest example of divine creation. Boole was elected a fellow of the Royal Society in London but, strangely, not a member of the Royal Irish Academy. Often, he used to work thinking in the dark for sparing his eyes. Boole wrote a fundamental book entitled so beautifully: *An Investigation of the Laws of Thought on Which are Founded the Mathematical Theories of Logic and Probabilities.* It has been printed several and several times since his times. I have a copy of it in my office and I am really marveled every time when I read some pages of it."

OTHER LOGICS

-"If I remember well, you have said classic logic. We say classic music when we refer to Mozart, Beethoven, Grieg, because there are also other kinds of music, like the music composed and interpreted by Beatles, for instance. Is there a logic which is different from the classic logic?"

–"Yes, there are other kinds of logic either. Continuing the analogy between sets and classic logic, suppose that a set A contains those elements that have a certain property p. For instance, dealing with positive integers, the set of even integers is defined by the property 'the integer is divisible by 2'. Everything is crystal clear here because every positive integer either belongs to the set of even integers or doesn't belong to it. Thus, it is true that 4 belongs to the set of even integers and it is false that 211 belongs to the set of even integers. True or false, like in the classic logic where we have only these two truth values.

Around 1930, Jan Łukasiewicz introduced the three-valued logic, where the truth values are: true, possible, and false, denoted by 1, 1/2, and 0, respectively. If now Mike says 'On 25 December, next year, I will be in New York,' this sentence could be true, possible, or false. The tables for negation 'non', disjunction $\vee$, conjunction $\wedge$, and implication $\Rightarrow$ in this logic are:

p	0	1/2	1
non p	1	1/2	0

			q	
$p \vee q$		0	1/2	1
	0	0	1/2	1
p	1/2	1/2	1/2	1
	1	1	1	1

			q	
$p \wedge q$		0	1/2	1
	0	0	0	0
p	1/2	0	1/2	1/2
	1	0	1/2	1

			q	
$p \Rightarrow q$		0	1/2	1
	0	1	1	1
p	1/2	1/2	1	1
	1	0	1/2	1

Another kind of logic is obtained if we consider properties which are not so clearly cut. Thus, if we refer to the men living now in Geneva and the property is 'being bald', it is not so easy to classify a man as being bald or not. There are many men who are more or less bald. We arrive to the so called fuzzy sets where we can talk not about true or false, yes or no, has a certain property or not, but only about several degrees of satisfying a given property, like several degrees of baldness for our example. Dealing with vague properties or concepts is very common in everyday life."

–"What is the relationship between classic logic and this fuzzy logic?"

–"If we go back to the classic logic and take a subset A of the total set Ω whose corresponding property or proposition is p, as I have said, for every element x of the total set Ω, $p(x)$ is either 1, if x belongs to A, or 0, if it doesn't. If 1 and 0 are taken to be numbers, corresponding to the truth values 'true' and 'false', respectively, then $p(x)$ is also called the membership function of the set A. Now, if this membership function is allowed to take any numerical values in the unit interval $[0, 1]$, it is said that A is a fuzzy set. In this case, the real number $p(x)$ represents the degree of membership of the element x of the total set Ω to the fuzzy set A. Things are now vaguer than in the classic logic and we can no longer say with certainty whether an element x of the total set Ω belongs or not to A. Instead, we are more cautious and say: 'The element x belongs to A with the degree of accuracy $p(x)$, which is a number in between 0 and 1.'

I want to give you another simple example of a fuzzy set, to see how different it is from a classic set. In the set of positive integers, taken as the total set Ω, the subset consisting of only the number 5, denoted by $\{5\}$, has the membership function p whose values are $p(5) = 1$, and $p(n) = 0$, for every positive integer n different from 5. A fuzzy set 'approximately 5', which allows the number 5 to be approximated by 4 or 6 with an approximation level 0.1, has the membership function p whose values are $p(4) = 0.1$, $p(5) = 1$, $p(6) = 0.1$, and $p(n) = 0$, for all positive integers n different from 4, 5, 6.

A systematic study of the fuzzy sets was done by Lotfi Zadeh. Being bald, as we have seen, is a fuzzy set. How much hair somebody should have in order to be called bald? A 'sharp 5' is a classic, or crisp, set, whereas an 'approximate 5' is a fuzzy, or vague, set. Somewhere, sometime, Zadeh said or wrote that Nature doesn't write with a sharp pencil but uses a spray can."

–"Therefore, except the classic logic, there are two other logics, the logic with three values and the fuzzy logic. Are there still other logics?"

–"Yes. The three-valued logic has been generalized to multivalued logics with more than three possible truth values. There are some more specialized logics like the deontic logic and the modal logic. Unfortunately, I am not familiar with them. I have mentioned only those logics that are closer to mathematics. There are topics in logic for which no adequate mathematics has been found. Thus, John von Neumann, a brilliant mathematician who was an active member of the group of experts who built the first powerful computer in Los Alamos during the World War II, said somewhere that computers are incapable of dialectical reasoning and the language of the brain is not the language of mathematics."

–"What is dialectical reasoning? I have seen the word dialectical in newspapers but, for me, it is something nebulous, even murky."

–"To be frank with you, it is nebulous to me too. Some philosophers insist, however, that the dialectic logic explains better the structure and evolution of systems in nature and society. As far as I can remember, some of its theses, as formulated in a relatively obscure way, long ago, by Georg Wilhelm Friedrich Hegel (1770-1831), and made a little clearer for me by Mario Bunge, are: Everything has an opposite; Every object is contradictory, consisting of mutually opposing components and/or aspects; Every change is an outcome of the tension or struggle of opposites within a system or among different systems; Progress is a helix every level of which contains, and at the same time negates, the previous rung; Every quantitative change ends up in some qualitative change and every new quality brings about new modes of quantitative change. I don't know any serious and consistent attempt at building a mathematical model for dialectic logic. Perhaps a new kind of mathematics would be needed. Maybe somebody from your generation will succeed in doing this. As things stay today, the mathematical proofs still rely on classic logic and the theory of crisp sets."

CANTOR

−"I prefer to deal with yes-no sets. It seems to be quite easy and natural to deal with such sets and perform operations on them. It seems to be very intuitive. For me, in order to understand something, it is very important to get a picture, or a diagram, or a graph, or some kind of concrete representation of things or concepts."

−"This is quite true when the sets have a finite number of elements. The complications appear when we take into account infinite sets. Georg Cantor (1845-1918) was the first mathematician who fully understood the subtleties of the infinite sets and that there are several and several types of infinite sets."

−"A set is either finite or infinite. Obviously, we can have different kinds of finite sets, depending on how many elements they have, but, for me, an infinite set is just a very large set with nobody knows how many elements. But what did Cantor do and how is it possible to have more kinds of infinite sets?"

−"He assigned to each set its cardinal number. Two sets have the same cardinal if there is a one-to-one pairing of their elements. If a set has five elements, its cardinal is five because its elements may be one-to-one paired with the elements of the set consisting of the integers 1, 2, 3, 4, 5. The set of positive integers is the simplest infinite set. Its cardinal number has been denoted by $\aleph_0$. Here $\aleph$ is the first letter from the Hebrew alphabet, called 'aleph'. The subscript 0 is to indicate that this is the smallest infinity. Any set which has the cardinal number $\aleph_0$ is called denumerable, or countable. The name is well justified because for such a set, its elements may be one-to-one paired with the set of positive integers which means that its elements may be numbered. In dealing with infinite sets our intuition doesn't help us. Indeed, as the set of even positive integers is also countable, we see that a subset of a countable set may be itself countable which, roughly speaking, says that an infinite set may have as many elements as a subset of it. This is something more difficult to understand because the finite sets, we are used to deal with, don't have such a property and we are tempted to extend, wrongly, the properties of the finite sets to the infinite ones.

Cantor showed that the set of rational fractions is also countable but the set of real numbers has a higher cardinal number, denoted by $\aleph$, than the set of rational fractions. In order to show that the set of real numbers between 0 and 1 is not denumerable, assume that it is in fact denumerable, in which case the real numbers between 0 and 1 may be arranged in a sequence: a_1, a_2, ... But every such real number a_i may be identified with a sequence of digits forming its decimal part. If we take the i-th decimal of the real number a_i, change it into any other digit, and take this altered value to be the i-th decimal of a real number denoted by b, this new number is a real number between 0 and 1 but doesn't belong to the sequence of real numbers between 0 and 1 because b differs from the real number a_i in at least the i-th decimal. Therefore, we have assumed that the real numbers between 0 and 1 may be arranged in a sequence but, by this diagonal procedure, we have constructed a real number between 0 and 1 which doesn't belong to the sequence. This is a contradiction. Thus, the set of real numbers between 0 and 1 cannot be arranged in a sequence and therefore is not denumerable."

–"Does this mean that there are two kinds of infinite sets?"

−"No, many many more. In fact, as shown by Cantor, we can construct 'bigger' and 'bigger' cardinal numbers. He built a whole hierarchy of infinite sets according to their different cardinal numbers. Indeed, if we have an infinite set, then all its parts, taken together, form another set which has a 'bigger' cardinal number than the initial set, and so on. As mentioned before, one of the most puzzling things in dealing with infinite sets is that a proper subset of an infinite set can have as many elements as the set itself. Cantor showed that the set of real numbers from the unit interval has the same cardinal number $\aleph$ as the set of points from the square of side 1, or as the set of points from the cube of side 1. When he proved this, Cantor himself was amazed and it is said that he wrote to a friend: 'I see it, but I don't believe it!' Also, the set of algebraic numbers, namely the set of numbers which are roots of polynomial equations with integer coefficients, is denumerable. If we keep in mind that a transcendental number is an irrational number which is not a root of any polynomial equation with integer coefficients, then it results that almost all numbers are transcendental because real numbers are not denumerable while the algebraic numbers are denumerable.

Cantor is the undisputed creator of set theory. When something fundamentally new is introduced, like set theory for instance, intuition and flair play an important role in the initial phase of the construction of the new theory which is being created. It takes a little time until it becomes clear on what system of axioms the new theory is to be based on. The usual axioms of set theory, nine of them, which are accepted today, have been formulated by Ernst Zermelo, Abraham Fraenkel, and Thokolf Skolem. Some of these axioms are simple, intuitive, and easy to be accepted, like: Two sets are equal if and only if they have the same elements; There exists a set with no elements (the empty set, denoted by $\emptyset$); For every set of sets, the union of its members is a set; If $\in$ means 'belongs to', and $\{x\}$ is the set containing the element x, then $x \in \{x\}$, but we cannot write $x \in x$; If A and B are sets, then the pair $\{A, B\}$ is a set.

One of the axioms, however, called the axiom of choice, has raised many discussions. It says that if we have a collection of nonempty sets $\{A, B, \ldots\}$, then there is a set Z consisting of exactly one element from A, one element from B, and so on, for all the sets of the collection.

Intuitively, this axiom seems to be very plausible, but some mathematicians recommend to avoid it because it doesn't say, anyway, how such a selection, or choosing, should be performed.

Cantor also made the assumption, called the continuum hypothesis, that any infinite set of real numbers has either the cardinality of the set of all positive integers or the cardinality of the set of all real numbers. In 1938, Kurt Gödel showed that one cannot disprove Cantor's conjecture using the usual axioms of set theory. Later, in 1963, Paul Cohen showed that it is also impossible to prove it. Therefore, if the usual axioms for set theory are used, the continuum hypothesis is formally undecidable."

–"I think that I am becoming dizzy with so many kinds of infinite sets."

–"I am sorry. I wasn't supposed to give you all these details. In fact, many mathematicians have been reluctant to accept the results on infinite sets published by Cantor. More than that, some embarrassing paradoxes started to appear inside the set theory. To give only one such an example, let us consider the set of all sets that are not elements of themselves."

–"How can a set be an element of itself?"

–"If we take the set of even numbers, such a set is not an even number and, therefore, doesn't belong to itself. But if we consider the set of all non-peaches, this set is not a peach and, therefore, it is an element of itself. The set of all sets that are not elements of themselves offers such a paradox of set theory because we cannot decide whether this huge set is an element of itself or not. If it is an element of itself then, according to its definition, it is not an element of itself. Conversely, if it is not an element of itself then, by its definition, it is an element of itself. We cannot get out of this dilemma because the set of all sets that are not elements of themselves is contradictory. A popular version of this paradox is the so-called barber of the regiment. But perhaps you know it."

–"No, I don't."

–"In a regiment there is one barber. According to the strict regulations, the barber has to shave those and only those members of the regiment who do not shave themselves. The paradox is about what is going to happen with the barber himself. If he shaves himself, then he cannot be shaved by the barber of the regiment. If he doesn't shave himself, then he has to be shaved by the barber of the regiment."

–"How did Cantor solve this paradox?"

–"He didn't. Due to his intensive work and the criticism of his results, Cantor suffered several attacks of severe depression in the last years of his life and died in a mental institution."

–"That was really tragic. Have his results been accepted after his death?"

–"Yes. In fact even before he died in 1918, because not everybody rejected what he did. The entire mathematics of the twentieth century was in fact written on set theoretical basis. Unfortunately, in his last years, Cantor was more preoccupied to convince people that Francis Bacon wrote William Shakespeare's plays than to pursue his work on infinite sets.

GEOMETRY

–"In school, I found algebra to be much easier than geometry. Once you get used to the algebraic rules for manipulating algebraic expressions and solving equations, everything goes relatively easy if you are careful. But in geometry you need a lot of intuition and sometimes the solution of a problem depends on some supplementary constructions, like drawing a useful parallel or perpendicular in a given geometrical figure. There are no general rules for solving a problem in geometry. Much depends on inspiration. I found particularly difficult to prove that some points are on the same line segment, or collinear as they are called, that several lines meet at the same point, or to describe the set of all points that satisfy a certain geometric condition."

−"Yes. Perhaps geometry is the best 'gymnastic of the mind'. The geometry taught in high school is still the old Euclidean geometry. Euclid's *Elements* came out about 300 years B.C. It put on axiomatic basis what was known at that time in the geometry of the plane and three-dimensional space. Perhaps the most important discovery of Greek mathematics was the concept of proof: To derive the conclusions of a theorem from its hypotheses, using the accepted axioms and the rules of the respective theory, including the classic logic as the way of correctly reasoning, and other theorems previously proved. The first proof is said to have been given by Thales of Miletus (600 BC) when he justified that the diameter divides a circle into two equal parts."

−"This seems quite obvious to me."

−"Thales understood that in mathematics we cannot rely on intuition. It is true that sometimes, when we discover something new, our intuition could play a major role. But, subsequently, we have to prove it rigorously, which means to show, step by step, that the claimed results are logically implied by axioms and intermediary results already proved to be true. If a sentence p implies a sentence q then, if p is true then q is true as well. 'True' cannot imply 'false', but 'false' can imply anything. Indeed, the above statement proved by Thales is very simple. But what is still called Thales's theorem, stating that a parallel to one of the sides of a triangle divides the other two sides in proportional line segments, is not obvious at all and had to be proved. Without mentioning another important result, Pythagoras's theorem, stating that in right-angled triangles the square on the side subtending the right angle is equal to the sum of the squares on the sides containing the right angle, which is also far from being intuitively obvious and whose proof is not trivial at all."

−"What obvious sentences did Euclid take as axioms?"

−"The first five axioms of Euclid's *Elements* were: 1. Given two points, there is a line that joins them; 2. A line can be prolonged indefinitely; 3. A circle can be constructed when its center and a point on it are given; 4. All right angles are equal; 5. If a point lies outside a straight line, one and only one straight line can be drawn through that point that will be parallel to the first line.

The fifth axiom is very different from the other ones and many unsuccessful attempts have been made to prove it from the other four. Much much later, in 1697, Girolamo Saccheri assumed the first four axioms to be true but the fifth axiom to be false and wrongly believed that he got a contradiction. In 1766, however, Johann Heinrich Lambert, who, by the way, left school at the age of twelve, taught himself, became a tutor in an aristocratic family of Coire, here in Switzerland, becoming a member of the Swiss Scientific Society of Basel, showed that in a geometry where the first four axioms are true and the fifth one is false no contradiction occurs.

After many years, two new non-Euclidean geometries have been developed, namely the so called hyperbolic geometry, created independently by János Bolyai and Nikolai Ivanovich Lobachevsky, which allows an infinite number of parallels to a given line through any exterior point, and the elliptic geometry, created by Bernhard Riemann, which allows no parallels to a given line through any exterior point.

Felix Klein (1849-1925) proposed to use group theory in order to unify different geometries. According to his so called *Erlangen program*, every 'geometry' is the theory of the invariants of a particular group of transformations. A transformation moves the points of a space into points of the same space, like a flow acting inside that set, mixing up its points and its subsets. Thus, Euclidean geometry is the study of invariants of the group of those transformations of the plane that preserve the distance between points. Anyway, synthetic geometry is not much taught in universities these days. There could be a marginal course about it, but not more."

DESCARTES

–"Is there another kind of geometry which is different from what we have been taught in high school, called by you synthetic geometry, because, as I said, I like it more than any other topics of mathematics I was taught about."

–"Yes, there are different continuations of it. Much more emphasis is put on analytic geometry, a happy marriage between geometry and algebra. It was initiated by René du Perron Descartes (1596-1650), a genuine 'mousquetaire', in the first half of the 17th century. He was a very unusual and interesting character. Being frail, he liked to stay in bed in the morning and think. He is famous for his maxim: 'I think, therefore I exist'. In the boarding-school, being a brilliant pupil, he was given a special right to wake up later than the time required by the severe rules of the old school. He studied law in Poitiers and mathematics in Paris but joined the army of the Prince of Orange. Later, he settled in Holland and, when he was 53 years old, already famous for his contributions in mathematics and philosophy, he went to Sweden, invited by Queen Christina. It is said that the scientific discussions between the 53 years old scholar and the eccentric 23 years old queen took place at five o'clock in the morning, in an unheated room. This could be true or not, I don't know. Unfortunately, Descartes died shortly after of pneumonia. There is no doubt that both the cold climate and the austere, early-rising rules at the royal court, preventing him from indulging in his habit of spending more time in bed in the morning, contributed to his premature death."

–"Wow! It would have been nice if Alexandre Dumas had written about René Descartes too, not only about d'Artagnan and the three musketeers Aramis, Porthos, and I don't remember the other one's name."

–"Athos. It would have been nice, indeed. A legend about him says that once, he was aboard a ship and he heard some thugs talking in a foreign language, I don't remember which one, planning to attack him. Descartes, who knew that language too, was well-prepared when they eventually attacked him and succeeded in overpowering them.

Another story about him, but this time an authentic one, is the following. Once, I had in one of my courses a student majoring in philosophy. He took my course just in case, as an elective course. Unfortunately, his mathematical background was very weak and eventually he dropped the course, to my regret because he was a fine individual. In one of my tests there was a problem with nine yes-no questions. I, generally, don't like multiple-choice problems and the students, with minor exceptions, don't like them either. But, on one hand, you can use them for rapidly testing whether the students know some details of basic theoretical statements and, on the other hand, such problems are easy to mark. The student I am talking about didn't do anything in the other problems of the test but got right seven out of nine questions in the yes-no problem, by answering 'no' to all of them. When I returned the marked tests to the students, I asked him how did happen that he had known seven correct answers out of nine in that yes-no problem but couldn't solve any other problem of the test. The student was very frank and said to me: 'Professor, I didn't know how to answer the questions in that problem either but I applied Descartes's recommendation about the power of negative thinking and I put 'no' to all of them.'

Descartes wasn't only a mathematician but also a philosopher and indeed, in his method for thinking correctly, he mentioned the cautious rule of choosing 'no' rather than 'yes' when you are in doubt. The so called principle of doubt is a basic component of the Cartesian reasoning. The adjective Cartesian, which is frequently used in mathematics when we talk about Cartesian system of coordinates or Cartesian product of sets, for instance, comes from the Latin name of René Descartes which is Renatus Cartesius."

−"At least your student had a reason for answering only 'no' to all your questions. I know a joke about a teacher who noticed that a student of his chose his answers to a yes-no test by flipping a coin. When the time was up, all students gave the   tests to the teacher except our fellow who continued to flip his coin. Then, the teacher approached him saying: 'You have answered the questions by simply tossing a coin. Why didn't you finish your test yet?' 'I have finished it, but now I am checking my answers!' said the student."

−"This is a good one. I will tell it to my students next year. Anyway, due to Descartes, geometry was reduced to algebra. He introduced the concept of coordinates and the concept of representing by the coordinate method any algebraic equation with two unknowns in the form of a curve in the plane. He took a reference system of coordinate axes, consisting of two perpendicular straight lines intersecting at a point called the origin. By the coordinates of a point in the plane he meant the abscissa and ordinate, therefore two numbers, representing the projection of the respective point on the horizontal axis and on the vertical axis, respectively. On the horizontal axis, an abscissa is positive on the right-hand side of the origin and negative on the left-hand side of the origin. On the vertical axis, an ordinate is positive above the origin and negative below the origin. It seems to be obvious today, but Descartes was the first one who 'arithmetized' the plane, a geometric point being replaced by a pair of numbers, its coordinates. This has changed everything in geometry. Any function $y = f(x)$ of one variable, viewed as an equation in two variables, namely $y - f(x) = 0$, or more generally, $F(x, y) = 0$, becomes now a curve in the plane. This is how the graphs of functions, so accessible today by using different computer softwares, have appeared. More than that, Descartes wanted not only to represent graphically some functions but used his method for finding the points where such a function has a local maximum or a local minimum value.

Once these truly revolutionary ideas have been introduced in mathematics, the so called analytic geometry has expanded to spaces with more dimensions, like the algebraic study of curves and surfaces in space, and to the algebraic study of functions in abstract spaces. We can say that analytic geometry and its abstract generalization called algebraic geometry, are parts of mathematics which investigate geometric objects by algebraic means. Marriages between different domains of mathematics have always been very fruitful. I have just mentioned the use of algebra in geometry. Another great achievement was the use of differential and integral calculus in geometry, resulting in the creation of the differential geometry, showing what kind of equations describe the curvature, curved triangles, angles between curves, and shortest distances between points, called geodesics, on different types of surfaces. It was like seeing what kind of intrinsic geometry has to be discovered and used by a thinking shadow living on an egg shell. Towards the middle of the 19th century, Bernhard Riemann, through his results on algebraic functions, brought geometry into contact with the theory of analytic functions of complex variables and with topology. In the first part of the 20th century, Marius Sophus Lie introduced continuous groups, named Lie groups, that proved to be important in differential geometry, in abstract group theory, and in mathematical models of the physics of elementary particles."

CALCULUS

–"Therefore, a student in mathematics has to start his study by taking a linear algebra course first. What else?"

–"Without any doubt, calculus, or mathematical analysis how it is called in many European countries. It can be taken simultaneously with linear algebra. Calculus could be covered in separate, easier so-called service half courses, meant for those interested only in acquiring some techniques to differentiate and integrate functions of one or several variables and manipulate series. A deep understanding of the basic concepts and corresponding proofs needs several full courses, at least two anyway.

Basically, calculus and its ramifications deal with the study of functions. A function is a correspondence between sets. To each element x of a set A, called domain of definition, a function assigns a unique element $y = f(x)$, from another set B, called codomain. Generally, the codomain is a set of numbers and sometimes the domain too is a set of numbers. The generic element x represents a variable. In multivariate calculus, the codomain B is still a set of numbers but x is a vector and the domain A is a set of vectors with n numerical components. In the one-dimensional case, in the original applications, the function $f(x)$ described a trajectory followed by a moving vehicle, and the variable x represented time, increasing from time instant t_1 to time instant t_2. The problem was to study different types of such trajectories, their continuity, their points of discontinuity, their maximum and minimum values, their rate of change, which is the velocity or first derivative, the rate of change of the rate of change, which is the acceleration or second derivative.

Conversely, if the rate of change, or first derivative, is given, we want to see how to find the function, called antiderivative, or primitive, that has such a given rate, which means to calculate indefinite integrals. Definite integrals were also introduced. In the one-dimensional case, the definite integral of a positive function on a certain numerical interval is just the area under the curve and above the corresponding interval. When such an integral is divided by the length of the interval of integration, it gives the mean value of the integrated function on that interval.

Another important problem is how to represent a complicated function, like the exponential, logarithmic, radical, sine, cosine, tangent, cotangent functions, in terms of simpler functions like polynomials with an infinite number of terms, called series. These and their generalizations to the multi-dimensional case, are some fundamental problems in calculus."

−"We did some calculus in high school and I know the basic rules to calculate derivatives and integrals of elementary functions. But our math teacher, who was quite good otherwise, didn't insist much on definitions and basic concepts. What is really essential in calculus?"

−"I am afraid that everything is essential and useful there. I could say, however, that the concept of limit is really new in calculus and causes headaches to students. Yet, the concept of limit is very intuitive but involves infinite sets. And infinity scares people. An infinite sequence of real numbers $\{x_1, x_2, \ldots, x_n, \ldots\}$ has the number x_0 as its limit if, except a finite number of them, all the elements of the sequence are as close as we want to x_0. We use to write this as $\lim_{n \to \infty} x_n = x_0$, but this explicitly means that for every small real number $\varepsilon > 0$, there is an integer n_0, depending on ε, such that $|x_n - x_0| < \varepsilon$ if $n > n_0$. Thus, the sequence $\{1, 1/2, 1/3, \ldots, 1/n, \ldots\}$ has the limit equal to 0, or converges to 0 when n tends to infinity, because whatever choice we make for the small number $\varepsilon > 0$, all the terms of this sequence, except a finite number of them, will be within a distance smaller than ε from the limit 0. Indeed, if $\varepsilon = 0.00001$, for instance, then $|1/n - 0| < 0.00001$ for all $n > 100000$. We write $\lim_{n \to \infty}(1/n) = 0$.

If $f(x)$ is a function defined on a domain D, this function has the number a as the limit at the point x_0, and we write $\lim_{x \to x_0} f(x) = a$, if for every small real number $\varepsilon > 0$ there is a small real number $\delta > 0$, such that for each x from D for which $|x - x_0| < \delta$, we have $|f(x) - a| < \varepsilon$. Again, this seems almost incomprehensible but in fact it simply says that the values $f(x)$ of our function are very close to the number a when the values of the argument x are close to x_0. The function $f(x)$ is continuous at the point x_0 if, in the above definition, $a = f(x_0)$, which again, may be made intuitive by saying that a function is continuous at a point x_0 if small variations of the variable x around x_0 result in small variations of the values $f(x)$ of the function around $f(x_0)$. A function $f(x)$ is continuous in a domain D if it is continuous in every point of this domain.

To the same extent to which we learn to hear a tuneful music reading the signs of a partition written for violin or piano, the secret in calculus is to read symbolic formulas feeling what they intuitively 'tell' you. This visualization of symbolic mathematics comes after a lot of practice in trying to particularize and make concrete our thoughts and concepts we are dealing with. We have to see, hear, and smell our formulas, so to speak.

The concept of limit is applied everywhere in calculus. Thus, a continuous function is differentiable at a point x_0 if there is the limit $\lim_{x \to x_0} [f(x) - f(x_0)]/(x - x_0)$. This limit is the first derivative of $f(x)$ at x_0, denoted by $f'(x_0)$. Calculated at different points of the domain of definition, the first derivative f' of the function f is also a function. The derivative of the first derivative f' is the second derivative, f'', and so on. If $y = f(x)$ denotes a function, where y is the value of the function f corresponding to the value x of its argument, sometimes we use the symbols dx and dy to denote small variations of x and y, respectively, and we call them differentials. In such a case, the derivative f' makes the connection between the two differentials and we write $dy = f'(x)\,dx$. A function $f(x)$ is smooth if it is continuous and has continuous derivatives. The trigonometric functions, like $\sin x$ or $\cos x$, the exponential functions, like e^x, and the polynomials of any degree, for instance, are continuous and have derivatives of any order. If a function depends of two variables, namely $f(x, y)$, the partial derivative of f with respect to the variable x at x_0 is the limit: $\lim_{x \to x_0} [f(x, y) - f(x_0, y)]/(x - x_0)$, denoted by $(\partial f/\partial x)(x_0, y)$.

If $\{x_1, x_2, \ldots\}$ is a sequence of numbers and $\{f_1(x), f_2(x), \ldots\}$ is a sequence of functions, the series of numbers $\sum_{k=1}^{\infty} x_k$ and the series of functions $\sum_{k=1}^{\infty} f_k(x)$ are defined as the limits of the finite sums, $\lim_{n \to \infty} \sum_{k=1}^{n} x_k$ and $\lim_{n \to \infty} \sum_{k=1}^{n} f_k(x)$, respectively, if these limits do exist. A numerical series is convergent if its sum exists and is a finite number. It is divergent if the sum is infinite. Thus, the harmonic series

$1+\frac{1}{2}+\frac{1}{3}+\frac{1}{4}+\ldots$ is divergent whereas the alternate series $1-\frac{1}{2}+\frac{1}{3}-\frac{1}{4}+\ldots$ is convergent and equal to $\ln 2$.

Finally, the limit is also essential to define the definite integral of a continuous function $f(x)$ on an interval $[a,b]$, denoted by the symbol $\int_a^b f(x)\,dx$. Thus, if we take a partition Δ_n of the interval $[a,b]$ in n equal subintervals, $a = x_0 < x_1 < \ldots < x_{n-1} < x_n = b$, this definite integral is the limit $\lim_{n\to\infty} S(\Delta_n)$, where the sum $S(\Delta_n) = \sum_{k=1}^{n} f(y_k)(x_k - x_{k-1})$, where y_k is an arbitrary point belonging to the subinterval $[x_{k-1}, x_k]$. Again, we can visualize what happens here and see that $S(\Delta_n)$ is a finite sum of rectangles erected on the n subintervals of $[a,b]$, and the definite integral represents the area between the curve $y = f(x)$ and the interval $[a,b]$."

–"What is the most important result in calculus, in your opinion?"

–"Except the rules for calculating derivatives and integrals, which now are being taught even in high school, and the central role played by the limits, I think that the concept of series is the most important. A series is a sum with an infinite number of terms. It is convergent if the sum is finite and divergent if the sum is infinite or cannot be calculated. Some series are very strange. Thus, the mysterious transcendental number

$\pi = 3.1415926535\ldots$, which appears in the formulas for the area of a circle πr^2, the length of a circle $2\pi r$, or the volume of a sphere, $4\pi R^3/3$, where r is the radius of the circle and R is the radius of the sphere, is the sum of a very regular infinite series: $\pi/4 = (1/1) - (1/3) + (1/5) - (1/7) + \ldots$. Similarly, the other mysterious transcendental number $e = 2.7182818284\ldots$, which plays an extremely important role in mathematics, being, among many other things, the base of the natural logarithm, for instance, is also the sum of a very regular infinite series: $e = 1 + (1/1!) + (1/2!) + (1/3!) + (1/4!) + \ldots$. What strikes me here is that even if Pythagoras's school hoped in vain that the integers and fractions would be the only possible numbers, we can see that the fractions may be used for approximating irrational numbers such as π and e. But, however, infinitely many fractions are used for getting such a transcendental number, like π or e, for instance.

The funny thing is that sometimes the sum of an infinite series could have a simpler form than the sum of a finite number of terms. Thus, if a and q are positive numbers, and $q \neq 1$, they generate a geometric progression with the initial term a and ratio q, namely: $a, aq, aq^2, aq^3, \ldots$. The sum of the first n terms is $a(1-q^n)/(1-q)$, while, if $0 < q < 1$, then the sum of the geometric series containing all, infinitely many terms, is equal to $a/(1-q)$.

Brook Taylor (1685-1731) jumped from the numerical series to the representation of sophisticated functions by polynomial series. His formula, $f(x_0 + x) = f(x_0) + f'(x_0)x/1! + f''(x_0)x^2/2! + \ldots$ is one of the main results in calculus. It shows how to expend a function which has derivatives of all orders in the vicinity of a starting point x_0, as a series whose coefficients are the values of that function and its derivatives at the starting point x_0. Very often we take the starting point to be the origin $x_0 = 0$, in which case the corresponding Taylor's series is known as the series of Colin Maclaurin (1698-1746). Thus, the Maclaurin series for the exponential function is: $e^x = 1 + x/1! + x^2/2! + x^3/3! + \ldots$, for sine function is: $\sin x = x - x^3/3! + x^5/5! - \ldots$ and for cosine function is: $\cos x = 1 - x^2/2! + x^4/4! - \ldots$. Taylor series show us how basic functions may be approximated by polynomials, the simplest functions possible."

–"As series are sums with an infinite number of terms, is it possible to approximate a function by taking only a finite number of terms from its series representation, which would be just a polynomial and, therefore, easier to calculate?"

–"Now, I am really amazed. This is a very pertinent question indeed. Good for you! It touches the delicate problem of approximating functions by polynomials, so important in applied mathematics. Unfortunately, if we take only the first n terms from the Taylor series of a function $f(x)$ in the neighbourhood of a point x_0, ignoring all the other terms, the approximation could be very rough indeed. The truncated Taylor's formula is: $f(x_0 + x) = f(x_0) + f'(x_0)x/1! + f''(x_0)x^2/2! + \ldots + f^{(n)}(x_0)x^n/n! + R_n(y)$, where the remainder, given by Joseph Louis Lagrange, is $R_n(y) = f^{(n+1)}(y)x^{n+1}/(n+1)!$ with y an intermediary value in between x_0 and $x_0 + x$."

–"Who invented calculus?"

−"It is difficult to say. As we discussed about it, the Greeks developed a wonderful geometry, but everything was static there. Find the properties of a triangle, a parallelogram, or a cone when they don't move, for instance. As far as motion was concerned, they looked at it in a too deep a way. For instance, Zeno of Elea (450 BC) arrived to the conclusion that motion is impossible because if a body moves from a point S (source) to a point D (destination) then, before it reaches D, it passes through the midpoint D_1 of the line segment SD. To move to D_1 it must first reach the midpoint D_2 of the line segment SD_1, and so on, which means that the body has to move through an infinite number of points and therefore, it cannot move.

On the other hand, Archimedes (about 225 BC), who could be called the first inventor of calculus, showed how to calculate the area of a segment of a parabola by the summation of an infinite series of its parts. He also found an approximation of the area of a circle, the volume and surface of a sphere, area of a cone, and the area of an ellipse. He seems to have been a remarkable character. Except what I have just mentioned, he is known for his famous cry 'Eureka!' when, sitting in a bathtub, how the legend goes, he discovered the principle according to which a solid body immersed in a liquid is pushed up by a force equal to the weight of the amount of dislocated liquid. He also invented engines of war for the defense of Syracuse against the Romans. When Syracuse was captured, Archimedes was slain by a soldier while, the legend says, he was thinking about how to solve a mathematical problem.

Jumping about 1850 years later, in the 16th century, Johannes Kepler used a kind of crude form of integration, looking at areas as sums of lines. The same idea, called the method of indivisibles, was used by Bonaventura Cavalieri, and refined in the 17th century by Giles Personne de Robertval, for whom the area between a curve and a line consisted of an infinite number of infinitely narrow rectangular strips. In fact, the 17th century was decisive in the real birth of what we understand today by calculus. Indeed, then Pierre de Fermat, in his correspondence with René Descartes, looked for maxima and minima of a smooth function by considering points where the tangent to the graph of the respective function was parallel to the horizontal axis, which is equivalent to locating points where the first derivative of the function is equal to zero. Isaac Barrow defined the tangent to a curve as being the limit of shrinking chords whose end points approach each other. The definition of the derivative of a function was almost there.

And then, came Isaac Newton (1642-1727), who put the basis of the differential and integral calculus. Interested in mechanics, he considered variables, like distance on a trajectory and speed, changing in time. Newton took a moving particle whose trajectory is described by the equation in two variables $f(x,y) = 0$. When the particle moves in time along this curve, the coordinate lines x and y are moving as well. The horizontal velocity x' and the vertical velocity y' were the fluxions of x and y associated with the flux of time. The fluents of flowing quantities were x and y themselves. The ratio y'/x' was the slope of the tangent to the trajectory $f(x,y) = 0$. Newton also considered the converse, or antidifferentiation problem: given the relationship between x and the slope of the tangent y'/x', which means that we know the slope as a function of x, namely $y'/x' = f(x)$, then the problem is to find y. He also calculated areas by antidifferentiation, which is called the 'fundamental theorem of calculus'."

LEIBNIZ

–"Therefore calculus was discovered mainly by Newton. Is it true?"

–" In some sense, yes. But about the same time, Gottfried Wilhelm Leibniz (1646-1716) thought about x and y as being arbitrary variables, each ranging over infinitely close values and denoted by dx and dy differences between successive values of these two variables. The ratio dy/dx gave the slope of the tangent of the graph of y with respect to the values of x. Like Cavalieri, he used integration as a sum of infinitesimals. The notations d for differential and $\int$ for integral, and the algorithms for differentiation and integration given by Leibniz are still used today. Leibniz found his new calculus between 1673 and 1676 in Paris, under the personal influence of Christiaan Huygens, and after studying what René Descartes and Blaise Pascal did. Leibniz's approach to calculus was geometrical. If I remember well, his seminal paper, written in Latin in 1684, had a very long title containing the words *Nova methodus pro maximis et minimis* and *tangentibus*. Just on the first page, it contained the differential symbols dx, dy and the rules of differentiation, including $d(xv) = v\,dx + x\,dv$ and $d(v/y) = (y\,dv - v\,dy)/y^2$, with the condition $dy = 0$ for extreme values and $d^2y = 0$ for points of inflection. This paper was followed, two years later, by another one, with the rules of the integral calculus, containing the $\int$ symbol we are still using today. Many mathematicians in Europe, including Leonhard Euler and Bernoulli brothers Jacob, Johann, and Daniel, eagerly absorbed Leibniz's method and notations. In fact, it was Leibniz who used the names 'calculus differentialis' and 'calculus integralis'. It is also said that he introduced the terms 'function' and 'coordinates', but I am not 100% sure about it. Newton's approach of calculus was primarily kinematical, building it as a necessary tool for studying mechanical motion."

From time to time, when some kind of simple formula had to be written down and shown to me, John took out, from one of his many pockets, a microscopic note-book to which a small size pen was attached. I noticed to him that he seemed prepared to do mathematics anywhere, anytime.

–"Not really," replied John. "In fact, it took me a very long time to realize that it is possible to do mathematics not only sitting at a desk or in front of the blackboard and writing on a piece of paper or using a piece of chalk. Walking, waiting for a bus to come, joining a waiting line somewhere, attending a boring meeting, or flying, there are so many opportunities not only to think about some general mathematical problems but even to perform some mental computations or analyze the details of some mathematical proofs. Sometimes, however, it is useful to scratch on a piece of paper, ready available, something essential to remember eventually. When you cross the road, however, it is safer to stop doing any kind of mathematics and focus on the lights and traffic. The same applies when somebody is talking to you. I don't remember how many times my wife told me: 'You don't listen to what I am telling you, do you?' But I have noticed that you have a notebook with you, yourself."

–"Yes, but I don't use it for mathematical formulas. I just take some notes about the trails we are hiking along, in order to help my memory. But I don't want to interrupt your comments about calculus."

– "Right. Let me go back to the early calculus. Some historians reproached both to Newton and to Leibniz some kind of vagueness and even obscurity in their way of dealing with differential and integral calculus. In Leibniz's case, for instance, it has been noticed that sometimes his differentials dx, dy were finite quantities, sometimes quantities less than any assignable amount and yet not zero. Such comments have always made me very unhappy. When you build a new theory it is very rare, if not impossible, to put its foundation on an absolute rigour and accuracy. You come with new, radical ideas; it is up to the army of disciples to put the missing bricks, fill in the missing details, polish the results, and look for more consequences. And, my God, both Newton and Leibniz basically did in the 17th century almost all which is learned in an undergraduate course of calculus these days. Even if Newton's approach and Leibniz's approach to calculus weren't crystal clear at that time, they definitely inspired further constructive work, pushing forward mathematics to new heights.

Later, among those who developed rigorous foundations of calculus were: Bernard Bolzano, and Augustin-Louis Cauchy, in the 18th century, Julius Wilhelm Richard Dedekind, Karl Theodor Wilhelm Weierstrass, and Georg Cantor, in the 19th century. The ramifications of calculus are numerous and very diverse. First, the theory of functions of real variables focused on all sorts of strange functions and introduced new types of integrals. The work done by Émile Borel and Henri Léon Lebesgue was continued by different mathematicians who, step by step, built the abstract measure theory, a modern and general way of looking at integration. Around 1930, Andrei Nikolaevich Kolmogorov put probability theory on rigorous measure theoretical basis."

COMPLEX VARIABLES

– "You have just said 'functions of real variables'. Are not all variables real?"

– "A very strange, singular, but beautiful extension of calculus is offered by the theory of functions of a complex variable. As I mentioned before, when we discussed about algebra and the different kinds of numbers, the imaginary numbers are met when we solve even simple algebraic equations, like $x^2 + 1 = 0$, for instance, and the solution contains the square root of negative real numbers. As I said before, a complex number is a number of the form $a + bi$, where a and b are real numbers and the symbol 'i' denotes the square root of -1. I also mentioned to you that Carl Friedrich Gauss gave the geometric representation of complex numbers, as points in a complex plane, where a, the real part of the respective complex number, is represented on the horizontal, or real axis, and b, the imaginary part of the respective complex number, is represented on the vertical, or imaginary axis. The corresponding complex number is the point of coordinates a and b in this complex plane. It seems to be like in Descartes's coordinate representation of the points of the plane. But it is not so. Due to the special properties of the operations (addition, subtraction, multiplication, and division) with complex numbers, we are in a very special field.

Giving credit to Gauss, who in 1831 made public his ideas on the geometric interpretation of complex numbers in a very clear way, let me mention that the Dane C. Wessel and the Swiss J. Argand, both amateur mathematicians, more or less self-taught, published independently similar results in 1798 and 1806, respectively, in two papers ignored for a long time by the scientific community. "

–"What is the difference between a complex number $a + bi$ and the pair of real numbers (a, b) because, if I understand it correctly, both are represented by a point of coordinates a, on the horizontal axis, and b, on the vertical axis, in the plane?"

–"To each complex number $a + bi$ we assign indeed the vector (a, b), which may be viewed as being a point in plane, but in Gauss's complex plane, due to the fact that $i = \sqrt{-1}$ and $i^2 = -1$, the addition and multiplication of two such complex numbers $a + bi$ and $c + di$ induce, as a consequence, the following rules: $(a, b) + (c, d) = (a + c, b + d)$ and $(a, b) \times (c, d) = (ac - bd, ad + bc)$ between the corresponding vectors. William Rowan Hamilton, on the other hand, gave a pure algebraic treatment of the complex numbers, viewed by him as simply being pairs of real numbers whose addition and multiplication are given by the two rules just mentioned, taken now as axioms.

Some functions defined on sets of complex numbers prove to have unique properties, never met before. It is a completely different world, like entering a totally new cave and finding all sorts of new, coloured stalagmites and stalactites, never seen before. These special functions, called analytical functions, are those that have any number of derivatives and, therefore, can be represented by infinite series at any point of their domain of definition. To give only one example of such a strange property the analytical functions possess, the integral of an analytical function in an oval domain from the complex plain over any closed contour lying in this domain is equal to zero. As a consequence, the value of an analytical function at interior points of a closed contour may be expressed as an integral of the values of the function on the contour itself. The applications of the theory of functions of a complex variable in fluid mechanics and aerodynamics are simply amazing. Major contributors to the creation of this singular chapter of mathematics were Bernhard Riemann and mainly Augustin-Louis Cauchy."

FUNCTIONAL ANALYSIS

–"Therefore, a regular course on calculus should be followed by a course on multivariate calculus, and then, either a course on the theory of functions of real variables or a course on the theory of functions of a complex variable. What else?"

–"Yes, what you are saying is correct if you replace 'either-or' by 'both-and'. Other courses that rely on a solid background in calculus are the theory of differential equations and the theory of equations with partial derivatives. These are specialized courses and the main problem is to find the families of trajectories when the current, or flow, of their tangents are solutions of systems of linear or nonlinear equations. For instance, the entire time evolution of a strictly deterministic system, like a system of many material points, whose state at each time t is defined by the values of a finite set of independent parameters depending on time t, is completely characterized when the rate of variation of these parameters with respect to time satisfy some algebraic equations, which may be integrated, and the state of the system at an initial moment t_0 is known. When the rates, which are total or partial derivatives of a multivariate function, satisfy systems of algebraic equations, we have to integrate these equations for getting the corresponding family of possible trajectories of the respective system in the so-called phase space of the possible values of its parameters. Differential equations describe the evolution in time of strictly deterministic systems. Classical mechanics is entirely based on solving differential equations. When the derivatives or partial derivatives of a certain unknown function, called state function, depending on the variable state of a mechanical system and describing the strictly deterministic evolution of the respective system, satisfy a set of generally linear equation then, if the initial conditions, like position and velocity at the initial time t_0, or the boundary values, namely the values of the state function on the frontier of its domain of definition, are known, then the unknown state function is uniquely determined and, therefore, the entire behaviour and evolution of the respective system may be predicted. Solving differential equations proved to be very successful in describing the evolution of celestial bodies and the mechanical motion at the macroscopic level.

You could see another ramification of calculus by taking a course on functional analysis. This was one of my favourite courses when I was a student. As a usual function assigns numbers to numbers, a functional assigns numbers to functions. Therefore, a functional is an application from a set of functions, called functional space, to a set of numbers. An operator, is an application from a set of functions to a set of functions. It assigns a function to another function. To the same extent to which the derivative of a function is another function, like $\cos x$ which is the derivative of $\sin x$, and therefore the operation of taking the derivative is an operator, a set of differential equations may also be viewed, at a big scale, as defining a differential operator on a set of differentiable functions. Functional analysis is the study of infinite-dimensional vector spaces. When some kind of distance is defined in them, we deal with infinite-dimensional metric spaces. Sometimes, some other structures, like topological linear spaces, normed linear spaces, Banach spaces, and Hilbert spaces, are introduced in order to build up a geometry in such infinite-dimensional spaces. Operators in linear function spaces and their duals, and very sophisticated distributions, measures, integrals and derivatives in such abstract spaces are introduced and studied.

I have mentioned how important Taylor's formula is. Functional analysis has pushed this point of view even farther, introducing the representations of the most different functions by means of series of functions. It is something like taking a sequence of simpler functions, but not necessarily polynomials this time, as an infinite system of coordinates in an infinitely-dimensional space, that are used for expressing other functions as series of these generalized coordinate functions. The origin may be found in Pythagoras's discovery that the sound produced by the vibration of a taut string may be decomposed into the harmonics of a fundamental sound. In the 18th century, mathematicians started to decompose a periodic function $f(x)$, which satisfies $f(x + 2\pi) = f(x)$, into a series of simple periodic functions like the infinite sum of trigonometric functions, as the sine and cosine functions. The systematic study began in 1807 due to Fourier. You can see how the generalizations went on: from numerical series, to polynomial series, and, eventually, to series of more general functions.

Joseph Fourier (1768-1830), who was a soldier during the French Revolution and accompanied Napoleon Bonaparte on his campaign to Egypt, showed that the trigonometric series may be used to represent a large class of functions. He showed that an 'arbitrary' function, more exactly a function capable of being represented by an arc of a continuous curve or by a succession of such arcs, could be represented by a trigonometric series, which may be viewed as an infinite linear combination of sine and cosine functions. Later, the trigonometric functions have been replaced by other systems of functions taken as generalized coordinates in series representations of very different classes of functions of interest.

The tools provided by functional analysis are essential for solving very applied problems in optimization theory. The standard calculus is routinely applied to find points where real-valued functions take on maximum or minimum values. An ingenious and simple Lagrange's multipliers method may be used for optimizing functions of several variables, called objective function, subject to equality constraints, but effective, exact results may be generally obtained only when the objective function is linear or quadratic. The strictly deterministic part of operations research deals with the optimization of linear functions subject to linear inequality constraints. But these are still relatively simple problems in optimization. In the 17th century, the Swiss mathematicians Jacob Bernoulli and Johann Bernoulli invented the calculus of variations, dealing with important problems from mathematical physics where the value of an integral was thought of as a function of the functions being integrated, and their objective was to minimize such a function of functions, called functionals. Calculus of variation is typically seeking functions, curves, or other geometric objects which maximize or minimize functionals.

Anyway, the functional analysis, as we know it today, is a creation of the 20th century, The word 'functional' was introduced by Jacques Hadamard (1865-1963) in 1903. He is one of the few mathematicians about whom I heard and read only superlatives as a human being. There was also a joke about him when, towards the end of his long life, a newspaper apparently published a little note announcing that: 'There is a crisis of candles in Paris; Professor Hadamard is celebrating his anniversary!' He died at 98.

The derivative of a functional was defined by Maurice Frechet in 1904. He had important contributions to the development of the functional analysis and lived 95 years. Once, he presented one of my short notes to the Academy of Science in Paris, before being published in their Comptes Rendus. I was very happy, back then, just to see his famous name mentioned on my short paper and, for a couple of days, I kept looking at it even during breakfast, lunch, or dinner. Towards the end of his life, Maurice Frechet was very much involved in urging people to pay more attention to the artificially created international language 'Esperanto' and to use it in their mathematical publications."

–"Why are so many spaces necessary?"

–"Some are not necessary but are introduced as logically possible generalization of more worldly spaces. For instance, a Hilbert space is a direct generalization of the Euclidean spaces, we are so familiar with, to the case when we have infinitely many dimensions. A point in such a space is identified with a vector having not two coordinates, like in plane, not three coordinates, like in our regular three-dimensional space, but infinitely many. We can still define a distance there, lengths between vectors, lines, angles between lines, and even the analog of Pythagoras's theorem from classic geometry. The funny thing is that such an artificial mathematical creation, which cannot be fully visualized by us, in fact we cannot visualize even a four-dimensional Euclidean space, where the shades are three-dimensional, proved to be very useful in quantum mechanics, for instance."

–"I am afraid that with so many important courses to take, I would need ten years to graduate if I decided to become a mathematician. It seems to be very tough indeed. Are there even other math courses which are offered?"

TOPOLOGY

–"Topology comes immediately to my mind but there are two different ways in which this name is being used. On one side, topology is used in functional analysis. On the real line, an open interval, denoted (a, b), is the set of all real numbers strictly larger than a and strictly smaller then b. It is unfortunate that the same notation is used for a point of coordinates a and b in the plane. If we start from the set of all open intervals and we take countable unions of such open intervals, we get so-called open sets. Once we have open sets available, we can use them to define neighbourhoods (the neighbourhood of a point being any open set which contains that point), accumulation points (a point is an accumulation point for a set if any neighbourhood of this point contains points of the respective set), close sets, as complementary sets of open sets, bounded sets, compact sets (closed sets which contain their accumulation points), like a closed interval $[a, b]$, which is an open interval containing its end points too, convergence of sequences of numbers, limits of sequences of functions, continuity of functions (small variations of the argument result in small variations of the values of such a continuous function), etc. The so called point set topology, does the same thing in abstract spaces, starting from a given family of open sets in these abstract spaces. Topology is used to construct a kind of geometric calculus in abstract spaces. In fact, this set point topology is just an essential part of functional analysis.

Apparently Georg Cantor, in the last quarter of the 19th century, introduced the concept of set of limit points, or set of points of accumulation, called the first derived set. He also defined closed subsets on the real line as subsets containing their first derived set, and introduced the idea of an open set as being the complementary of a closed set. About the same period, Karl Theodor Wilhelm Weierstrass (1815-1897), proved the important result that every bounded infinite set of real numbers possesses at least one point of accumulation. Following the steps of Cauchy and Riemann, Weierstrass is renowned for being very concerned about promoting and using the most-needed absolute rigour in the definitions and proofs of mathematical analysis. It is not without interest to notice that, for a long period of time, he was a secondary school teacher, a position which didn't prevent him from becoming the father of modern analysis, how he was later called.

Later, at the beginning of the 20th century, Maurice Fréchet called a space compact if any infinite, bounded subset contains a point of accumulation. He extended the concept of convergence from the set of real numbers, on the real line, dealing with abstract metric spaces, where a distance is possible to be defined and where the open sets are unions of open spheres. Frédéric Riesz and Felix Hausdorff defined abstract topological spaces without using any metric considerations, simply starting from a given set of open sets, which is enough to build up a type of abstract, set-theoretic, geometric mathematical analysis.

David Hilbert studied spaces with a countable infinity of dimensions, where a vector is characterized by a series of coordinates and where the distance is defined from an inner product between such points. This inner product allows also to talk about a generalization of the length of vectors and the angle between vectors with an infinite set of countable components. Stefan Banach (1892-1945), one of the founders of the functional analysis, who, before the World War II, liked to do mathematics in a café in Warsaw, sometimes writing down formulas on the marble of the table, generalized Hilbert spaces, moving from inner product spaces to normed spaces. Finally, Henri Poincaré (1854-1912), introduced new topological methods when, in his research on the systems of differential equations that describe autonomous systems, looked at the totality of all solutions rather than at particular solutions or trajectories, as it was done in classical mechanics.

On the other side, there is a more general topology, as a distinct geometric discipline, which, trivializing a little, deals with those properties that would remain unchanged if the geometric objects, supposed to be made from some flexible and stretchable material, were subject to continuous deformations. Under a topological transformation of an arbitrary figure, the parts of this figure that are in contact remain in contact, and the parts that are not in contact cannot come in contact. More explicitly, in a topological transformation neither breaks nor fusions can arise. In particular, two distinct points cannot be united into a single point. Thus, a topological transformation of any geometrical figure, considered as a set of points forming it, is not only continuous but also a one-to-one transformation and any two distinct points of the figure are transformed into two distinct points, whereas the inverse transformation is continuous as well. But the distance between points and, therefore, the shape of the figure could change. For example, in plane, when a closed rubber ring is given in the form of a circle, then we can stretch it, which is a topological transformation, into the shape of an ellipse, but we cannot, by a topological transformation, turn a circle into a figure with two loops, like an eight, because this would require the fusion of two distinct points of the circle, or into an interval, because this would require the fusion of one semicircle with another or else a break of the circle at an arbitrary point.

Once, I attended a lecture given by a well-known topologist. He started his talk by saying: 'Let us take a circle,' and drew a potato on the blackboard. In topology, they are equivalent. The surrealistic Spanish painter Salvador Dalli did a famous painting 'Persistence of memory' in which several distorted watches hang around, looking like being made either from thin rubber, or from melting soft plastic, or unbaked dough. Mathematically, they are circles that have suffered topological transformations. In such an approach, the distance is absolutely irrelevant. It seems strange to even talk about geometry without using the concept of distance between points but there are problems where it may be ignored, or the distance between points simply changes during some transformations."

−"But distorting figures like that could give very strange shapes, like molding a piece of plastic substance."

–"Topology deals with strange monsters, indeed, like: surfaces with holes, spheres with handles, ring-shaped surfaces, surfaces looking like sophisticated bottles. They could have strange properties. To give you one simple example, you may construct easily the so-called 'Möbius band', which is obtained when we take a rectangular strip of paper, like a rectangle ABCD, and paste together the two opposite short sides AB and CD so that the vertex A coincide with C, and B with D. The surface thus obtained has only one side, not two. Starting from an arbitrary point E and moving along the surface we arrive again at the point E, but on the other side of it, although we haven't crossed the edge. Therefore, we can paint the entire surface with only one colour, while keeping the brush in contact with the surface. By pasting, a two-sided strip has become a one-sided surface."

–"Who was the first one who thought about such problems?"

–"In the old town Königsberg, where the philosopher Immanuel Kant was born and lived, taking his afternoon walk at 3:30 sharp daily, the river Pregel, running through the town, has two islands that are joined to each other and to the shores by seven bridges. The first island is joined by two bridges with the right bank of the river and by two bridges with the left bank. The second island is joined by one bridge with the right bank of the river and by one bridge with the left bank. There is a seventh bridge joining the two islands. Starting at any point, the puzzle is whether it is possible to walk so that we get back to the starting point having walked across all seven bridges but only once over each bridge. In 1736, Leonhard Euler showed that the problem of crossing the seven Königsberg bridges in a single journey is impossible. Indeed, the 14 end points of the seven bridges may be considered as being the vertices of a graph. There is a line between two points when we can move directly from one of these points to the other one. A figure can always be drawn by using one line ending at its starting point if there is an even number of lines meeting at every vertex. The Königsberg problem cannot be solved because there are vertices with odd numbers of lines meeting at each of them. As the distance between points was irrelevant, this problem marked the beginning of topology as a special kind of geometry.

Fourteen years later, Euler gave a simple but amazing formula, stating that in any polyhedron, of any shape, we have the relation $v-e+f = 2$, where v is the number of vertices of the polyhedron, e is the number of edges, and f is the number of faces. For a cube, for instance, $v = 8$, $e = 12$, and $f = 6$. Later, Antoine-Jean Lhuilier generalized Euler's formula for a solid which has h holes, namely: $v-e+f = 2-2h$."

–"Who was the greatest mathematician of all times?"

–"I am afraid that I cannot answer this question. The great contributors to the development and progress of mathematics, as a science, have been very different and cannot be objectively compared; anyway, not by me. Subjectively, however, it is possible because, depending on his own background and field of work, everybody has favourites among the big names. This is like in classical music, where I would prefer Beethoven and Schubert to anybody else, whereas Mozart's fans could be outraged by my choice. Therefore, objectively speaking, I cannot answer your question but, subjectively, I would start with Isaac Newton and Carl Friedrich Gauss. I cannot say that I love them, but I do respect and admire them."

NEWTON

–"But I heard about Newton from my physics teacher and not even once in math classes."

–"This is one of the reasons why he was so great. He was a first class mathematician who is known in other sciences as well. He built the foundations of classical mechanics, developing it from three fundamental laws and, for achieving this goal, he invented a new mathematical tool, the differential and integral calculus, or the method of 'fluxions', how calculus was called during his time. He lived in the second half of the seventeenth century and the first quarter of the eighteenth century. He needed a new kind of mathematics in order to build a grandiose deterministic model of the universe in motion.

Newton used to say that he did what he did in science because he stood on the shoulders of giants, learning from René Descartes the elements of analytic geometry, the first symbiosis between geometry and algebra, from Johann Kepler the three laws of the planetary motion discovered empirically, and from Galileo Galilei the first two of the three laws of motion. Newton used to say that he didn't frame hypotheses, but in fact he dealt with mechanics in an axiomatic way, starting from three fundamental laws and deriving from them subsequent results using his method of fluxions. He used derivatives, as rates of change. Thus the velocity was defined as the rate of change of space with respect to time, and acceleration as the rate of change of velocity with respect to time.

Briefly, Newton's three laws of motion may be stated as: (a) Every body will rest or move uniformly in a straight direction if no force is acting on it; (b) The product between mass and acceleration of a body is proportional to the force acting on the body; (c) In any mechanical interaction, action and reaction are equal and opposite. His major discovery was the law of universal gravitation according to which the attraction between two bodies is proportional to the product of their masses divided by the square of the distance between them. How somebody put it, such a great discovery may be done only once and it was Newton who did it. The great success of Newton's mechanics in explaining the motion of celestial bodies gave him a mythical stature."

–"What about his life?"

–"His life was long. He was born in 1642 and lived about 85 years, if I remember well, but without spectacular events. He travelled in a very small triangle in England, never got married, had no children, worked all the time during his youth and mature life, believed in God, and became interested in alchemy and religion towards the end of his life when he lost interest in mathematics and physics. Some commentators said that he was in fact deeply religious during all his life. Who can know for sure? Anyway, his father died before Newton's birth. Both his stepfather and the brother of his mother were priests.

The decisive years of his creativeness were 1664-1666, when Cambridge University, where Newton was a student at that time, was closed due to the bubonic plague which decimated many lives in Europe. During those years, he retired to his native hamlet Woolsthorpe where he had enough time to think and work on his ideas. In this brief period he made roughly all his fundamental discoveries in mathematics, mechanics, and physics.

As far as I read about him, later, when he became a professor in Cambridge, Newton wasn't rich, often complaining about lack of money to the Rector of the University. In the last part of his life he was a highly paid government official in London. Due to his scientific achievements, he was highly admired by his disciples who looked up at him as being a demigod.

Unfortunately, he was engaged in a bitter dispute with the German mathematician Gottfried Wilhelm Leibniz about priority in creating the differential and integral calculus. I cannot be an objective arbiter in this dispute because I don't know all the facts. Very often, similar ideas appear simultaneously in different places. I read somewhere that as far as printed publications are concerned, the priority belongs to Leibniz who gave a substantial account of the basic ideas of calculus in papers published in *Acta Eruditorum* during the period 1682-1686. On the other hand, Leibniz began his research in the analysis of infinitesimals only in 1673, whereas Newton came upon the fundamental ideas of the differential and integral calculus in the short period of maximum creativity mentioned above and, by 1671, had assembled his results in *Methodus fluxionum*.

What really matters is that Newton and Leibniz approached the new calculus from completely different viewpoints. Newton started from mechanical and geometrical concepts, rigorously defining the limit of a variable quantity and introducing 'fluxions', or 'derivatives', based on finding the limits of ratios of two infinitesimal quantities that vary jointly, being in a mutual dependence. He carefully dealt with the fundamental problem of the integral calculus, that is, how to determine a primitive function from its given derivative, or using his terminology, how to determine a 'fluent' from its given 'fluxion'. Leibniz, on the other hand, introduced the new term of 'infinitesimal' which allowed him to get an easier, algorithmic approach in dealing with differentials. Starting with Leibniz, a new period of rapid development of mathematics occurred, culminating with the contributions of Euler. This period put the emphasis more on getting new results rather than paying attention to absolute rigour. Operating with divergent series or integrating complex functions like dealing with real functions, for instance, were characteristic for that period. By contrast, a cautious Newton underscored the necessity of analyzing convergence in order to justify the use of series expansions in calculus. Anyway, looking today into Newton's fundamental book *Principia mathematica philosophiae naturalis*, is not an easy task. The proofs and justifications are presented using cumbersome and complicate geometric figures. Paying respect to Newton and Leibniz, as the creators of the differential and integral calculus, it is necessary, however, to mention that later, Augustin-Louis Cauchy and Karl Weierstrass focused on rigour and succeeded in putting calculus in the modern form we can find it in today's textbooks. Newton's mechanics also has been transformed later into an elegant chapter of mathematical analysis by Comte Joseph Louis Lagrange, in France, who created the analytical mechanics."

–"Are you on Newton's or on Leibniz's side in this dispute on whose approach of the differential and integral calculus is better?"

–"I am not such an important personality to judge them and reach a verdict about this. As an applied mathematician, however, I am definitely on Newton's side. It seems to me that, for him, applying the new mathematics for solving problems in mathematical modeling was more important than polishing and looking for elegance inside pure mathematics. I can give you a simple example to this extent. Many important mathematicians have spent a lot of time trying to solve rigorously general algebraic equations. Many types of such equations cannot be exactly solved. In fact we could talk about this some other time. For Newton, however, it was more important to approximate the solutions of algebraic equations instead of running after solving exactly general equations, an objective which, anyway, often proved to be an empty dream. How did he do it? Ingeniously, as always.

Let me take a cubic equation, say $x^3 - 3x - 10 = 0$. Today, if we use a modern computer package that does symbolic computing, like Stephen Wolfram's MATHEMATICA for instance, we get the solutions: $x = 2.6129$, and $x = -1.3064 \pm 1.4562\,i$, where $i = \sqrt{-1}$. Now, let us have a look at what Newton did in order to approximate the real solution of the above equation. We look first for the integer which makes the left hand side of the equation closer to zero; it is $x = 2$. This would be the best integer approximation. Now, we replace x by $2 + u$ in the initial equation. Using the cube of a binomial, $(2 + u)^3 = 8 + 12u + 6u^2 + u^3$, from elementary algebra, we get the equation: $u^3 + 6u^2 + 9u - 8 = 0$. Neglecting the terms which contain powers of u, it gives the linear equation $9u - 8 = 0$, which gives the decimal approximation of the solution, $u = 8/9 = 0.88889$. At this stage, the approximation of the solution is $x = 2 + 0.88889 = 2.88889$. For getting a better approximation, we replace u by $0.88889 + v$ in the cubic equation $u^3 + 6u^2 + 9u - 8 = 0$; we obtain:$v^3 + 8.66667v^2 + 22.0371v + 5.4431 = 0$. Neglecting the terms that contain powers of v, we get the linear equation: $22.0371v + 5.4431 = 0$, whose solution is $v = -0.247$. At this new stage, the approximation of the real solution of the initial cubic equation is: $x = 2.88889 - 0.247 = 2.64189$. Doing one more step, if we replace v by $-0.247 + w$ in the last cubic equation in v and neglect the terms containing powers of w, we get: $w = -0.028631$, and the new approximation of the real solution of the initial equation becomes: $x = 2.64189 - 0.028631 = 2.61326$, which is quite good."

–"This means that Newton knew the formula for the cube of a binomial, which we learned to be: $(a + b)^3 = a^3 + 3a^2b + 3ab^2 + b^3$."

–"Not only the cube of a binomial but even the elegant formula of the n-th power of the binomial, which in fact is called Newton's binomial theorem, $(a + b)^n = \sum_{k=0}^{n} C_k^n a^{n-k} b^k$, where the symbol C_k^n, which is equal to $n!/(k!(n - k)!)$, is the number of combinations of n objects taken k at a time or, equivalently, the number of subsets of k distinct elements that may be taken from a set containing n elements. It is just this general formula that allows to apply Newton's method presented here to approximate solutions of algebraic equations of any degree. These last comments illustrate that, except big scale discoveries like classical mechanics, differential and integral calculus, and the law of gravity, for instance, Newton had smaller scale discoveries, but also very important, like the binomial theorem just mentioned, which is taught even in high school today, giving such an elegant formula for how to raise the sum of two terms at an arbitrary positive integer power, which was used by him for getting series expansions for functions. He was also interested in optics and pleaded in favour of the corpuscular nature of light."

−"How could somebody create so much in science?"

−"I have absolutely no idea. Newton mentioned somewhere that he discovered the law of gravity because he had thought about it continuously, for a long period of time. This is nice but, certainly, doesn't explain why he was so successful in discovering it. An anecdote says that he was also asked why he never got married and his answer was: 'Because I had no time to think about it.' But no anecdote should be trusted, of course."

−"You have just mentioned that Newton created classical mechanics and discovered the law of gravity. What did he think about time because, as I know from high school, speed, or velocity, measures the variation of distance with respect to time and acceleration reflects the variation of velocity with respect to time? Time is so important everywhere. Almost everybody has a watch at his wrist. Adding extra time, or injury time how it is sometimes called, at the end of a soccer game, or getting into overtime during a hockey or basketball game, could be disastrous and many dramas have developed during these added minutes. Time-tables are everywhere. Any delays are bothering us. Everybody is expected to be punctual. In Canada, like in some other countries, we change time twice a year. I find this to be particularly annoying. The Eastern time is different from the Western time. Geneva is six hours ahead of Toronto. Even if the distance is the same and the same type of airplane is used, it takes seven hours to fly from Toronto to Amsterdam, but eight hours to go back. Can we play games with time, changing it when we want? Sometimes, I ask myself what is time after all?"

−"Not talking about the calendar business either, which is even more obscure. My father never really knew when to celebrate his birthdays: following the present Gregorian calendar or the previous Julian, old calendar?

Philosophically speaking, the problem of time is quite messy and I am not competent to mention the details of the disputes and controversies about it. For some, time is a category which exists independently of us. For others, time doesn't exist at the larger scale and we invent and use it because, locally, we report the changes occurring in a certain system to more regular or periodic changes occurring in another system. For Immanuel Kant, to say that the universe is finite in space and had a beginning in time, which would be a 'thesis', or to assume that the universe is infinite in space and there was no beginning in time, which would be its 'antithesis', is to generate a contradiction, called by him 'antinomy' of 'pure' reason, which cannot be solved because there are arguments both in favour and against both of them and, therefore, a 'critical' reason has to leave them both undecided upon. For those who assume that time is infinite, it could increase linearly from the past to the future, passing through the present, or could move on cyclically, in a kind of eternal, periodical return.

Not so long ago, Stephen Hawking, who by the way holds the post of Lucasian Professor of Mathematics at Cambridge University, once held by Newton himself, published an interesting book, *A Brief History of Time*, which was meant to be accessible to a large audience. In fact, it is not an easy book at all. The book became an instant bestseller, showing the wide interest of the general public in any scientific debate on time. A good friend of mine told me that in her institution, which wasn't an academic one by any means, a lot of people used to walk on the corridors or in the lounge with this book under their arms. Fortunately, the book is not very big or heavy. This reminds me that once, I had to give a specialized talk in a nonacademic institution as well, and to my surprise, the big room reserved for general meetings was fully packed. Later, I found out that the director of the institution had announced my talk suggesting that only intelligent people were expected to attend.

Anyway, the mathematical time, as considered by Newton in his mechanics and as it is viewed even today in calculus or in the theory of differential equations, is a linearly increasing real variable t, taking values on the real axis, from $-\infty$ to $+\infty$, even if, in many applications, it belongs to a finite interval $[t_0, t_1]$."

–"Who was the other name mentioned by you along Newton's?"

GAUSS

–"Carl Friedrich Gauss. He lived one century later and I put him in such a high position because, in my opinion, he imposed the standards of perfect rigour, clarity, precision, and economic thinking in modern mathematics. Apparently, he wasn't interested in public recognition and published papers only when they were extremely polished and perfectly finished, in an condensed form that risked to become incomprehensible. It is said that he sent for publication only a small part of his results but I cannot check the accuracy of such a statement. Anyway, the Latin dictum 'pauca sed matura', which would mean 'few but ripe', is attributed to Gauss. His contributions have been amazing. His book *Disquisitiones Arithmeticae* on number theory is still considered a paragon of how to do mathematics and how to write a treatise on mathematics.

Gauss was fascinated by the mysterious distribution of the prime numbers in the set of positive integers and conjectured the fact the the number of primes less than the real number x, which is denoted in literature by $\pi(x)$, behaves, roughly speaking, like $x/\ln x$, for large values of x, or asymptotically, how mathematicians use to say. For small values of x, however, he made a somehow different assumption. In 1849, in a personal letter to the astronomer Encke, after heuristically examining the distribution of the primes between 2 000 000 and 3 000 000, Gauss conjectured that $\pi(x)$ might be approximated by the logarithmic integral $Li(x) = \int_2^x (1/\ln t)\, dt$.

Gauss also gave the first genuine proof of the fundamental theorem of algebra, according to which every polynomial equation of degree n, with rational coefficients, has exactly n solutions, as real or complex numbers, with the corollary that the field of complex numbers is algebraically closed, which implies that solving algebraic equations we don't need other numbers than the complex numbers for describing their solutions. He mastered the complex numbers, differential and integral calculus, optimization, probability theory, differential geometry, and astronomy. He was one of the first mathematician, if not the first, who introduced existence proofs, but was also a master in suggesting effective mathematical constructions."

–"Was something special in Gauss's life?"

Gauss was born in Braunschweig, also called Brunswick, in 1777, in a very modest family. His father had several menial jobs and, at some point of his life, he was a brick layer. His mother was more educated and concerned about the education and future of her son. The young Gauss proved to be a wonder kid in school. The legend says that when the teacher gave the problem of summing up the integers from 1 to 100 to his students to keep them busy, the eight-year old Gauss immediately wrote down the answer 5050. I don't know how he did it. One possibility is that he noticed that if we put in one row the numbers 1, 2,..., 99, 100, in increasing order and below, in the second row, the same numbers in decreasing order, namely 100, 99,..., 2, 1, then, summing up the corresponding numbers from the two rows, we get 101 times 100. Dividing by 2, we obtain the sum asked by the schoolteacher.

Fortunately, his teacher Büttner, whose given name I don't remember, and a young assistant teacher, Martin Bartels, were impressed by his unusual talent in mathematics. They provided the young prodigy with some excellent mathematical books and mathematical works of classics like Newton and Euler. Apparently, he was 19 years old when he obtained his first success, proving that the regular polygon with 17 sides, called 17-gon, may be constructed using only an unmarked ruler and a compass. It is said that this success made Gauss decide to become a mathematician instead of specializing in philology."

–"Why was this important?"

–"Well, this goes back to Plato and his school, where nobody could enter without being a geometer. According to Plato, the only perfect geometrical figures are the circle and the straight line, which could be constructed using a compass and an unmarked ruler, respectively. The Greek geometers became interested in using only these two instruments for constructing all sorts of figures in two or three dimensions. Thus, they could divide line segments into arbitrarily many equal disjoint subsegments, bisect arbitrary angles, draw parallel lines, and construct a square whose area is equal to, or is twice, the area of an arbitrary regular polygon. It was an obsession for them to show that more and more geometric constructions could be performed only by using a ruler and a compass. Unfortunately, three problems couldn't be solved by them using only these two perfect instruments, namely, the duplication of cube, which means to construct a cube whose volume is twice the volume of a given cube, the trisection of the angle, which means to divide a given angle in three equal parts, and the quadrature of the circle, which means to construct a square whose area is equal to the area of a given circle."

−"Even in the everyday language, sometimes a very difficult problem is compared with solving the quadrature of the circle. But I didn't hear about the other two. Have they been solved?"

−"No. In fact, more than that, using the modern theory of algebraic fields, it is quite easy to prove that all three famous problems mentioned above cannot be solved using only a ruler and a compass."

−"What other contributions did Gauss make later in his life?"

−"So many that I have time to mention only very few of them now, namely, only those I am somehow aware of."

−"But if Gauss's family was so poor how could he pay for his education?"

−"The Duke Ferdinand of Braunschweig, impressed by the young Gauss, became his generous sponsor for about 20 years, until he died fighting the French army. After the death of his benefactor, Gauss became professor in Göttingen. In the last 20 years of his life, he lived in a relative reclusion, in the astronomic observatory in Göttingen. He didn't teach much, had little interaction with younger generations, and preferred to do research and long numerical calculations in his astronomical investigations. Politically, he was conservative, in contrast with many other mathematicians who very often rebelled against the establishment and injustice. I don't know much about his personal life except that he was married twice and had five or six children. I admire him for his unique place in the history of mathematics, where he has been called the 'prince of mathematics'. I cannot say, however, that I love him, but who cannot admire him?"

– "Why not love him?"

– "I don't really know why. Everybody has his or her own favourite or favourites. Maybe because several times he claimed that he had previously discovered, but kept for himself, some mathematical results published by other mathematicians. Whereas there are no reasons to doubt his words, it is a little annoying to see that such remarks and even debates about priority occurred several times during his life. Another reason for my lack of special affection is that he lived a long life, of 78 years if I remember well, without anything spectacular, except his exceptional mathematical results, of course.

Apparently, the only adventure of his life occurred when, around 1820, he was asked by the government to do a geodesic survey of the kingdom of Hanover. It took him almost a decade to deal with this mission. Gauss spent weeks and months outdoors, travelling and collecting data. Then, he came back to his office and processed the data set obtained by him. It is very probable that from dealing with such a practical but not very exciting problem, he made two of his major discoveries in mathematics. First, moving and making geophysical observations in his travel between two distant localities, Gauss realized that, on a larger scale, the earth is not flat and that the Euclidean geometry of a plane cannot be applied, having to be replaced by a new geometry of curved spaces. Like a shadow moving on the surface of an egg, he developed the intrinsic differential geometry of curved spaces, defining and giving formulas for measuring important concepts like the distance between points on curved surfaces and the curvature of surfaces. Before talking about the second major contribution, I have to ask you a question. Do you know what a random variable is?"

– "Not really, but give me an example."

– "Well, take the temperature X, measured in degrees Celsius, recorded in Geneva at noon, on every May 22, during the 20th century. This temperature is definitely not the same. Looking at the numerical values registered, we can see that some values are more frequent than other values. We can calculate the absolute frequencies of the possible values by simply counting how many times each value has been recorded. Dividing the absolute frequencies by the total number of observations, we obtain the relative frequencies of the possible values. The absolute frequencies are positive integer numbers but the relative frequencies are always fractions between 0 and 1, whose sum is always equal to 1. The relative frequencies of values recorded form a so-called probability distribution of the possible values of the temperature in Geneva, at noon, on May 22, in the 20th century. If by temperature we understand its possible values together with the probability distribution of its values, then it is viewed as being a random variable. In fact, it is a so-called finite discrete random variable because the set of possible numerical values of it is finite.

The mean value μ of this temperature is a number obtained by multiplying each possible value x_k with its occurrence probability, or relative frequency, p_k and summing up with respect to all possible values of the random variable, which, symbolically, is represented by $\mu = \sum_k x_k p_k$. The mean temperature μ is important because it summarizes, in only one number, the trend or the expected average value. The standard deviation σ of a random variable is the square root of the variance, which is obtained by taking the mean value of the squared differences between the possible values of the random variable and the mean value of the random variable. More explicitly, for obtaining the variance of the temperature, we take the sum of the squared differences between the possible value of the temperature and the mean temperature multiplied by the probabilities, or relative frequencies of the corresponding possible values. The corresponding formula for the variance is $\sigma^2 = \sum_k (x_k - \mu)^2 p_k$. Finally, the standard deviation is obtained by taking the square root of the variance. The standard deviation σ is important because it shows the mean spread, or deviation, or scatter of the possible values of the temperature around its mean value. Now, if we plot the possible values of the temperature on the horizontal axis and the numerical values of the corresponding relative frequencies, vertically, we obtain the two-dimensional graph of the probability density of the temperature.

A random variable X is continuous if the set of its possible values is an interval, like $[35, 42]$ for human body's temperature for instance, or the set of positive real numbers, or even the set of all real numbers. In such a case, the probability that X takes on values between two arbitrary values a and b is given by the definite integral $\int_a^b f(x)\,dx$ of a probability density function $f(x)$ between a and b. A random variable is called normal if its probability density looks like a symmetric bell-shaped curve centered at the mean value μ, with two inflexion points at $\mu - \sigma$ and $\mu + \sigma$, respectively, where μ is the mean and σ the standard deviation of the corresponding random variable, resembling Napoleon's hat."

–"Now, I remember. Our physics teacher showed us some graphs for the distribution of the values of some functions measured in our laboratory which looked like a bell and called them Gauss's curves."

–"Right, and very often a normal random variable is called Gaussian random variable. In Germany, a couple of years ago, before they switched to Euros, I saw a 10-Deutsch-mark bill, or 5-Deutsch-mark bill, I don't remember exactly which one, having Gauss's picture on it along with a nice, bell-shaped curve representing the normal probability distribution.

In fact, Gauss didn't discover the normal distribution. The French mathematicians Abraham De Moivre (1667-1754), who died before Gauss was born, and Pierre Simon Laplace (1749-1827), who was 28 years older than Gauss, did. Gauss, on the other hand, did much more than that and this is his second major discovery I was talking about. Dealing with a lot of geophysical and later astronomical measurements and with the inevitable errors induced by performing operations on the observed values, Gauss discovered a special case of what is called today the 'central limit theorem' in probability theory. He noticed that, in general, summing up a lot of errors, which may be viewed as being independent random variables, uniformly distributed in a given interval, subtracting the mean value of the sum of errors, and dividing the result by the standard deviation of the sum of errors, the possible numerical values of such a standardized random variable, obtained this way, are distributed like a bell-shaped symmetric curve centered at origin and having the standard deviation equal to 1. Such a bell-shaped probability distribution centered at origin and with the standard deviation equal to 1 is called the standard normal distribution. In general, if from a random variable X we subtract its mean μ and then divide by its standard deviation σ, we use to say that we standardize the respective random variable. The mean of the standardized random variable $(X - \mu)/\sigma$ is equal to zero and its standard deviation is equal to 1.

Therefore, Gauss didn't introduce the normal distribution for the first time but he proved a special case of the central limit theorem which says that the standardized sum of independent, identically distributed random variables is distributed asymptotically, namely when the sum contains a large number of terms, according to the standard normal probability distribution. This theorem, as its name suggests, has major applications in probability theory and statistics."

–"From what you are saying, Gauss seemed to be interested both in pure and in applied mathematics."

–"He wasn't only interested in applied problems but, in dealing with them, he always tried to develop a general methodology for solving these types of problems. To give an example, at the beginning of the 19th century, the largest asteroid Ceres was detected. Having very little luminosity, after a short time interval, it disappeared near the sun and it seemed to be lost. The astronomers published their previous observations of the location of Ceres but wanted to determine the asteroid's orbit. Gauss succeeded in fitting the best ellipse to the observed data by using the method of least squares and his tremendous skill in numerical computation. Later, Ceres was located precisely as predicted by Gauss. The 'method of least squares' fitting is still being used today, as a powerful tool in time series analysis, for predicting the trend hidden by random fluctuations. It was Adrien-Marie Legendre (1752-1833) who first published this method. Gauss claimed that he had used it ten years before. There is some evidence in support of Gauss's claim but, however, Legendre has the printing priority."

–"This method seems to be very important if the 'prince of mathematics' used it in practical applications."

– "The method of least squares is intensively used today in fitting the 'closest' polynomial to a given set of numerical data. Intuitively, when we measure something like the amount of rain, for instance, falling at different times in a certain place, behind the apparently chaotic variation of the data set, due to random fluctuations, we want to discover some kind of regularity, or trend, that could be represented by some kind of curve. In a class of possible curves chosen to describe the trend, we select that one which is the closest one, in the sense of the Euclidean distance, to the empirical values available."

– "What is the Euclidean distance?"

– "This is the simplest distance used in calculus and analytical geometry. More exactly, if we have two points in the plane, each of them is defined by its two coordinates, say (x_1, y_1) and (x_2, y_2), respectively. The Euclidean distance is then the square root of the sum of the squared differences between the corresponding coordinates, namely $[(x_1 - x_2)^2 + (y_1 - y_2)^2]^{1/2}$. The distance between two points in the three-dimensional space or between two vectors in an m-dimensional space, is defined in the same way.

Thus, if we are interested in a trend described by an arbitrary polynomial of degree n, whose variable t is time, we determine the coefficients of such a polynomial in order to minimize the distance between the values of the polynomial and the empirical values, obtained from observations, at the time instants at which the observations of the amount of falling rain have been recorded. As I said before, the square of the Euclidean distance between two vectors with m components is simply the sum of the squared differences between the corresponding components of the two vectors. If the coefficients of the polynomial which describes the trend are given, as real numbers, then the values of this polynomial at the given m times form the components of one vector and the empirical values recorded at these m time instants form another vector. The distance between them is a positive number. It is equal to zero if and only if the two vectors have exactly the same components. Now, if the $n+1$ coefficients of the trend polynomial of degree

n are unknown, then the distance between the vector generated by the arbitrary polynomial of degree n and the given vector of empirical data, at the m time instants taken into account, is a function depending on the unknown coefficients of the trend polynomial. These coefficients are chosen in order to minimize the distance between these two vectors. It is a typical problem from multivariate calculus: minimize a quadratic function of $n + 1$ variables. Solving this optimization problem reduces to solving a system of linear equations which, normally, can be done. The particular values found for the $n + 1$ coefficients will give the polynomial, or the corresponding curve, that fits best the set of empirical data, describing the trend followed by the amount of falling rain in that place. Once the trend is described by a function of time, we can use it to predict values of the amount of falling rain at later times, if these future times, called the prediction horizon, are not too far from the times at which observations have been performed and if the random fluctuations are not very large.

In a more concrete way, assume that we have a certain unknown function depending on time. If we have registered the observed empirical values $y_1, \ldots, y_m$, not necessarily different, at some times $t_1, \ldots, t_m$, and we want to fit a polynomial of degree three, namely $ax^3 + bx^2 + cx + d$, to this empirical set of values, we take the square of the Euclidean distance between the values of the polynomial and the empirical values, $\sum_{k=1}^{m} [(at_k^3 + bt_k^2 + ct_k + d) - y_k]^2$, which is now a function of the unknown coefficients a, b, c, d of the polynomial we want to determine. Now, we minimize this distance, in order to make our polynomial to be as close as possible to the empirical set of observed values. In order to get a so-called stationary point of this distance, we equate to zero the partial derivatives of the Euclidean distance with respect to a, b, c, d, respectively. We obtain a system of four linear equations with four variables a, b, c, d which, once solved, allows us to finally find the best polynomial approximation of degree three for our empirical data. Now, this polynomial could be used for finding approximate values of the unknown function at times t different from the given time instants $t_1, \ldots, t_m$, by replacing such a value t in our polynomial which now is fully determined.

In fact, this is the basic problem in the so called time series analysis: from a set of numerical data obtained by observing the behaviour of a certain entity, we want to detect a possible regular trend, a possible periodicity, and the kind of random fluctuations that have to be taken into account, and use all this in order to make predictions about the future behaviour of that entity. This is a common problem these days and its results are applied in the most different areas like predicting the trajectory of a meteor, anticipating the stock market for the best money investment, or doing the weather forecast. I know some brilliant mathematicians who resigned from very good tenured academic positions in order to focus on the time series provided by the continuous huge flow of data from the stock market, for finding the most profitable ways of investing money. Sometimes they were successful, sometimes not, and sometimes, some of them, spent some time in jail. But this is a different story, about collecting information and using time series for getting rich.

Anyway, the weather forecast, for instance, has improved tremendously in the last couple of years due to the consistent applications of time series analysis and much better ways of collecting data about the global and local weather, for instance, using observations obtained from satellites."

–"What was the controversy about this new 'method of least squares' during Gauss's time?"

–"Legendre's paper on the least squares method was published before the corresponding paper of Gauss's, but Gauss, supported by some comments made in letters sent to the astronomer Wilhelm Olbers, claimed that he had used this method long ago. What is certain is that Gauss successfully used this fruitful optimization method for predicting the orbit of the largest asteroid Ceres, based on a very limited number of astronomical observations about its position. All in all, the least square method is so intuitive and simple that we can only wonder why it wasn't discovered long long ago. But, as it happens with every scientific discovery, somebody has to come up with it and convince the other members of the community that there is something valuable in it."

–"You have mentioned Newton and Gauss as being the greatest mathematicians of all times. Why not Albert Einstein, about whom so much has been written and said?"

–"Albert Einstein was a genius and is considered by many as being the greatest scientist of the twentieth century. His theories on special relativity, general relativity, the photo-electric effect, and many other contributions, belong to physics, cosmology, and even philosophy. But he did nothing new in mathematics. More exactly, he used mathematics but made no discoveries in mathematics. This is also why he got the Nobel prize for physics in 1921."

–"As far as I know, there is no Nobel prize in mathematics? Why?"

–"I really don't know. Some mathematicians like to say that this happened because Nobel's wife cheated on him with a mathematician, but this is just not true because Alfred Nobel was never married."

It was about six o'clock in the evening when we reached La Fouly. John invited me again to have dinner at Edelweiss, but I refused, politely. In fact, I was anxious to eat what I had bought from the Supermarché in the morning and to write down the impressions of the day in my thick notebook. I washed some personal stuff, took a shower, and I had an excellent dinner in front of my tent, with good bread, fantastic Swiss dry sausage, a slice of La Gruyère smelly cheese, and a hot tea with biscuits. Everything tastes better outdoors. Withdrawing inside my tent, I spent the rest of the evening filling in about a dozen of pages, sketching the main points of the trip and trying to reproduce, as accurately as I could, John's comments about mathematics and mathematicians discussed during the day. I also carefully numbered and added to my notebook the small pages with mathematical formulas scratched by John, in a surprisingly legible form under the circumstances, during his explanations. All this time, not far from my tent, somebody put some music loud enough but I didn't mind because it happened to be quite acceptable, at least to my tastes. And writing went better with music in the background. I switched off the light at 11 p.m. and, once I closed my sleeping bag, I ceased to exist, losing any conscious contact with reality as we know it.

SECOND DAY

PETIT COL FERRET

Early Wednesday morning was very similar to the previous one. Fifteen minutes of physical exercises, a shower, a good breakfast consisting from cheese, marmalade, and coffee with biscuits, followed by a rapid shopping at the Supermarché to replenish my thermally insulated food bag. The weather looked good, with very few white clouds around the tall peaks, but less dry than on the previous day. All in all, at eight o'clock I was in front of the Hotel Edelweiss where John was waiting. About ten other people were also there, not far from a beautiful brown horse, with a blond mane, who was eating some seeds from a basket. On horse's back, a large saddle had already been fixed, specially designed to allow about a dozen big bags to be hanged on it. I looked with sympathy at the horse while John joined me and we shook hands.

–"It's the Mont Blanc Tour group who came yesterday from Italy, passing through the Grand Col Ferret. Some of them are still inside, finishing their breakfast. Yesterday night was tough because they made a terrible noise during and after dinner. Some of these groups are relatively quiet but not this one. Probably they knew each other before joining the Tour. Today's breakfast also showed that they have a tremendous appetite. The orange juice and dry salami have disappeared in a couple of minutes from the buffet table. Tonight, another group will come, from the opposite direction, going to Italy through the Grand Col Ferret. But this happens only twice a week. The other days are relatively quiet at Edelweiss."

As previously settled, our objective for Wednesday was to go to the Petit Col Ferret.

–"Petit Col Ferret and Grand Col Ferret are close to each other, separated by the relatively smooth peak Tête de Ferret. The routes to follow for reaching them are, however, very different, as you are going to see."

He was right. Indeed, the trail to Petit Col Ferret proved to be much more difficult, and the 'little' Col looked very differently than the 'big' Col. To be honest, as the two Cols have almost the same altitude, I would have rather called them the 'narrow saddle' and 'large saddle', respectively.

Stage 1. As yesterday, we went south along the paved main road. The wide arrow of the signpost with indications for tourists, located on the main road in the middle of the village, informed us that we needed 2h 30 min until the final destination for the day, Petit Col Ferret. But this time, we didn't pass through the hamlet Ferret. After about 10 minutes, at the point called Le Clou, for unknown reasons, because there were only two little cottages there, we left the main road, crossed Drance de Ferret, on a simple wooden bridge, to its left side, mounting west in a zigzag on a dirty path through an old, dark forest. I told John how nice was to walk in the cool shade made by the big trees after marching on the main road under a surprisingly hot sun for the early hours of the day.

–"I like it too but, unfortunately, there are not many trees at high altitude. Along the trails around Val Ferret there is a mixture of spruce, fir-tree, larch, and sometimes leafy trees such as alder. But, as the path mounts, the trees become rarer and rarer, disappearing around 2200 meters and sometimes even at a much lower altitude, depending on the slope, being replaced by juniper bushes and, obviously, bare boulders and rocks. There is, however, plenty of alpine grass everywhere, and as you have already seen, many many flowers. I am not very good at botany and the only flowers I could identify in this region are: the blue gentiane, the purple saxifrage cassepierre, miraculously growing from rocks, the yellow anémone soufrée, the delicate lily, the omnipresent white daisy with yellow center, the beautifully red-mauve rhododendron, and, for the lucky ones, the gentle white velvet-like edelweiss.

Sometimes, there is a mixture of different flowers but, more often than not, they live in distinct colonies of the same kind of flowers."

–"You told me already that, except the mysterious but highly problematic wolf, apparently seen by nobody in the region, there are no big and dangerous animals in the Swiss Alps. What about venomous snakes? Are there?"

–"I read in a book that there are some vipers in the southern valleys of Switzerland, at low altitude only, because they have a cold blood and need a lot of sun to warm up. I haven't seen any during my trips and absolutely nobody told me anything about incidents involving vipers in the area. In fact, they are as afraid of humans as we are of them. Elementary caution is needed mainly before you decide to sit on a stump. Long, long ago, after graduating, I went with a group of friends on a ten-day trip in some mountains renowned for a high density of vipers that lived there. Very afraid, we got somehow a syringe and a rare anti-viper serum from a medical research institute and we took them with us. Fortunately, we haven't met any viper and the serum was passed to some friends of ours, who passed it to some friends of theirs, and so on. But, in that particular viper rich region I heard many awful stories. Thus, one mountaineer, hiking alone, was bitten by a viper. Soon he lost his consciousness, fainted, and fell down in a precipice. Miraculously, he was found later and didn't die because falling down from rock to rock, he was severely hurt and luckily lost a lot of blood, and, therefore, he lost a lot of deadly venom which entered his blood stream too. I cannot guarantee that this story was really true. It is plausible, however, as an example about how a misfortune, falling in a precipice, could compensate another misfortune, being bitten by a venomous snake, like a double negation which results in something positive, namely, surviving. In fact, I personally met a forester whose thumb was bitten by a viper and who, immediately and bravely, severed it with his axe, to prevent the venom from spreading inside his body and stopping his heart from beating. But let give up talking about snakes because, as I said before, there is no reason to panic about them here."

After ten minutes through the forest, the narrow path crossed an inclined meadow leading us to an unpaved road. To the left, the road went a little down to Gîte de Léchère, a former sheep farm, recently transformed into a rustic Cabane with a kitchen and three dormitories that can accommodate about 35 people. We turned to the right instead, and the road mounted slowly in a large serpentine, basically heading west and, in about 35 minutes, we arrived to La Léchère, or Léchère Dessus how it is also called, a complex of two closed sheep farms. Unfortunately for us, very close were a flock of sheep guarded by four dogs. One of the dogs didn't pay any attention to us, but the other three rushed towards us, barking aggressively. Two of them, still barking, stopped, keeping some distance between them and us. The third hostile sheep dog, white and big, didn't stop, however, and moved fast to attack us. Not so far, the shepherd was calmly sitting, talking on a mobile telephone and doing nothing for restraining his dogs. I was terrified but the dog went directly to John who at least had two climbing sticks in his hands. Instead of hitting the dog, however, John crouched down, looking directly in the eyes of the dog and saying 'Good dog, good dog!' The sheep dog proved to be fluent in English and, flattered by the compliment, smelled John and me and left to his sheep.

Stage 2. For obvious reasons, we didn't take any break at La Léchère, even if I was tempted to ironically thank the shepherd for his total lack of concern for our fate. The altitude there was 1850 meters and two arrow-indicators told us that 30 minutes were needed for descending to La Fouly and 1h 50 min for going up to Le Petit Col Ferret.

As the unpaved road had ended at the sheep farm, we followed a steep path, marked, from time to time, with a red strip with white margins, mounting south-west, and a little later in zigzag towards west, in a bleak environment. Grass and hillocks. Sometimes, we saw some round holes, with a diameter of about 10 cm.

−"They are entrances into underground labyrinths made by marmots, burrowing rodents that resemble your Canadian groundhogs," explained John. "And if you have noticed, from time to time, you can hear a ferret, which is a small and extremely rapid, supple feline, relatively frequent in the region, detecting us and informing about our presence by whistling."

After a quarter of an hour, we arrived on a plateau and, for the next
ten minutes, the path slowly mounted towards west, eventually turning to the left, going almost linearly south-west, through a vast field
of green rhododendrons with a lot of red flowers, and dense juniper
bushes. On the left-hand side we had a not so deep valley, ramification of the main Val Ferret, having patches of snow, remained from
the previous winter. On the right-hand side there was a long vertical
rock. Eight minutes later, the path entered a narrow valley mounting
slowly towards south-west, and then switched on the west side of the
valley which became deeper and deeper as we ascended. After climbing
a ridge, we left the narrow valley to our left and, turning to the right,
we entered the upper part of the large valley of the Combe des Fonds,
where, very down there, at the cascade, I met John on the day of my
arrival at La Fouly. From now on, we would remain on the left-hand
side of this newly met, large valley until our final destination, but the
difficulties were only now to come. We needed just one hour from La
Léchère up to this point of joining the valley of the Combe des Fonds.

Stage 3. We took a break, mainly to admire the high peaks on
the right-hand side of the large valley, unaccessible to normal mortals.
Then, we followed our narrow path that turned left, soon starting to
climb drastically. The scenery became really alpine, with almost only
rocks and patches of snow and, surprise, absolutely nobody around.

−"I am really surprised," said John. "It is true that fewer tourists
come to Petit Col Ferret, compared with what happens on the trail to
Grand Col Ferret, but still, normally there are plenty of them here too.
What happens today seems to me quite unusual."

The weather was so so. From time to time local clouds suddenly
appeared, some of them even dark grey, at the beginning around the
tall peaks, but sometimes descending above our heads, hiding the top
summits from us. The temperature also dropped and we had to wear
something warmer. Everything is calm and reassuring when the sky is
blue and the sun is shining. By contrast, when the weather changes,

and the dark clouds show up, it is impossible not to feel some strange kind of vulnerability, especially when there are no other human beings around and no houses or shelters in sight. Soon, a slow but cold rain started. Fortunately, it lasted only about 15 minutes. And again, small clouds came and left, sometimes with a great speed. The path descended a little, crossing some patches of snow, and then an arduous climb followed, of about 100 meters in altitude, just through the middle of the valley Combe des Fonds, much narrower now, whose slope became more inclined than before. The arduous ascent ended in a hollow from which, above us, Le Petit Col Ferret became fully visible, up there, in front of us and completely covered by a snow surprisingly white, an obvious proof that a fresh powder had fallen in the previous night or nights.

Stage 4. The last portion of the trail proved to be the most difficult one. I didn't complain but everything was quite different compared with the friendly trail to Le Grand Col Ferret. A steep climb started, on the left-hand side of the upper portion of the valley Combe des Fonds, among big rocks and boulders. The bottom of the valley was compact with snow. There was no clear path among rocks, perhaps because the amount of snow changes from year to year, forcing the hikers to choose different paths that avoid the existing snow. From place to place there were some visible pyramids made of smaller rocks by caring predecessors, who wanted to help the newly arriving climbers.

Approaching the last part of the climb, there was no alternative but go on the snow, present now everywhere around, until we finally reached the top of the saddle called Petit Col Ferret, at 2539 meters altitude, as written on a little stone marking the frontier between the two countries. Again, behind us, to north-east, was Switzerland and in front, down to south-west, was Italy. France was also very close, somewhere to the right. We were now much closer to the high mountains surrounding the Mont Blanc, but just because we were now too close to them, we had a more limited panorama than we had from Le Grand Col Ferret. We took a break, but not as long as we had planned to have because it was cold, perhaps around five degrees Celsius, and a strong wind was blowing from Italy. Again, there was no hut or shelter there. Just snow, rocks, and, here and there, some patches of grass.

−"From here, it is relatively easy to go to the Refuge Fiorio, also known as Bivouac Fiorio," said John. "Crossing to Italy, by descending a little to the west and then climbing about 200 meters towards north-west, the Refuge Fiorio may be reached in a little more than one hour, when the weather is good. From there, you can admire the long Glacier de Triolet."

As on the previous day, the descent to La Fouly took us a much longer time than the ascent itself, which, normally, is not supposed to happen. Just at the beginning, we somehow lost the tortuous path in the rocky upper portion of the valley. After a couple of unfortunate deviations, going to nowhere, we had no choice but plunge towards the bottom of the valley, jumping from rock to rock and even sliding on a steep and long patch of snow. When we regained the marked path, we slowed down and took several long breaks, sitting, eating the scarce food brought by each of us in our light knapsacks, and chatting. The weather suddenly improved, the clouds simply melting away. On our way down, we met a group of four senior Dutch men, carrying very heavy staff on their back and heading to La Vachey, down in Italy, on the southern side of Petit Col Ferret. Approaching La Léchère, I wasn't excited by the perspective of meeting again the four sheep dogs but, by a true miracle, there were no traces of them or of the sheep guarded by them, who moved somewhere out of sight. God be with them!

HILBERT

The discussion also turned to mathematics. When John asked me what kind of mathematics I liked most in high school, I mentioned immediately the geometry. Then, it was my turn to bring John himself into it and I asked:

−"As you mentioned yesterday, geometry starts from some axioms, stated very long ago by Greek mathematicians. Does this happen in other domains of mathematics, like calculus, for instance?"

−"This is a very long topic to talk about. To make the long story short, the Euclidean geometry was for a long time presented to be a model of axiomatic field, envied by any science that aimed at precision, rigour, and correctness. It started from some definitions of basic entities, a couple of axioms, which were statements accepted as being obvious, and inference rules, based on classic logic, leading to lemmas, theorems, and corollaries. But even the Euclidean geometry was put under the microscope and dissected.

Towards the end of the 19th century, David Hilbert challenged Euclid and, in an excess of precision and rigour, proposed 20 axioms for geometry, instead of the five postulates of the Euclidean geometry. His book *Grundlagen der Geometrie*, published in 1899, put geometry on formal axiomatic basis, claiming that the new system of independent axioms is noncontradictory, self-consistent, and complete. The book started from three distinct sets of objects, called points, lines, and planes, respectively, among which there are certain mutual relations denoted by words like 'lie', 'between', and 'congruent'. Then, the axioms of the geometry are grouped in five groups: eight axioms of incidence, four axioms of order, five axioms of congruence, an axiom of parallels, and two axioms of continuity.

In the new axiomatic presentation, intuition has been completely eliminated and even obvious things and properties are supposed to be meticulously justified and proved. For instance, the first axiom of incidence says that: 'For every two points A, B there exists a line a that contains each of the points A, B.' The first axiom of order states that: 'On a line, if a point B lies between a point A and a point C, then the points A, B, C are three distinct points on a line, and B then also lies between C and A.' And so on and so on. For Hilbert everything had to be carefully defined and nothing left to common sense and a 'matter-of-fact' intuition.

The axiom of parallels, called Euclid's axiom, is formulated in a weaker form, like: 'Let a be any line and A a point not on it. Then there is at most one line in the plane, determined by a and A, that passes through A and doesn't intersect a.' As a consequence, we obtain that there is exactly one parallel to a line through a point not on the given line, as originally stated by Euclid in his 'parallel postulate'.

In high school, I had an excellent textbook on the plane geometry, written in the old Euclidean style, and I really enjoyed solving problems, very much based on imagination and a little fantasy in drawing an inspired supplementary line or circle or any auxiliary geometric construction, in order to approach the final answer. Later, an academic, who didn't know much about what was going on in high schools, has restructured the elementary geometry manual according to Hilbert's approach and the Ministry of Education made it compulsory in all public schools. I remember how many difficulties the students and even their teachers had in coping with the new style. The most obvious steps and constructions had to be absurdly rigorously justified and simple problems suddenly needed extremely long and tedious proofs."

–"Maybe Hilbert didn't write his book for high school students."

–"This is a very debatable question. How much from modern mathematics has to be taught in schools or to people who are not going to become professional mathematicians, like engineers or economists? Sometimes, pushing the rigour too far and trying to prove absolutely everything with absolute precision could become frightening and detrimental for learning and getting confidence in our ability to understand and solve problems by using a mathematical tool. Even in my fourth year course on operations research, I prefer to use often the word 'justification' instead of 'proof' because really proving something would imply going very very far into the finest details. Our 'proofs' still rely on prerequisites assumed to be known from other courses and therefore can not be complete. And there is no time to perform such an absurd dissection for analyzing all subtleties of a complete proof if we still want to cover all the new topics, results, algorithms, and methods we are supposed to cover according to the demanding curriculum of the respective course.

On the other hand, I find very depressing when even some good students are asking me the very frequent question: 'Are we responsible for the proofs?' or 'Are you going to put proofs in the test or final exam?' Then, I always answer: 'Of course, if the proof was done in class.' And, at this moment, I preach the sermon about mathematics as being the only science where we can prove our statements and how the students themselves can check whether I was right or not instead of simply believing what I was saying or writing on the blackboard.

A favourite moment for me is when I spend a lot of time proving all the details for getting a formula for the probability that a customer has to wait more than an arbitrary amount of time t in a queuing system in steady state condition, with s servers, waiting to be served and being served. When the final formula is finally obtained, I tell my students: 'In some popular textbooks this important formula is given without any justification. Without proving it, how could you trust that there is no printing error in it?' Every time, however, I feel that some students are not impressed and would rather prefer to believe that everything is OK with the respective formula and skip the proof."

–"Did Hilbert something more than being so picky about Euclid's axioms?"

–"As a matter-of-fact, he did. First of all, he published a lot of papers on the invariant theory in algebra, integral equations, algebraic number theory, and calculus of variation, which is a kind of optimization with boundary constraints. He also constructed an example of a strange curve that can fill a two-dimensional domain. In functional analysis, whose general objective is to study entire sets of functions collectively, he systematically constructed the geometry of infinite-dimensional spaces, called today Hilbert spaces, which have important applications in quantum mechanics. A Hilbert space is somehow similar to an Euclidean space but it has infinitely many dimensions and its elements are either functions or sequences of numbers. But we can still deal with distances, angles, and orthogonality, like we do in an Euclidean space where the elements are vectors with a finite number of numerical components.

Being obsessed with axiomatic theories, his dream was to do for the entire mathematics what he did for the Euclidean geometry. More exactly, towards the end of his life, he published two volumes of *Grundlagen der Mathematik*, intended to lead to a general 'proof theory' that would allow a direct check for the consistency of the whole mathematics, viewed as a grandiose formal axiomatic system. Unfortunately, a famous paper, published about the same time by Kurt Gödel, showed that Hilbert's dream wasn't possible. But this is another story.

Remaining still to Hilbert, let me mention that in 1900, at the Second International Congress of Mathematicians held in Paris, he gave a famous speech during which he outlined his philosophy on mathematics and formulated 23 famous open problems. Some of the problems were vague, like the need to get an axiomatic treatment of physics (problem 6), but some were very specific, like Goldbach's conjecture (all even positive integer numbers larger than 2 could be written as the sum of two primes), the Riemann hypothesis (about the location of the zeros of Riemann's function from number theory, a generalization of Euler's zeta function to complex variables), about which I intend to say more sooner or later, and the continuum hypothesis (the order of infinity of the real numbers is the next one after that of the natural numbers). Afterwards, a lot of mathematicians focused on Hilbert's problems and some of them are still unsolved. Thus, Hilbert said that the Riemann's hypothesis would be solved during his lifetime but, in fact, it has remained unproved so far. Anyway, Hilbert's talk was somehow surprising because, normally, at conferences or congresses the participants report on the results obtained by them and not on unsolved problems. The majority of the mathematical textbooks also present the facts proved to be true and are quiet about questions remained unanswered."

–"And what about Hilbert's life?"

–"Not too much to talk about. Or, more exactly, I don't know much about it. He was born in Königsberg and attended the university in his native town. When he was 33 years old, Felix Klein, a great geometer, brought him to Göttingen, where Hilbert became full professor and spent the rest of his long life there. In Göttingen, he enjoyed taking long walks with friends, very often talking about mathematics or physics, used to go to the market on his bicycle, and I read that he liked very much to dance. Even a great mathematician is a human being after all. He was 81 years old when he died."

–"I have read that the discoveries in mathematics are made by young people. Is this so indeed?"

–"Well, the history of mathematics contains many examples of very young mathematicians who had great contributions to the development of different areas of mathematics and, in general, the talent in mathematics is revealed at an early age. However, Carl Friedrich Gauss wrote a masterpiece on differential geometry when he was 50 years old and Leonhard Euler, one of the most prolific mathematicians ever, did high quality mathematics until the end of his long life."

EULER

– "I saw Euler's picture on a 10-Swiss-franc currency bill. Perhaps he was very important because it is very unusual to see scientists printed on paper money. In Canada you can see only the pictures of former politicians or Queen Elizabeth II on our 5-dollar, 20-dollar, 50-dollar, and 100-dollar bills."

– "Leonhard Euler was born indeed near Basel, in Switzerland, at the beginning of the 18-th century (1707) and lived 76 years. His house was burnt during a big fire. His father was a Protestant clergyman. Euler had a special gift for languages and an extraordinary memory. He could perform complicated arithmetical computations without using pencil or paper. He entered the University of Basel when he was 14 years old. He was influenced by Johann Bernoulli, whose son Daniel went to Russia to take a position in mathematics at the Saint Petersburg Academy, newly created. Euler went to St. Petersburg himself, accepting an offer for a position in physics, and resided at the home of Daniel Bernoulli. Five years later, Daniel returned to Switzerland and Euler took the chair in mathematics remained vacant in Saint Petersburg. He married the daughter of a Swiss painter living in Russia and, during a happy marriage of about 40 years, they had 13 children but only five survived to adolescence and only three outlived their parents.

He published and published, without interruption, and his reputation went up and up. In spite of the loss of vision in his right eye, Euler obtained many fundamental results in number theory and a monumental treatment of Newton's mechanics in the general framework of differential and integral calculus. His excellent memory compensated his partial loss of vision. Generally, he had a good life in St. Petersburg. But the death of Catherine I, the political turmoil, and the growing suspicion of foreigners, made him move to the Berlin Academy when he was about 34 years old. In Berlin he worked for about 25 years."

–"What made him famous in mathematics?"

–"I dare say that Euler was fascinated by series and the logarithm function. If we sum up the inverse positive integers, namely $1/1+1/2+\ldots+1/n$, we obtain the so called finite harmonic series. Euler showed that the difference between this finite harmonic series and the natural logarithm $\ln n$, when n increases indefinitely, is a certain constant value called today 'Euler's constant', namely: $\lim_{n\to\infty}(\sum_{k=1}^{n}(1/k)-\ln n)=0.577215\ldots$.

He also obtained an important formula showing that for any real number $s>1$, summing up the terms of the form $1/n^s$, for all positive integers $n=1,2,3,\ldots$, which defines the so called zeta-function $\zeta(s)=\sum_{n=1}^{\infty}(1/n^s)$, we obtain the same result as taking the product of all numbers of the form $p^s/(p^s-1)$, for all prime numbers $p=2,3,5,\ldots$, a surprising connection between analysis and number theory. Later, in 1859, Bertrand Riemann extended Euler's zeta-function $\zeta(s)$ to the case when s is a complex variable and this generalization proved to be crucial in the proofs given independently, in 1896, by Jacques Hadamard and Charles Jean Gustave Nicolas de La Vallée Poussin, to the famous 'prime number theorem', according to which the number of primes less than or equal to the real number x, denoted by $\pi(x)$, behaves like $x/\ln x$, for large values of x, a result conjectured by Carl Friedrich Gauss in 1793, when he was about 15 years old. Obviously, there is no connection between $\pi(x)$, whose values are positive integers, and the transcendental number $\pi=3.14\ldots$ from geometry. Both notation are standard and used by everybody. Unfortunately, mathematicians use sometimes the same symbol for different things.

Euler published an important text on the theory of functions, where he constantly manipulated infinite series and series representations of sine, cosine, or logarithm functions, and another text on differential calculus. More than two centuries later, it is very easy for some picky fellow mathematicians to criticize Euler who sometimes used divergent series, which means series whose sum is infinite, as the convergent series, whose sum is finite, forgetting or ignoring that he was a pioneer in this important field.

Apparently for the first time, Euler introduced techniques of differential calculus to solve problems in algebra, like the relations between the roots and coefficients of an arbitrary polynomial, and he gave a new proof for solving a quartic polynomial equation by radicals. He also mastered the complex numbers, defining the multivalued radical and logarithm of complex numbers and discovering, among many other things, the much celebrated Euler's identity connecting the trigonometric functions sine and cosine to the exponential function with complex exponent. Mathematically, this is the simple but very important formula: $e^{i\alpha} = \cos\alpha + i\sin\alpha$, where $i = \sqrt{-1}$.

Only this last formula would have been enough for making him famous. A particular case of it gives an unbelievably simple relationship between the imaginary unit i, which is the square root of -1, and the most important transcendental numbers e, so important in number theory or calculus, and the circular constant π, which you certainly know from trigonometry or from the formula for the area of a circle. Thus e raised at power $i\pi$ is equal to -1, which means $e^{i\pi} = -1$. If you think that the transcendental numbers are real numbers with infinitely many decimals, without any kind of repeated pattern inside their decimal part, and the square root of -1 has scared even brilliant mathematicians like Descartes or Leibniz, it is almost miraculous that e at power $i\pi$ could give such a simple result as -1. Against common sense, something very complicated combined with something even more complicated give something amazingly simple."

–"If I understand correctly, during the times of Newton, Leibniz, and Euler, calculus was created and developed. But Euclid's geometry remained unchanged. Even if Hilbert tried to reformulate its axioms, basically what we learn in school today are old results as known by old Greek geometers."

–"No field in mathematics is closed for ever. There is always something new to be done, some old results to be continued, and the possibility to look at things from a different angle. Knowing is a never ending process. Believe it or not, Euler was interested even in elementary plane geometry and proved that in any triangle the orthocenter, the intersection of the three altitudes, the centroid, the intersection of the three medians, and the circumcenter, the center of the triangle's circumscribed circle, are collinear, which means that they must lie in a straight line, called 'Euler's line'. Yesterday, I mentioned his seminal contribution to the birth of topology when he solved the Königsberg's bridges problem. "

−"From so many contributions, which one was considered to be the most important?"

−"It is difficult to say. It is not without interest to notice, however, that the most widely read work done by Euler wasn't a mathematical text but a series of volumes entitled *Letters of Euler on different subjects in natural philosophy addressed to a German princess*, resulted from a series of introductory lectures in elementary science provided by him to a young Princess, whose name I don't remember, while he resided in Berlin. Unfortunately, the sophisticated Frederick the Great, who had reorganized the Berlin Academy and had brought Euler there, didn't like him very much. Also, the brilliant Voltaire, also a member of the Berlin Academy at that time, and the modest and quiet Euler didn't get along very well either. Consequently, Euler moved back to St. Petersburg, where the situation had improved mainly under Catherine the Great. He continued to work hard and be extremely productive in spite of becoming virtually blind and losing his wife. During this time, he wrote a huge book on algebra and a three-volume text on integral calculus. It is said that even on his last day, when he was 76 years old, he made some calculations on the orbit of the planet Uranus, in the morning, before dying, in the afternoon."

VIEWPOINTS ON MATHEMATICS

−"I wouldn't like to lose my sight but I would prefer to have a death like Euler's. And everything he created remains valid forever because mathematics is the only rock solid science."

−"First, don't even mention death at your age. You still have an entire life ahead of you. Enjoy every minute of it.
Second, even about mathematics, as solid as it seems to be, com-

pared to other sciences, there are different viewpoints about what it should be looked at. The 'logicism', promoted by Gottlob Frege (1848-1925), Bertrand Arthur Russell (1872-1970), Giuseppe Peano (1858-1932), and Alfred North Whitehead (1861-1947), looked at classical mathematics as being a part of logic. The form rather than content is more important. Its axioms, rules, and theorems, are discovered but not created, because they exist independently of the human mind.

The 'intuitionism', promoted mainly by Luitzen Egbertus Jan Brower (1881-1966), who taught at the University of Amsterdam during his entire career, claimed that mathematics is a mental activity and not a collection of theorems. The definitions, theorems, and proofs have to be constructive. A theorem which proves that a solution of a problem exists without showing, however, how to construct it effectively, has no value and should be ignored.

Finally, the 'formalism', promoted mainly by David Hilbert (1862-1943), should try to formalize the different axiomatic branches of mathematics and to prove that they are free of contradictions. This was a very ambitious program, trying to reach the absolute rigour in mathematics. Unfortunately, later, Kurt Gödel (1906-1978) showed that not even arithmetics can be proved to be free of contradictions."

–"You have mentioned many names of mathematicians and all are men. What about women mathematicians?"

–"Until recently, becoming a professional mathematician wasn't considered to be a proper career for a young woman. Things have changed. In fact, in the last years, I have had more girls than boys in my fourth year math courses. Looking back in time, there are some women who should be included in any serious treaty on the history of mathematics.

Sophie Germain, born in 1776, successfully worked in number theory. In her correspondence with Joseph Louis Lagrange and with Carl Friedrich Gauss, she preferred to sign her letters using the name Mister Le Blanc. She got a prize from the prestigious French Academy of Sciences for a paper on the vibrations of thin elastic plates but died relatively young, at the age of 55.

Sophia Kovalevska, or Sophie Kovalevski, born in 1850, worked with Karl Weierstrass and obtained prizes for papers on theoretical mechanics and the theory of partial difference equations. She was appointed professor for life in Stockholm but died young, at the age of 41, if I remember well.

I think that the most famous woman mathematician was Amelie Emmy Noether, born in 1882. She had an overwhelming contribution to the development of the abstract general algebra. Until 1933, when she emigrated to the United States, she had a modest position in Göttingen in spite of the fact that foreign mathematicians used to come to attend the algebra course taught by her there. Among her students in Göttingen was Bartel van der Waerden, a Dutch who later published two volumes on abstract algebra that are the best in the field even today, in which he mentioned that he had intensively used the fundamental ideas of Emmy Noether and the notes taken during her lectures. The preface of a modern book on category theory, one of the most recent abstract developments of the already very abstract algebra, mentions that there are several fathers of category theory but only one mother, Emmy Noether. She also died at the early age of 54."

−"You seem to have a fantastic memory. I have a good visual memory myself, or I think I have, but I cannot remember proper names at all."

−"Not really. As you have mentioned memory, let me tell you a joke about what a good memory means. A psychologist found out from a friend of his that there was an old man who had an unbelievable memory, a real encyclopedia. He made the necessary arrangements and got an appointment with him. The old man welcomed the psychologist in his modest apartment, served him delicious scrambled eggs prepared by him, and they started talking about all sorts of personalities, things, and events from history, politics, and arts. Overwhelmed by the unusual memory of his host, the psychologist thanked for the meeting and left very impressed. About ten years later, he met the old man again, by pure chance, and wanted to greet him with the usual 'How are you?' But he barely started saying 'How...', that the old man immediately snapped back: 'Scrambled!' "

−"I hope that my own memory is good enough to remember this

and tell the joke to my friend Stephen. The only joke that comes to my mind about memory, or lack of it, is about a usually absent-minded professor who comes home from school and proudly waves an umbrella telling his wife:

    –'Look, today I didn't forget to bring back my umbrella.'

    –'But today you didn't take any umbrella with you,' said the wife."

–"I am afraid that I am not very far from behaving like this professor. Anyway, whatever people say, a good memory helps. Gauss, who wrote his papers in Latin, started a systematic study of the Russian language towards the end of his life. He strongly believed that learning foreign languages is an excellent exercise for improving the memory, in particular, and our intellect, in general."

FERMAT'S LAST THEOREM

–"Routinely," I said after a while, turning back to mathematics, "mass media don't mention names or stories about mathematicians. For instance, I never heard something about Euler or Hilbert. Not long ago, however, I saw some articles in the newspaper *The Globe and Mail* about how the last Fermat's theorem has been solved after more than 300 years. I am sure that you know many details about."

–"Indeed, a lot of noise has been made about it. At least two books, meant for the general public, have been published on this topic recently. Pierre de Fermat (1601-1665) was a very interesting character. He wasn't a professional mathematician. He studied law and having later a comfortable life and a high job, as a judge for the parliament in Toulouse, that allowed him enough free time, he did mathematics as a hobby, which is meritorious if we take into account that he had five children who perhaps took their share from his free time. In number theory, a domain in which he excelled, he was in the habit of formulating different statements without proofs. Many of them have been later proved to be true, whereas a few of them have been later proved to be wrong, and some of them remained unproved and became so-called conjectures, keeping many brilliant minds busy to prove them true or false in the coming years.

In order to formulate Fermat's last theorem, let me notice that there are different positive integers that can be the lengths of the sides AB, AC, and BC of a right-angle triangle ABC, for instance the integers 3, 4, and 5, respectively. Indeed, according to Pythagoras's theorem, $AB^2 + AC^2 = BC^2$, the square of 3, which is 9, plus the square of 4, which is 16, is equal to the square of 5, which is 25. Fermat's conjecture was that there are no different positive integers x, y, z, such that the n-th power of x plus the n-th power of y is equal to the n-th power of z, which means $x^n + y^n = z^n$, if $n > 2$. He scratched this conjecture, called later 'Fermat's last theorem', on the margins of an old book on number theory, mentioning that he had a truly beautiful proof for it but not enough space to reproduce it there. In fact, I heard about Fermat's last theorem, when I was in high school, from my mathematics teacher who, making the story more mysterious, told us that Fermat, attending a party, had written the solution of his conjecture on the cuff of his immaculate white shirt but forgot about it and the proof was erased when the housekeeper washed the shirt on the following day.

So, two questions arose: is Fermat's statement true and, if the answer is yes, did he possess indeed a general proof for it? Whatever happened, a general proof hasn't been found among his papers. Leonhard Euler proved the conjecture for $n = 3$. Apparently, Fermat proved it for $n = 4$, and Adrien-Marie Legendre for $n = 5$. Since then, the conjecture has been proved to be right for many values of n, by different mathematicians along the years, and by using powerful computers more recently, but not for an arbitrary integer n larger than 2. Checking its validity for a huge amount of values of the exponent n is still not a proof of the respective conjecture. In fact, in number theory sometimes it is easier to discover an interesting property of some special kind of numbers than to prove it.

Thus, we come to the second half of the 20th century. Without technical details, the winding course of events that happened in Japan, Germany, the United States, and Great Britain, heading to the final proof of Fermat's last theorem, may be summarized in the following steps:

First, we have to go back to the second half of the 19th century. One of the greatest mathematicians ever, Jules Henri Poincaré (1854-1912), a very respected professor at the University of Paris and member of the French Academy, dominated every part of the mathematics of his time, introducing new ideas and mathematical techniques in analysis, differential equations, theory of functions of a complex variable, non-Euclidean geometry, and topology. Among many other things, he introduced the so called 'modular forms', a special class of automorphic functions defined in the upper half of the complex plane. An automorphic function, or Fuchsian function how Poincaré called it, is a function defined in the complex plane, which remains invariant when the complex variable z is transformed into $(az + b)/(cz + d)$, where the real numbers a, b, c, d satisfy the condition $ad - bc \neq 0$. In fact, for the modular forms, $ad - bc$ should be positive. Poincaré was fascinated by the strange symmetries these functions possess and their study made him get a very ingenious model for the non-Euclidean geometry of János Bolyai and Nikolai Ivanovich Lobachevsky. But this is another story.

In 1954, 100 years after Poincaré's birth, a young Japanese, Yutaka Taniyama, made an unexpected conjecture, known today as either Goro Shimura-Taniyama conjecture or Shimura-Taniyama-Weil conjecture, according to which every elliptic curve is a modular form. Conjecture means a statement expected to be true but still remained unproved. An elliptic curve, is a particular class of cubic equations in two variables, having the elementary form: $y^2 = ax^3 + bx^2 + cx$, where a, b, c are integers or rational numbers. Four years latter, Taniyama committed suicide. In his death note he mentioned that, while he couldn't understand himself the cause of his suicide, he was tired, both physically and mentally, and had lost confidence in his future.

Later, Gerhard Frey suggested that if the conjecture were proved, then Fermat's last theorem would be proved as well because if there are three integers for which Fermat's theorem is not true for a certain n larger than 2, then the corresponding elliptic curve, defined by these three numbers as coefficients, will contradict Shimura-Taniyama conjecture. It is not without interest to notice that Gerhard Frey arrived to this unexpected connection between Fermat's last theorem and Shimura-Taniyama's conjecture on the elliptic functions without proving it. Often, intuition and an educated guess have precedence over fixing a rigorous proof when something new is discovered in mathematics. In 1987, Kenneth Ribet proved that Frey's suggestion was true.

Finally, in 1993, Andrew Wiles, who had learned about Fermat's last theorem when he had been 10 years old, subsequently remaining obsessed with it, proved a weaker form of Shimura-Taniyama's conjecture, namely that a class of elliptic curves, the so-called semi-stable elliptic curves, are modular forms, which, based on what Frey and Ribet did, was still sufficient to imply that Fermat's last theorem was true. A very sinuous way of indirectly proving Fermat's last theorem, indeed! Anyway, after the conference in Cambridge, where he had announced his astonishing achievement, Andrew Wiles instantly became famous. His long paper was dissected by specialists and, unfortunately, a flaw was eventually found. Wiles, who before had liked to work in total isolation and secrecy, went back to do more research and hopefully fix the flaw, but this time under public scrutiny. Richard Taylor, a former student, joined in. After more than a year, with periods of uncertainty, deception, followed by a sudden inspiration about how to eliminate the flaw, the long proof of Fermat's last theorem was declared clean by the experts. In the month of May of 1995, the prestigious journal *Annals of Mathematics* published Wiles's original Cambridge paper and the correction signed by Taylor and Wiles.

Once Fermat's last theorem was proved, a certain 'sense of melancholy' remained, as Wiles himself put it. A challenge, who inspired many to do mathematics, was gone. But, two things are still lingering in the background. First, the final justification was about two hundred pages long, which somehow is not what we expect from an elegant proof. Second, the mathematical concepts and techniques used in all these successive steps of the proof were certainly not available during Fermat's lifetime. Therefore, if Fermat proved indeed his last theorem, then he ought to have used a totally different approach. But did he, and if yes, what approach? Therefore, the mystery remains."

–"Is this such an important achievement that it deserves to be made public in newspapers?"

–"Well, it depends on what we think to be important. Important for what and for whom? For an applied mathematician, Fermat's last theorem has little importance if any, because he would approximate the solution of Fermat's equation using rational numbers instead of integers. There are some open problems in mathematics, and number theory is full of them, that are nothing more than challenging curiosities. Getting an answer to them would not have ramifications and consequences in other domains. For instance, Christian Goldbach's conjecture, already mentioned when we talked about Hilbert's open problems listed by him in 1900, formulated in 1742 in a letter to Euler, that every even integer number larger than 2 is at least in one way the sum of two primes, remained unproved as far as I know. As you ought to know, a prime is a positive integer that may be divided only by 1 and itself. We have plenty of examples confirming the conjecture, like $4 = 2 + 2$, $6 = 3 + 3$, $8 = 3 + 5$, or $10 = 3 + 7 = 5 + 5$, but the problem is to prove that this is true for an arbitrary even integer number. Fermat's last theorem is not far from such a relatively innocent mathematical statement. Carl Friedrich Gauss, for instance, did not show any interest for dealing with it and mentioned that he had a long list containing many other similar puzzles in number theory. However, Fermat's last theorem proved to be important in pure mathematics because, trying to solve it, some new concepts were introduced in mathematics, like Ernst Eduard Kummer's so-called 'ideal', whose theory was later developed by Julius Wilhelm Richard Dedekind and Ferdinand Gotthold Eisenstein, a concept that proved to be useful in number theory and abstract algebra."

–"Ideal in mathematics? It's a funny name. Only humans can have an ideal ahead of them!"

–"I don't know why this name was chosen. It is only a name, but mathematically, an ideal is a very well defined concept, without any ambiguity. Using the standard notations $\mathbf{Z}$, $\mathbf{Q}$, $\mathbf{R}$, and $\mathbf{C}$ for the set of integers, the set of rational numbers, the set of real numbers, and the set of complex numbers, respectively, with respect to the operations of addition and multiplication, as we discussed yesterday, $\mathbf{Z}$ is a ring (a group with respect to addition but not a group with respect to multiplication because dividing two integers – which is the inverse operation with respect to the multiplication of numbers – we don't obtain always an integer), but both $\mathbf{Q}$, and $\mathbf{R}$, and $\mathbf{C}$ are fields, because they are groups both with respect to the addition and with respect to the multiplication. Obviously, any field is a ring but not every ring is a field, for instance $\mathbf{Z}$. More than that, $\mathbf{Z}$ is a subset of $\mathbf{Q}$, which is a subset of

R, which is a subset of **C**. Or, as algebraic structures, **Z** is a subring of **Q**, which is a subfield of **R**, which is a subfield of **C**. All four sets are infinite, but **Z** and **Q** are countable, or have the 'smallest' infinite cardinal or power $\aleph_0$, whereas **R**, and **C** are infinitely continuous, having a larger power or cardinal $\aleph$, according to Georg Cantor.

By the way, the continuum hypothesis, one of Hilbert's 23 famous problems we talked about, stating that the order of infinity of the real numbers is the next after that of the natural numbers which, with the above notations, means that there is no cardinal in between $\aleph_0$ and $\aleph$, has remained undecidable.

Anyway, in general, an ideal of a ring R is a subring I such that if a is an arbitrary element of I and r is an arbitrary element of R, then the products ar and ra lie in I. For instance, the subring of even integers, denoted by $2\mathbf{Z}$, is an ideal of **Z**, called the ideal generated by 2. Similarly, the ideal generated by the natural number n, denoted by $n\mathbf{Z}$, is the subring formed by the integer multiples of n or, equivalently, the set of integers divisible by n. Ideals are very important."

–"Why are they important?"

–"I am happy that you have asked about ideals, because they allow us to look at Fermat's last theorem from an angle not very much mentioned in literature. Once an ideal I in a ring R is given, all the elements of R could be grouped in classes, such that two elements of R whose difference belongs to I are considered to be equivalent with respect to I, and put in the same class. The set of all these classes of equivalence with respect to the ideal I is called the quotient ring of R with respect to the ideal I and is denoted by R/I. In particular, the quotient ring $\mathbf{Z}/n\mathbf{Z}$, denoted simply by $\mathbf{Z}_n$, is the ring of integers modulo n, or mod n. It is extremely important to notice that even if the ring **Z** and the ideal $n\mathbf{Z}$ are infinite sets, the quotient ring $\mathbf{Z}_n$ is a finite set containing just n equivalence classes. It is like wrapping up the infinite set of nonnegative integers $\{0, 1, 2, 3, \ldots, n-1, n, n+1, \ldots\}$ around the finite set of the first n nonnegative integers $\{0, 1, 2, \ldots, n-1\}$, such that $\{n, 2n, 3n, \ldots\}$ overlap 0, and are considered to be equivalent to 0, $\{n+1, 2n+1, 3n+1, \ldots\}$ overlap 1, and are considered to be equivalent to 1, and so on, $\{2n-1, 3n-1, 4n-1, \ldots\}$ overlap $n-1$ and are consid-

$$
\begin{array}{c|cc}
+ & 0 & 1 \\
\hline
0 & 0 & 1 \\
1 & 1 & 0
\end{array}
\qquad\qquad
\begin{array}{c|cc}
\cdot & 0 & 1 \\
\hline
0 & 0 & 0 \\
1 & 0 & 1
\end{array}
$$

Figure 1: Addition and multiplication modulo 2.

ered to be equivalent to $n - 1$. Conventionally, we continue to denote the equivalence classes of $\mathbf{Z}_n$ by 0, 1, 2, $\ldots n - 1$, but now: 0 represents the class of all integers divisible by n; 1 represents the class of all integers which, once divided by n, give the remainder 1; 2 represents the class of all integers which, once divided by n, give the remainder 2; and so on, $n - 1$ represents all the integers which, once divided by n, give the remainder equal to $n - 1$. This is why, sometimes, the quotient set $\mathbf{Z}_n$ is called the set of residues modulo n.

When we deal with $\mathbf{Z}_n$, it is like living in a simpler world where only the numbers 0, 1,$\ldots n - 1$ are known and used. Generally, the integer a is congruent with the integer b modulo n, and we write $a \equiv b$ (mod n), if the difference $a - b$ is divisible by n. This notation was introduced by Gauss in his book *Disquisitiones Arithmeticae*, which also contained the first systematic study of congruences. When n is a prime number, the ring $\mathbf{Z}_n$ is a field, which means that it is a group both with respect to the addition and to the multiplication of equivalence classes modulo $n\mathbf{Z}$."

–"Can you give a simple example?"

–"I can and I have to, in order to show you what funny things happen with Fermat's last theorem once we move from the infinite set of nonnegative integers to the finite, and highly remarkable set of equivalence classes modulo p, where p is a prime number. If we take $n = 2$, all integers may be grouped in only two classes modulo 2, namely 0 and 1. The addition and multiplication modulo 2, that operate on 0 and 1 and have as the result only 0 or 1, are very easy to be obtained, if we take into account that $1 + 1 = 2 \equiv 0$ (mod 2). This binary-$\{0,1\}$ case, is the only case when the arithmetic operations (addition

+	0	1	2	3	4
0	0	1	2	3	4
1	1	2	3	4	0
2	2	3	4	0	1
3	3	4	0	1	2
4	4	0	1	2	3

·	0	1	2	3	4
0	0	0	0	0	0
1	0	1	2	3	4
2	0	2	4	1	3
3	0	3	1	4	2
4	0	4	3	2	1

Figure 2: Addition and multiplication modulo 5.

+ and multiplication ·) have the same tables as the logical operations (nonexclusive disjunction 'or', and conjunction 'and') if 1 means 'true' and 0 means 'false'. This is a good reason why, in modern computing, the software is compiled in a binary-$\{0,1\}$ machine language that could be better understood and used by computers.

There are five classes of equivalence, or integers, modulo 5, namely: 0, 1, 2, 3, and 4, and the addition and multiplication tables may be obtained in a very easy way. It is like dealing only with these five numbers instead of the infinite set of nonnegative integers. Fermat's last theorem doesn't hold in $\mathbf{Z}_5$, because $1^3 + 2^3 \equiv 4^3$, consequence of the fact that: $1^3 + 2^3 = 9 \equiv 4 \pmod 5$ and $4^3 = 64 \equiv 4 \pmod 5$.

In general, if $x^n + y^n = z^n$ has an integer solution, then $x^n + y^n \equiv z^n \pmod m$, for any modulus m. Conversely, if for a certain prime modulus p we have $x^n + y^n \not\equiv z^n \pmod p$, then $x^n + y^n \neq z^n$ for $0 < x < y < z < p$. In fact, for any prime number p, the equality $x^p + y^p = (x + y)^p, \pmod p$ is true.

It is interesting to notice that Fermat's last theorem could be proved, using methods that had been accessible to Fermat himself, if somebody would be able to show that the set of congruences $x^n + y^n \equiv z^n \pmod p$, where $n \geq 3$ and p is an arbitrary prime number, induce absurd conditions on the integer variables x, y, z. In fact, it is easy to show that for every prime $p \geq 5$, we have $x^n + y^n \not\equiv z^n \pmod p$ for $n = p$ and $n = (p - 1)/2$, which is very nice, but not enough to prove Fermat's last theorem in an elementary way."

−"Did you read the long proof of Fermat's last theorem?"

−"No, because it is not my field and it would have taken me an excessively long time to understand and check every detail. Also, I had many other things to do. It was unusual to see a two-hundred-page proof for a simple one-line statement. But this case is not singular. Another old problem, called the four-colour problem, claimed that every map drawn on paper may be coloured using only four colours such that countries sharing a common border get different colours. After many attempts made by different people, either professional mathematicians or just amateurs, Kenneth Appel and Wolfgang Haken came up with a proof which wasn't only 274 pages long but was also based on an analysis of the enormous number of configurations possible made by a powerful computer. As I belong to the old generation, I am not prepared yet to accept excessively long proofs, more likely to contain flaws, and computer-assisted proofs."

NUMBER THEORY

−"Listening to the story of Fermat's last theorem it seems that number theory is an interesting math course to take. Which other problems are covered in a standard such course?"

−"It depends who is teaching it and at which level. The elementary number theory doesn't use techniques from other parts of mathematics. It basically deals with the properties of integers such as divisibility, greatest common divisors, least common multiples, and the unique factorization of integers into primes. The study of congruences, we have just talked about, is definitely a part of it. By the way, Fermat stated, also without giving a proof, that in the ring of integers modulo an arbitrary prime number p, the power $p-1$ of any integer is congruent to 1 modulo p, which means $n^{p-1} \equiv 1 \pmod{p}$. But, unless Fermat's last theorem, this result may be proved in an elementary way. In the previous example involving $\mathbf{Z}_5$, we have indeed: $1^4 = 1 \equiv 1 \pmod 5$, $2^4 = 16 \equiv 1 \pmod 5$, $3^4 = 81 \equiv 1 \pmod 5$, and $4^4 = 256 \equiv 1 \pmod 5$.

Elementary number theory contains many conjectures and open problems. I mentioned Christian Goldbach's conjecture. Another example is the twin primes conjecture, stating that there are infinitely many pairs of consecutive primes whose difference is equal to 2, like 3 and 5, or 5 and 7, for instance. As I mentioned before, the funny thing is that in number theory, unless in the other domains of mathematics, it is relatively easier to notice some properties satisfied by some integers and to formulate conjectures about them, but it is much more difficult, and sometimes even impossible, to prove them true or false.

An important technique for proving in number theory is the so called principle of 'mathematical induction'. It is well known and intensively used in many chapters of mathematics where statements involving arbitrary positive integers have to be proved. Denoting by $P(n)$ a statement involving the positive integer n, according to this principle, if $P(1)$ is true and, for an arbitrary n, the fact that $P(n)$, supposed to be true, implies that $P(n+1)$ is also true, then they have as consequence the fact that $P(n)$ is true for every n. Less known is the so called 'method of infinite descent', discovered and used by Pierre de Fermat. It says that if for an arbitrary n, $P(n)$, supposed false, implies that $P(n-1)$ is false but $P(1)$ is however true, then $P(n)$ is true for every n.

More advanced chapters of number theory are: 1) Analytic number theory, which uses tools from calculus and the theory of functions of a complex variable, and deals mainly with formulas approximately describing the mysterious distribution of prime numbers among the positive integers. 2) Algebraic number theory, which deals with algebraic numbers which are roots of polynomials with rational coefficients. The important part here is Galois theory about the intimate connection between group representations and finite fields. 3) Geometric number theory, dealing with counting involving convex sets, like polygons in a plane and polyhedrons – solids formed by plane faces – in a three-dimensional space, curves, and other geometric objects.

Number theory has benefited more than any other domain of mathematics from the tremendous and rapid progress in computation, using the powerful computers available today, and from the software packages doing both numerical and symbolic computing. People doing specialized research have computers designed specially for solving only specific problems from number theory, like generating bigger primes or numerically checking conjectures involving integers."

CRYPTOGRAPHY

–"Yesterday, you used several times the words 'function', 'functional', 'operator', and 'transformation'. They seem to be similar but not quite so. What is the difference between them?"

–"Well, they are all applications from one set, called domain of definition, to another set, called set of values, or codomain, such that to each element from the domain it corresponds only one element from the codomain. More often than not, an application is called 'function' when the codomain is a set of numbers, 'functional' when the domain is a set of functions and the codomain is a a set of numbers, 'operator' when the domain and codomain are spaces with a certain structure, like groups or fields, for instance, and 'transformation' when the domain and codomain are the same set. This distinction is not always strictly followed. Often, only the term 'function' is used, regardless which particular domain or codomain is taken into account. But, because I have just mentioned the general word application from one set to another set, I can give you simple examples from cryptography, where the main objective is to mix up the letters of the alphabet or to assign numbers to words in order to hide the content of an important message. While by ciphering we want to make the message incomprehensible for the enemy, it has to be easy to be deciphered by the intended receptionist."

–"Now, this seems to be really exciting. Tell me about some safe ciphers I could use in my communication with my friend Stephen when I go back to Toronto."

–"Well, people were interested in hiding the content of some messages from very old times. In the *Bible*, a Hebrew ciphering, called 'atbash cipher', is mentioned, consisting of the following simple transformation of the alphabet: the first letter of the alphabet *A* is replaced by the last letter *Z*, the second letter *B* is replaced by the last but one letter *Y*, and so on, *C* by *X*, *D* by *W*, *E* by *V*, *F* by *U*, *G* by *T*, *H* by *S*, *I* by *R*, *J* by *Q*, *K* by *P*, *L* by *O*, *M* by *N*, and vice versa, *N* by *M*, ..., *Z* by *A*. Thus, if you want to hide the fact that you are in *LA FOULY*, you can write to your friend that you are in *OZ ULFOB*. If he

	1	2	3	4	5
1	A	B	C	D	E
2	F	G	H	I	J
3	K	L	M	N	O
4	P	Q	R	S	T
5	U	V	W	X	Y/Z

Figure 3: The square cipher.

knows what cipher you have used, he can apply the key, which is the inverse transformation, and recover your message meant for him. You can see how fragile our language is; a simple transformation like this, called substitution, makes our words strange and unintelligible.

Gaius Julius Caesar, not trusting people around him, used a cipher, known as 'Caesar cipher', provided by the following substitution: each letter of the alphabet is shifted two places through the alphabet, which means that:

$A\ B\ C\ D\ E\ F\ G\ H\ I\ J\ K\ L\ M\ N\ O\ P\ Q\ R\ S\ T\ U\ V\ W\ X\ Y\ Z,$

are replaced by:

$C\ D\ E\ F\ G\ H\ I\ J\ K\ L\ M\ N\ O\ P\ Q\ R\ S\ T\ U\ V\ W\ X\ Y\ Z\ A\ B,$

respectively.

The Greeks used the square method, arranging the letters of the alphabet in a 5×5 square matrix, with the rare letters Y and Z occupying the same position. The rows and columns are numbered from 1 to 5 and each letter is replaced by the pair of its integer coordinates representing the numbers of its row and column, as shown in Figure 3. Thus, G is replaced by 22, R by 43, Y and Z by 55, and so on. The word BUS becomes 125144.

The so called Playfair cipher, introduced by Lyon Playfair and Charles Wheatstone, was used during the World War II. It consists of randomly arranging the letters of the alphabet in a 5×5 square, excluding the letter J from the initial message. The text to be transmitted is divided into adjacent pairs. As a common practice, the space between words is often ignored. The two letters of each pair are located in this square and a rectangle is formed, taking the two letters at op-

$$
\begin{array}{ccccc}
A & F & Z & M & O \\
P & B & G & K & N \\
T & Q & C & H & L \\
W & U & R & D & I \\
Y & X & V & S & E
\end{array}
$$

Figure 4: A Playfair cipher.

posite corners of the rectangle, the top corner first, as a replacement for the initial pair. If the two letters fall in the same row or in the same column they are simply interchanged. Such a cipher is generated by a transformation of the set of pairs of letters into the set of pairs of letters. This is important because it makes the frequency distribution of the letters in the written language to be less important to the enemy who wants to decipher the message. As you know, the letters of the English alphabet have different frequencies, such that E and T are the most frequent ones, for instance. Thus, if the transformation, or substitution of pairs, is given by the square shown in Figure 4, we replace: *AR* by *ZW*, *SP* by *KY*, *TC* by *CT*, *OL* by *LO*, and so on. Thus, *MIKE* would become *ODNS*.

The matrix from Figure 4 may be also used to define an application where each letter is replaced by a pair of letters indicating the row and column in which the respective letter lies. In such a case *C* is replaced by *TZ*, *U* by *WF*, *A* by *AA*, *W* by *WA*, *M* by *AM*, and so on. Using this cipher, *MIKE* becomes *AMWOPMYO*.

To give only one more example, the so called 'Vigenère cipher', introduced by Blaise de Vigenère, assigns the integers from 0, for *A*, to 25 for *Z* to the 26 letters of the alphabet. Then, a key word is chosen, say '*TWO*'. This key is repeated below the message to be transmitted, say '*I AM HUNGRY*', ignoring the space between words, which is always done in ciphering. We have:

$$
\begin{array}{ccccccccc}
I & A & M & H & U & N & G & R & Y \\
T & W & O & T & W & O & T & W & O
\end{array}
$$

(the message),
(the repeated key).

The corresponding numerical vectors are (8,0,12,7,20,13,6,17,24), for the message, and (19,22,14,19,22,14,19,22,14), for the repeated key. Summing up the corresponding components of the two vectors, we get (27,22,26,26,42,27,25,39,38) and, modulo 26, which means to replace each number larger than 25 with the remainder obtained when it is divided by 26, we get (1,22,0,0,16,1,25,13,12), giving the ciphered message: *BWAAQBZNM*."

–"Which I cannot even pronounce."

–"Right. But I am really hungry and I am sure that you are hungry too. Time is up to end our today's trip."

When we reached the village around six o'clock in the evening, John invited me again to have dinner at Edelweiss. I protested mildly but he was very firm:

–"I don't take no for an answer. The main reason is that today would be a culinary experience for you because they are going to serve a typical Swiss meal."

I went to my tent to refresh myself and change my clothes but at seven o'clock sharp, just when the sun disappeared behind the western side of Les Aiguilles du Tour Noir, I joined John at his reserved table in the dining room of Edelweiss Hotel. The room was full because the second Tour de Mont Blanc group of the week was there. The majority of its members seemed to be British and to know each other very well. There were only one waiter and two waitresses, all of them very young, on summer jobs perhaps, but very skilled and polite, coping with so many customers quite well. The dinner, however, took a much longer time than when I was previously there.

Food was very good indeed. The 'entré', solemnly announced as an 'assiette valaisane', was a plate generously filled with different kinds of smoked dry sausage and ham, followed by a clear chicken consommé, as hot soup. 'La pièce de résistance' was the Swiss cheese dish called 'raclette', which is being served with great pomp. First, the waiter brings at each table a basket containing a lot of hot boiled small potatoes, black pepper. and plenty of pickles consisting of baby cucumbers and small round onions. Then, a dish is fetched to each customer, with a little good, hot melted, smelly cheese. From time to time, when the cheese is consumed, the waiter brings, without being asked, another dish with another helping of hot melted cheese and so on, until you say: 'Thank you, it was excellent but I had enough.' As dessert, we got a cup of stewed peaches in plum brandy. For drinking, we ordered the local beer. After a long hiking on a summer-day nothing could be better than a very cold light beer. We really enjoyed our dinner but, at some point, I noticed that the Swiss food seemed to be heavy.

–"Don't forget that, most of the time, it is cold in the Swiss mountains and people living here need a lot of calories," said John. "Without mentioning the physical effort required by working and simply moving at high altitude. But, definitely, referring to those living in towns and big cities, perhaps they are changing the traditional diet, switching on more fruits and vegetables. Life was very different before. Many villages in the mountains were isolated. I remember that once, in a local newspaper, I read an interview with a very old woman, almost 100 years old, who proudly declared that she had spent all her life in her native village, except a trip to Interlaken, a town situated at about 25 kilometers from her place. Not so long ago, the village Saas Fee, for instance, could be accessed only by horses. Now, there is a paved road and a comfortable postal bus that goes there several times a day. And there are now plenty of modern hotels there. 'Even too many,' how the owner of a small hotel there told me."

TRAVELS

–"You have come to Switzerland so many times. You obviously like this country and its mountains. But have you travelled in other countries as well?"

–"Yes and no. Yes, because I travelled in many countries from Europe. No, because I didn't travel to any country in Central America, South America, Australia, and, with one exception, in Asia."

–"Which exception?"

–"Turkey. Very long ago, when I was about 30 years old, I went to Istanbul and Ankara, by train, coming from Greece. In Istanbul, arriving in the amazingly crowded central train station very tired, after a whole night travel, I left behind, in the coach, important official documents. Even worse, I realized that only on my way out of the central train station. Obviously, I panicked, and ran back to the train which, luckily, was still there because Istanbul was the final destination for it. Fortunately, all the documents were there, untouched, where I had left them. From Istanbul I remember the monumental mosques, notably the Blue Mosque, the beautiful Topkapi palace, rich in golden stuff, the picturesque Oriental market called bazaar, and the impressive long bridge over Bosphorus, joining Europe with Asia. From Ankara, I took a one-day trip, in a mini bus, to the ancient Cappadocia, where the first Christians, to defend themselves, built an amazing underground town, digging a labyrinth with rooms, passages, and even churches, five levels down in a volcanic rock. They even had a system of flooding the upper level, hiding in the other lower levels in case of danger."

–"What about the other trips?"

–"There are too many and I am afraid that we don't have enough time to talk about all of them now."

–"You may mention at least some of them and just the first impressions coming up to your mind about the visited places, as you have done about Turkey."

–"Well, let's give a try. Following your suggestion, choosing places randomly, and the first impressions about them, as they come up to my mind now, I would take Paris first. I was there several times. Montmartre is my number one there. Very romantic, still old houses, climbing to the white church Sacre Coeur from where all Paris can be seen down there. Like in old times, there are painters, making your portrait with a tremendous speed and accuracy, for a relatively reasonable price. Then, walking along the big river Seine and spending time on the left bank of it, where many students eat in cheap restaurants and live in modest apartments around the old Sorbonne, was very romantic. Or, maybe, I was influenced by reading too much about poets, writers, and scientists who had spent time there. It was nice to visit Sorbonne, the famous old university, and on one of its walls I read the slogan 'It is forbidden to forbid', scratched by some liberal student. Louvre Museum is famous but crowded. When I finally got into it, I wasn't very impressed by Mona Lisa, surrounded by Japanese tourists clicking their electronic equipment, but I spent a lot of time, with nobody around, in front of a painting entitled 'Le Déluge'. A torrent is sweeping a family in a precipice. The father is hanging with one hand from the unearthed root of an almost falling tree. With his other hand he is holding his wife, who is holding the children, one or two, I don't remember well. The grandfather hangs, with a feeble hand, from the foot of his son. What I remember very well are the regards from the eyes of the characters: panic, but still different degrees of hope, except for the father. All depend on him but he is the only one who realizes that the disaster is inevitable and the tree is going to collapse, together with all of them, in the abyss."

For a while, John remained silent, with some of his thoughts still somewhere in Paris, and I did nothing to bring him back. But soon, he resumed his telegraphic recollections from past travels.

−"I was about 26 years old when I went to a short study trip to Oslo and Boston, with travel and maintenance offered by Carnegie Endowment. I remember the acrobatic landing to Oslo's airport made by the pilot of the Nordic SAS air company when I had the strong impression of an inevitable nose diving into the sea. I spent one week in Oslo, going every day to the Institute for Peace Research, which had a very liberal atmosphere inside and a small but excellent library, where you had free access to the books and journals and nobody asked you any kind of questions. The only request I got from a blonde young secretary, looking really like an angel fallen from some kind of white heavenly cloud, was to leave the lights on during the day-time because paying for electricity was much cheaper than buying new electric bulbs. Even a modest hotel was too expensive for my means back then and, after a couple of nights, I took my luggage and I spent the last three nights in an attic of the Institute, following the advice given by a young American who was preparing his PhD thesis there and who, having no money either, slept there in exchange for cleaning the main rooms with a vacuum cleaner every early morning. In the first evening there, he and his girl friend, a young and beautiful Norwegian who used to show up after all other people had left, invited me to a simply improvised dinner prepared by both of them. I still remember them, sitting in front of an open fire, poor, with an uncertain immediate future, but looking into each other's eyes and being really happy together."

–"Did you like Oslo?"

–"It seemed to me, back then, to be a quiet, almost provincial city, with friendly people who could speak good English and were willing to assist and help foreigners. I noticed that many cars were left unlocked during the night and I enjoyed a general feeling of safety. My idyllic image about that place was augmented also by the fact that the month of May is perhaps the most beautiful time of the year in Norway. A lot of green, sun, and fresh, cool air. During the only weekend there, I took a ferry, crossing to an island, visiting the Fridtjof Nansen Museum, and offering to myself a picnic on the seaside, just before the sunset. I also remember, quite vividly, the little boats arriving in the port, at the end of the day, with fresh fish, offered to the few customers at a very low price.

From Oslo, I took a flight to New York. It was my first voyage to North America and my first flight on the board of a Jumbo Jet Boeing 747. I looked at it before embarking, amazed and puzzled about how such a huge monster could take off and cross the Atlantic Ocean. In fact even now, after so many flights, in spite of the laws of classical mechanics and fluid mechanics, I still cannot understand how such a big plane can fly."

–"Who can? Have you ever had a really bad flight or an accident during one of your numerous flights?"

–"Not really. And this is why every time when I think that I never got more than four out of six winning lottery numbers, and that happened in fact only once, I try also to remember that, by compensation, I was very lucky to have so many flights without anything bad happening. The only somehow adventurous flight was during a trip from Montreal, where the temperature in the previous night had been −41 degrees Celsius, the lowest temperature ever experienced by me, to Paris, where the temperature was +10 degrees Celsius. This unusual difference in temperature was the cause of a very turbulent flight and, for the first and last time in my travels by plane, the captain asked us to keep the belts tied, not as an optional security precaution but as an imperative must, since the take off until the final landing. Obviously, nobody really was in a good mood to enjoy any kind of meal during the long flight but, in the end, nothing bad happened. Another time, during a short flight from Zürich, the plane had to take an unscheduled landing in Budapest, due to a severe snowstorm. But that was all, fortunately."

– "So, from Oslo, back then, you made your first trip to the United States. What was your first impression about the New World?"

– "The flight was pleasant, with considerably fewer passengers on board than what happens these days and, late in the evening, I arrived at J.F. Kennedy airport in New York. Generally, it is not an excellent idea to arrive in a new place in the evening. Worse than that, I had to continue my travel taking another flight to Boston, on the same day. I was overwhelmed by the big airport, with a lot of people around, and totally confused about what to do, mainly when I found out that the flight to Boston had to continue from the LaGuardia airport and the departure time was very close. Then, I witnessed for the first time the American efficiency. Somebody put me on a service microbus, as the only passenger, and with great speed, like in the movies, took me to LaGuardia, where I got on the right plane in the last minutes before the departure time. It was a smaller plane and because the distance between New York and Boston was relatively short, the flying altitude was low. This allowed me to look down and be amazed by the bath of lights of different colours floodlighting the East coast of the United States, like a huge Christmas tree, shining in the dark of the night.

When I arrived at Boston airport, I took a taxicab and, having no reservation, I asked the driver to take me to any cheap hotel in Cambridge. Tired and completely ignorant about where we were going in the middle of the night, I had nothing to do but completely rely on the taxi driver, against my lifetime principle to avoid taking a taxi in a foreign country. The driver didn't take advantage of his innocent passenger and took me in the shortest time possible, as I later realized, to a modest but very decent hotel, not very far from the famous Massachusetts Institute of Technology, known as MIT, which was my final destination in the United States. The hotel was fully booked but, somehow, the receptionist, seeing me in distress, found a solution to accommodate me. Due to three unknown but very kind persons, namely, the driver of the microbus at the Kennedy airport, the taxi driver at the Boston airport, and the receptionist at a small hotel in Cambridge, I wasn't lost in America.

On the next day, without a map, I didn't know where the MIT was and, after crossing by foot the long bridge over Charles River, to the amazement of the car drivers unused to see pedestrians on the bridge on a very windy day, I finally asked for directions a student passing by. Jennifer, this was her name, took me to the university campus, showed me where the residence for visiting fellows was, and gave me the address of an apartment shared by her with nine other colleagues, 'just in case you cannot find a room in the residence', as she told me in a simple and most friendly way. I found a room but, one day, I paid a short visit to Jennifer and her friends to thank her for her kindness. They treated me with a cup of tea and biscuits and we talked about all kind of things as we had known each other for a very long time. Thus, during my first days in the United States I was impressed not so much by skyscrapers as by the kindness of simple people. But because I have just mentioned skyscrapers, in Boston, which is a city not famous for tall buildings, I still remember that one afternoon, after a violent but short summer thunderstorm, when the low clouds started to dissipate and melt away, one little cloud remained isolated, surrounding the middle of a glass-and-aluminum skyscraper whose upper part was now rising above the cloud, like flying to the blue sky."

– "I am sure that you have visited other places in the United States since then."

–"Unfortunately, not too many, and I am sorry for that because there are many remarkable places to be seen there. I was a couple of times in New York which, except the overwhelmingly tall buildings, resembles European cities, or this was my feeling every time when I was there. I liked to walk along Manhattan, from the Central Park to the Battery Park at the Ocean, facing the Statue of Liberty, and to visit some of its extraordinarily rich museums, like Guggenheim, the Metropolitan Museum, or the Museum of the Modern Art. It is impossible to get bored in New York and many funny things and events could be seen only there. I remember a huge parade of incredibly diverse dogs and their owners through the Central Park, the amazing Canal Street, where a very large number of people were selling thousands and thousands of almost identical watches with nobody really interested in buying them, or some corners of some streets where you could buy, very cheaply, amazing art objects or wooden African sculptures.

In the South-east of the United States, I traveled to Durham, to attend two conferences at Duke University. A very quiet place, surrounded by a lot of heavy forests, one of the three summits of the so called Research Triangle, the other two being the University of North Carolina, in Reileigh, and the University in Chapel-Hill, a region where there is the largest density of PhDs, as I was told. As a general remark, I was impressed how many trees are in the United States. Flying from New York down to North Carolina on a clear day, I saw many lazy rivers winding amidst a lot of dense forests, in deep contrast with the bare mountains and hills from the Mediterranean countries like Greece or Spain.

In Florida, I attended a conference in Orlando, a very picturesque place, remarkable not only for the Disney World, but also for funny buildings in the city itself, including a house built upside down, spacious hotels with generous gardens, black-tie taxicab drivers, good Mexican and Cuban food, and symphonic music as background at the airport. I regret for not going farther south to Mexico, Central America, and South America, especially because I like very much the Latin music, dances, and soccer. I know that they are poorer than we are but perhaps they know how to enjoy life more than we do in the western part of the North hemisphere. Maybe, I will do this after taking my retirement."

–"What about Canada? I am anxious to know what you liked in my own country."

–"Many things in fact. First, the dimensions and the open space. It was exciting to be one day in Saint John's, looking at the Atlantic Ocean, and a couple of days later in Vancouver, cooling my feet in the waters of the Pacific Ocean, still remaining inside the same country. In Toronto, I saw the most beautiful sunsets I have ever seen in my life; each different but all amazing. In Victoria, which seemed to me very British, I enjoyed the five o'clock tea party at the Empress Hotel and the flowers present everywhere around the city. I can never forget an evening spent in a remote small village on the Vancouver Island, looking at the immensity of the Ocean, listening to good western country music, watching a demonstration of skill performed by some vigorous rangers, and eating clam chowder soup and fresh salmon grilled on burning wood charcoal by local fishers. Unforgettable was also the crossing of Rocky Mountains by bus from Calgary to Vancouver with stops to visit the breathtaking Lake Louise, Jasper, and the mysterious Spirit Island on the Maligne Lake, where the authorized boats go only to the middle of it, for keeping its waters as clean as possible. Finally, Niagara Falls, easy to reach from Toronto by bus, have impressed me so much that I went there three times. Professionally, I was positively shocked by how the libraries are organized in Canada. Not only the classification system of the books and periodicals is the same in any university, but the direct access to the shelves and the computerized search system is open to anybody. I found this amazing. You can spend days and days working in a spacious library without having any kind of permit. A library card is needed only for taking books home."

–"Have you been in Eastern Europe as well?"

–"I know better Romania because my good Romanian friend Marius, I met in Manchester, invited me to go and spend one summer-month there. It was quite interesting. I couldn't understand their language, of course, but the educational system there has always included two compulsory foreign languages in the curriculum of any school. French was more popular with the old generation and now English with the young. The Romanian seashore of Black Sea is east oriented and the beaches with fine sand are excellent. So is the food in Romania, a blend of local, Balkan, French, Hungarian, and German cuisine. I enjoyed a visit to a renowned vineyard, Cotnari, tasting an amazing sweet wine and delicious local thin pork sausages, on my way to the northern part of the country, Bucovina, where there are some unique old medieval churches, beautifully painted on the external walls, never seen elsewhere, built in picturesque natural surroundings, in green glades of dense forests. The popular music, with a lot of harmony and a very regular rhythm, is lovely. So are the popular costumes in the countryside, mixing mainly red, white, and black colours. Marius took me to Buşteni, in the middle of the Romanian Carpathian mountains, from where we climbed on some very rocky and quite wild trails, going up to about 2300 meters. Later, we went to the western side of the country where the mountains are not very high but the scenery is great and where there are many caves and torrents in a wild wooden large area. Only there I saw a torrent suddenly and completely disappearing underground, only to reappear, from nowhere, somewhere farther. I found this simply frightening. I remember a descent in a huge cave Meziad, which has five long and contorted levels, accompanied by a local guide equipped with special carbide lamps, without whom we definitely couldn't get out from there. Another unique experience was the descent on a huge subterranean glacier in another cave, Scãrişoara, where only professional speleologists could go deeper, using special mobile ladders, cords, and inflated boats. I talked to one of them who, in a perfect English, explained me that they were still discovering new galleries never ever visited by humans."

–"Many friends of mine complain all the time that life in Canada is too hectic and people work much too much, having little time to travel or enjoy what they have already achieved. I don't want to become such a robot and I am not very certain about how my future life is going to be. I admire Sarah, for instance. She was one of my colleagues in high school and now she is travelling by herself, with a simple knapsack on her back and a very modest budget, somewhere in China, India, and Pakistan, sleeping in modest hostels, convents, and even outdoors. Recently, she sent me a card from Taj Mahal containing only two sentences: 'It is not easy, but I have never been happier in my entire life. Wish you were here.' Perhaps, she indirectly influenced me when I decided to take a trip overseas."

–"Once, I had a Greek student in my statistics class. He was very intelligent but not very hard working and one day he complained about giving them a tough home assignment. I tried to comfort him by saying something like: 'Well, life is difficult!' He promptly replied: 'No, life is not difficult. We make it difficult.' I enjoyed his use of the plural pronoun 'we', meaning that I made his life difficult and he made my life difficult. But, later, I thought about his words and I had to admit to myself that he was right. Perhaps, we often make difficult the life of other people and sometimes our own life. It is true that we have to eat, raise children, need a home, electricity, water, heat, and pay a lot of taxes. But very often we don't distinguish between what is really essential and what is not. We are too much concerned about material things and end up by being surrounded by a lot of useless things that only complicate our everyday life. I remember that, somewhere, I read that before dying, Queen Victoria looked around and said: 'My properties, for a while.' Professionally, we are also under the threat of the three 'r': routine, rust, ruin.

Life in the Southern Europe, especially in the Mediterranean regions, seems to be much more relaxed, with something the French speaking people call 'joie de vivre'. I have had this feeling when I was in Malaga, Palma de Mallorca, Madrid, Toledo, Perugia, Assisi, Pesaro, Urbino, Udine, Venice, Budva, Athens, and Thessaloniki. There are many people there who are poor and have to work very hard for affording a relatively decent living but, obviously from a very limited amount of information I got from a few observations made during very short trips, I still got the impression that they worked for living and didn't live for working as it is the case in some industrialized countries from Western Europe or North America. I could be wrong, of course."

–"Have you been in all these places?"

–"For very short visits, generally within one week in each place. But

I still have shots of remembrances about. Thus, in Malaga, on Costa del Sol, it doesn't rain indeed and, in January, I needed only a thin pullover when I went out in the evening. The popular market looked very picturesque, there were small and cheap restaurants serving fresh fish and good wine in a friendly atmosphere, and I walked through the romantic ruins of a Moorish castle just on the seashore. In Palma de Mallorca, I attended a conference, and the organizers kept the participants inside a very good but isolated hotel on the rocky island. I barely saw the town, dominated by a huge cathedral and a beautiful palace, but all the participants seemed to enjoy the mild climate, the sea, the food, and the unbelievable Spanish music. In Madrid, I was impressed both by the broad boulevards, the monumental buildings, the Royal Palace, the Prado Museum, which fully deserves its fame, and by how generous, friendly, and helpful people were everywhere. At the hotel, before the departure, I had to convince some clerks from the desk that I still had to pay something they had omitted to include on the final bill. This reminds me that once, in Amsterdam, checking out at a hotel on the main road Damrak, close to the Central Station in the old town, I almost lost the last good train for going to the airport because the only clerk at the reception desk, already well tipsy by drinking too many cocktails generously provided by a waiter, didn't want to give me the bill and take my credit card, keeping saying 'Don't worry, be happy! Life is short!'

But let me go back to Spain. The day spent in the old town Toledo, built on a high hill, with its labyrinth of narrow and inclined streets with sudden openings revealing big churches or small palaces, cannot be forgotten. In the middle of Italy, the old towns of Perugia and Assisi were also built on high and abrupt rocks. Going there by train from Milan, I was amazed by how many tunnels we had to go through between Bologna and Florence. Perugia and Assisi, like many places in Italy, are full of old palaces, monuments, statues, ruins, and an enormous number of beautifully painted churches, each looking different. A lot of old stuff but with people everywhere, filling the streets, the restaurants, the piazzas, the shops. In Perugia, I remember very well, I became ice-cream addict. They had such a diverse and excellent fruit ice-cream that I could not abstain myself from eating a big portion, three times a day, and I still didn't have enough of it. Every time I bought some sandwiches, the bartender always added something extra without charging more. At the end of our visit there, when a taxicab took us to the train station at 5 o'clock in the morning and I gave the driver a very normal tip, he warmly embraced me and wished me all the best in the world. In Pesaro, a small town on the Adriatic cost of Italy, I had the best cappuccino I ever tasted. At midnight people filled the streets. One day, I took a bus from there and I went to Urbino, a town kept almost unchanged from medieval times. I wouldn't have been surprised if I had met Raphael on one of the narrow, steep streets of the citadel. In Venice, starting from the train station, I lost the shortest way of reaching the famous San Marco piazza, with its beautiful Dodge's Palace and thousands of omnipresent daring pigeons, and I strayed in a labyrinth of canals, passages, and bridges, without any hope of finding a shortcut. I needed a lot of time and help, using the very few words I knew from Italian movies, for finally getting out from the mess I was in.

In Budva, close to the well known resort Dubrovnik in the former Yougoslavia, I arrived shortly after a powerful earthquake had shaken a large area there. It was impressive to see the terrible effects on buildings and environment. I still remember palms almost completely buried on the Adriatic seashore, and how some local people marveled at a new minuscule rocky island born, from the depth of the sea, after the tremor.

In Thessaloniki, I remember the large number of restaurants along the seashore of the Adriatic Sea, with thousands and thousands of outdoor chairs, where people spent hours, consuming almost nothing, but talking and talking in front of a glass of juice, mineral water, or wine. Maybe, the fair weather, favourable to dialogue and debates, has contributed to the flourishing of philosophy and mathematics in the old Greece. In Athens, in the month of August, around noon many shops are closed and the city seems almost dead. It becomes alive again after five o'clock in the afternoon. It is not unusual to see people filling the squares at midnight, talking and eating the delicious souvlaki. Going south from Thessaloniki to Athens, along the Adriatic seashore, I passed by the highest peak of Olympus Mountains, rising from almost the sea level up to 2918 meters, with the top lost up in the sky, like connecting the earth with heavens. I am not romantic at all but, looking at it, as far up as I could, I had to admit that it was rightly identified with the abode of the gods in Homer's *Iliad*. Not far from it, on a lovely green lawn with apricot trees around, was the place where Aristotle had his famous outdoor school. Green grass, sweet apricots, big like melons, and excellent sunny weather; what do you need more for philosophizing outdoors? Once, in Athens, I was invited by a math professor to dinner. He came to my hotel around seven o'clock and took me and my wife to his home where he opened the refrigerator, serving us cold beer and hors d'oeuvres nicely prepared by his wife. We started talking and I said to myself that that was it. But I was very wrong. At about eleven o'clock in the night, they took us to a restaurant in Pireus, on the border of the sea, where two friends of his were waiting for us and the real dinner, or say supper, started around midnight and lasted until after three o'clock in the morning. It was really very pleasant, the hosts were lively, and the total lack of wind made the sea look like a quiet lake with no waves whatsoever."

–"Have you visited places where famous mathematicians lived long ago? Are they still remembered somehow?"

–"Not on purpose. I looked once for the former house of Euler in Basel but I was told that it was completely destroyed by a fire long ago. In general, mathematicians are not so popular as the artists are. In Amsterdam, for instance, the house where the famous painter Rembrandt lived is a nice museum which can be visited, and there is a big statue of him in the picturesque old city. Nothing of the kind for mathematicians, as far as I know. Once, however, I attended a conference in the lovely town Goslar, not very far from the big city Hanover, in the North of Germany. Once an imperial city, it has kept its beautiful old houses intact or rebuilt them as they were, unaffected by the modern architecture which spoils almost all old cities around the world. It really looks like in fairy tales. Long ago, the town was very prosperous due to its lead, zinc, copper, and silver mines, worked during the Middle Ages. But, less and less silver could be extracted, which brought an economic decline. And then came Gottfried Wilhelm Leibniz. The philosopher and brilliant mathematician, who co-invented calculus, proved to have also a very practical mind. He suggested to build a system of huge interacting wheels which restarted the production of silver at much deeper levels, revitalizing the moribund economy. As a result, Leibniz's name is still much revered there. After so many years, the mines still work but the tourism has become the main local industry there. I visited a part of the mine, which is now the Rammelsberg Mining Museum, going down to the first of Leibniz's wheels. I also remember the nice reception parties given by the organizers of the conference both at Rathaus, which is the Town Hall, and in the monumental Imperial Palace Kaiserpfalz. The only dark spot was at the end; when I and my wife checked out after one week spent in a romantic old hotel in the center of Goslar, the only words an elegant lady at the reception desk had to say to us, as farewell, were: 'The key!' Not a smile, not even 'please!' And we did nothing wrong, kept quiet, and asked for nothing during our stay there. This reminds me of another incident, in Koblenz this time, a very nice town, beautifully located at the confluence of the Rhine river and the Moselle river, where, after the last night of our stay there, in a fancy hotel which, by the way, was almost empty, we found our luggage put on the corridor, with no access allowed to our room, when we returned from the breakfast, at ten o'clock in the morning."

It was well after nine o'clock when I said 'Good night' to John. I walked slowly to the camping site. It was much warmer than in the previous two nights. I could hear La Drance de Ferret running and I could even see the refection of the moon in its waters from time to time. Apparently, there were no clouds but no stars were blinking from the sky. There was no wind at all. Just a heavy and still summer night. I crossed the bridge over the torrent. The forest to my left-hand side, so innocent during the day, seemed mysterious and dangerous in the dark of the night. I followed the road and, turning to the right, I saw a big fire at the left side of the camping. There had been some small fires in the previous evenings, in front of some tents, with a few people around them, eating, drinking, or warming up, but this one was really big, with a much larger group of campers gazing at the flames and listening to two young men who were singing and playing guitars. I have to admit that they were quite good and the songs, with Spanish flavour, were interpreted almost professionally. I went closer and I sat on a log, joining the quiet audience. Half an hour later, I went to my tent, feeling a deep calm inside me.

THIRD DAY

CABANE DE L'A NEUVE

After two demanding hiking days, we both decided to meet on the next day only at 9:00 in front of the Edelweiss Hotel. Therefore, on Thursday morning, I had enough time to exercise a little, mainly raising small rocks for stretching my arm muscles, do the food shopping, without any rush, and enjoy my breakfast consisting of cheese, fresh bread, plum jam, and strong flavoured coffee. I couldn't stop thinking, however, that the individual who said that breakfast is the most important meal of the day, certainly never had dinner at the Edelweiss Restaurant.

The weather was splendid, with cloudless sky, but I sensed some kind of humidity and tension in the air. I carefully closed and locked the tent and went to the meeting place. The members of the second group of this week doing the Mont Blanc Tour, more numerous than on the previous day, were preparing for departure in a somehow chaotic way. The poor horse, covered by a mount of luggage, stood calm, resigned about his hopeless life. I really felt sorry for him. A true hiker is supposed to carry his or her own knapsack. What a shame! Anyway, I don't know exactly what happened in the meantime but, when we started our hiking trip of the day, it was already 9:48.

–"It is later than expected," said John. "In fact, it is recommended to start hiking very early in the morning, around five o'clock, when it is not warm and the snow on the glaciers doesn't melt, and be back in the village around noon. I know the theory but I could never stick to it."

–"Well, we are not robots. And if we do what is recommended in books, we are supposed to eat no fat, no cholesterol, no carbohydrates. What the hell to eat then? According to my friend Stephen, one of his neighbours decided to eat only carrots and this is what he did, but died soon afterwards. I am sure that Stephen made it up but he had a point there."

– "We can eat anything but with moderation and do regular physical exercise. Even walking fast helps. The receipts for a healthy life are relatively simple; what is really tough is to apply them, every day."

– "This reminds me of a joke about somebody, a very robust and fit fellow who, in front of a large audience, boasted himself by saying that he didn't suffer of any disease because he took a cold shower every morning. Then, a miserably looking little men said: 'Big deal! You didn't suffer of any disease but you had to suffer the cold showers!' But where are we going today?"

– "To Cabane de l'A Neuve, or de La Neuvaz, how it is called in the local dialect. Linearly, it is not far from La Fouly but the difference in altitude is more than 1100 meters and the trail is quite sinuous. The Cabane cannot be seen from here. It is located in a marvelous alpine zone, among glaciers, and hiking up to reach it is 'la pièce de résistance' around La Fouly."

On the signpost from the middle of the village, an arrow pointing to the north-west indicated: Le Désert 30 min, Cabane de l'A Neuve, 3h 40 min.

Stage 1. From La Fouly, we took the road that goes to the Camping des Glaciers. We reached a bridge that spans the Drance de Ferret, crossed the campsite from south to north, and then, turning west, we made our way through a forest with very tall fir trees for a few minutes. There was moss and fir tree needles under our feet, like a carpet very comfortable to step on. When the forest was passed through, the path started to rise in the middle of shrubs on a very arid soil, with broken stones, properly named The Desert. Coming out of bushes, the path, heading towards the frightening Glacier de l'A Neuve, hanging menacingly above us, became a serpentine rising, among small larch trees, along the fast and noisy torrents Reuse de l'A Neuve, to our left-hand side, and Reuse de l'Amône, to our right-hand side. Gradually, we came closer and closer to the rapid waters of the right-hand side torrent. We stopped for a couple of minutes to take some pictures of the many red flowers of rhododendrons, at the border of the torrent, contrasting to the white, foamy water of the torrent falling noisily amidst big, gray boulders. Towards north, on the other side of the torrent Reuse de l'Amône, there was an almost vertical stone wall, full of natural scratches, with layers of alternate black and gray rocky structures, a couple of patches of snow at its base, and some thin but long waterfalls coming from the heights of a steep mountain facing Mont Dolent which was now located a little farther, on our left-hand side. Seeing me looking at this bleak, huge mass of massive rock, John introduced it to me, as being an old friend of his:

– "Here, to our right, is a massive, steep, bleak, and long chain of approximately constant height of 3000 meters, which has six peaks, hardly discernible because there is no much variation of altitude in between them. The entire chain is called Pointes des Six Niers. Obviously, it is much smaller than Mont Dolent, at our left, or Tour Noir, in front of us, whose impressive and snowy peaks measure 3820 meters and 3835 meters, respectively. Anyway, our trail will mount along the base of this chain, and the Cabane de l'A Neuve, our destination, is implanted into it."

– "What does the word 'Niers' mean?"

– "I have no idea. Once, I looked for it in a French dictionary, but I could find only the well-known verb 'nier', to negate. There is no similar noun. Perhaps it means something in the local dialect otherwise 'six' in front of it would have no sense. But there are so many geographical names, and proper names in general, apparently meaning nothing, and it would be an impossible task to get an explanation about how they were born. The linguists know much more but certainly not about all of them."

Compared to the previous days, the atmosphere was more dense, with more and more humidity in the air. Some isolated clouds made their appearance. It was very warm. Warm and humid. Only when the path, in its winding way, came from time to time closer to the torrent on the right-hand side, we got some breath of wind and a gentle breeze, due to the cold and fast current of running water coming down from glaciers. Our path started to climb relatively abruptly, in a short serpentine, on the edge of a long moraine, towards a vertical rocky peak, about 25 meters high, which had to be climbed using several long, thick chains, some of them not very firmly fixed in the rock, hanging loose. It was really funny to climb on the top of the big rock. There, we took a longer break.

The scenery was just great. Facing west, in front we had the huge Glacier de l'A Neuve, seeming to be ready to collapse over us, with the long chain Aiguilles Rouges in the background. To the left we had Mont Dolent, like a silent giant. A little to the west-north the svelte silhouette of the peak Tour Noir. On the right-hand side, the torrent Reuse de l'Amône, very close now, and the long chain Pointes des Six Niers beyond the torrent. Down to the east, we could still see the village left far behind. Using John's binoculars, I looked at the crevasses of the Glacier de l'A Neuve. Just frightening, mysterious, dark traps. In different places, huge masses of snow were barely hanging up there, as waiting impatiently for a signal to start falling and rolling down. Being so warm, I wanted to drink something, but John curbed my enthusiasm saying:

–"Don't drink yet. It is too early. We have much more to climb. Later, you will appreciate having all your drink still intact. There is no source of drinkable water in our way."

Stage 2. From the top of the big rock, we had to descend about five meters, using shorter chains this time, on the other side of the rock, towards north. The path continued with the cross of a narrow but very solid bridge over the torrent. Following a large serpentine, going north at the beginning, and west later, the climbing path went closer to the chain Pointes des Six Niers, traversing a peaceful alpine zone full of grass and flowers, leaving the Glacier de l'A Neuve up to the left. A scenery very different from the one we had in Stage 1. From time to time we passed among some isolated big rocks that looked like brown meteorites fallen from the sky. There was plenty of alpine grass around and even some timid, shy little flowers. I couldn't stop thinking that, if I had been a movie director, I would have chosen this place to shoot a western. Anyway, it was 12:20 when the path passed a ridge, turning to the north-west. At this point, looking back down, the village La Fouly disappeared from our sight, blocked by the passed ridge.

Stage 3. The scenery changed. Looking forward, our valley became arid, narrower and steeper, with a lot of smaller rocks, rusty, red, brown, and later grey, fallen from the right-hand heights, and almost no grass. The path continued to climb, in much shorter serpentine, along the massive Pointes des Six Niers to the right and a smaller ridge to the left, beyond which the dormant Glacier de l'A Neuve was still there, but a little closer than before. In fact it was only apparently dormant because, from time to time during the third stage of our climbing, we heard deep noises, like the sounds of far explosions. Once, when the noise was bigger and longer, John pointed to the Glacier saying:

– "Look, Mike, it is a cracking going on and a small avalanche down there."

I heard the noise but, as the Glacier was spread on such a huge area, I didn't know where to look. Finally, I located a spot where the rupture produced a patch of white powder formed by falling ice and snow. This spectacle repeated several times during our climbing. It was no danger for us because the Glacier de l'A Neuve wasn't so close to our left flank. More frightening was a much smaller but menacing glacier, covered by snow, hanging up there, in front of us, on the top of the narrow valley we were climbing right now.

– "It is amazing how many changes are happening from year to year up here. It mainly depends on how much snow fell in the previous winter. When I came for the first time to La Fouly, with my wife, we were told that they had had seven meters of snow in the village during the past winter. Even if it was the beginning of the month of July, like now, we were kindly advised to avoid going up to Cabane de l'A Neuve. We didn't listen and went up. In fact we couldn't reach it and we had to stop a little up from here. Everything around here was completely covered by snow. We couldn't see any rock and any path. Only white snow and, of course, no coloured signs to guide us. Somehow, however, the climbing looked easier and more exciting, because we could choose shortcuts in our way up but, sometimes, in some places, mainly around big rocks superficially masked by snow, the foot just stuck unexpectedly, plugging into the thinner snow, down to above the knee. Walking on snow could be really risky and I don't recommend it to anybody. And look now, the path is clean. We haven't walked on snow yet."

The narrow path was clean indeed but, from time to time, it was crossed by trickles of water coming from the glacier reigning above the valley we were climbing. But I had good boots, not looking very fancy, but very comfortable inside and waterproof. There are some good small shops in Toronto selling very reliable mountain equipment, like my tent and hiking boots. Then, showing a point far, up to the north, on the rocky wall of Pointes des Six Niers to our right, John said:

– "Look! You can see now Cabane de l'A Neuve, up there."

Using John's binoculars, I could indeed locate it; a little stone cottage perched on a rocky platform implanted into the wall of the mountain. It was still far for my tastes because I was already tired and more clouds came and passed above us. But it looked great, like a citadel made of stones assembled by humans, barely distinguishable from the surrounding big rocks put there, long long ago, by the mighty Nature. After a small break, we continued our climbing on the short serpentine of the path, well marked with a red stripe on white background painted on bigger rocks, from time to time. I no longer could follow John's advice to save my drink reserve and I finished more than half of it, with no regrets whatsoever. When the serpentine ended, we arrived to the base of a narrow moraine.

Stage 4. We climbed on the top of the long moraine, oriented towards north-west, and we walked along it for about 10 or 15 minutes. When we reached its end, Cabane de l'A Neuve was already clearly visible, approximately at the same altitude as the moraine we were climbing, but on the massive on our right-hand side. In order to reach it, however, we had to descend a little from the moraine, turn to the right, and cross about 25 meters of the tip of a white 'tongue' of snow hanging down. It was the point where the valley climbed by us met the glacier coming from above us. After crossing the slippery snow, to reach the alpine hut we had to go almost vertically through the crevice of the promontory, using mobile chains. It was like taking by assault a medieval castle. I did it with great satisfaction seeing the end of the trip approaching. We reached our destination after 3h 55 min since we left the village.

Cabane de l'A Neuve (2735 meters) offers some amazing views: opposite it rises Mont Dolent (3820 meters), on the top of which the Italian, Swiss, and French borders meet. Even in July, we had the possibility to watch small, local avalanches downwards the Glacier de l'A Neuve spread between Tour Noir (3835 meters) and Mont Dolent. I had the deep feeling that I did belong to the alpine zone myself. At least for a short while, I was just there, in the middle of it, and I felt just great about. The hut overlooked the Glacier and allowed to clearly see the north face of the Dolent, the Tour Noir, the Aiguilles Rouges de l'A Neuve, and the head of the Val Ferret, far down in the south.

There were a couple of people there, resting or eating inside the hut or in the little space in front of it. Behind the hut, however, there were a lot of boulders and rocks. We sat on two of them and had lunch from what we brought in our light knapsacks. I noticed that we were at the end of a hiking trail with no possibility to go farther up, in any direction.

–"During the winter time," explained John, "when more fresh snow covers the rocks around, experienced mountaineers, a rare breed today, do the tour of glaciers on skis, and go north from here to Cabane de Saleina (2691 meters), facing the long Glacier de Saleina. I wanted to go there during the summer time but the marked trail from Val Ferret starts not from La Fouly but from Praz de Fort, a small village you passed through when you came on Monday by bus. My wife has an obsession with it and always puts it on the list of places that ought to be seen. Maybe we will do it sometime in the future."

We couldn't really enjoy our lunch and have a long talk afterwards, as we did in the previous days, because more and more clouds, some of them quite dark, kept coming from west and north-west.

–"I think that it would be better to leave right now," said John, looking at the sky.

We started our descent. At one moment, I got the impression that I heard the sound of a remote thunder. Or, was it another cracking in the glacier? Unfortunately it proved to have been indeed a thunder and more menacing similar sounds followed. When we did Stage 4 and half of Stage 3, in reverse direction, the sky was already completely covered by very low and dark clouds and we walked in a dense humid haze . A massive shape-shifting cloud descended menacingly just above us. And then the thunderstorm started. I am very sorry that I have no literary talent to describe what happened. It is enough to say that I never experienced something even close. Without any doubt, the high altitude essentially contributed to this. We suddenly weren't under but just inside the thundering clouds. The wind, blowing in different directions, contributed even more to the surrounding confusion. The flash of lightning, heavy rain, strong winds, lack of visibility, and the noise produced by thunderbolt created a state of sudden infernal chaos. As we had objects from metal in our knapsacks, all we could do was to drop them far from us and remain seated with our heads on the knees, covered by both hands, in a fetal position, as recommended by the stewardesses in case of a plane crash. I kept the eyes shut but I still could perceive somehow that several times the lightning slid down along the rocks, perhaps because couldn't enter the ground. Then the hail came as well. To understand how a thunderstorm really works is to be in it, to hear it, to taste it. 'The safest place to be is in the basement of your house', recommends the weather television channel in Toronto in similar situations. 'Move indoors immediately!' But there was no indoors around us up there. I was really scared but I had no time to think that my life could be over any minute then. In a state of shock, my mind was just blank. Empty. Fate had to decide what to do about me. I was absolutely without any power.

I really don't know how long the first storm lasted. To me, it seemed much too much. But it went south as suddenly as it came. The amount of fallen rain, however, was incredibly large. When we dared to stand up, look for knapsacks thrown around, and start descending again, John couldn't abstain from bitterly saying:

–"It is so easy to arrogantly defy nature and feel to have power over it when you are inside a solid concrete building during a thunderstorm, looking outside through a double window. Being outdoors during it, however, it teaches you a fine lesson in modesty and humility."

–"If you are lucky enough to survive!"

–"I think that we have to speed up. The atmosphere is still heavy and I am afraid that the storm is not over yet."

And this is what we did. We continued our alert descent in spite of the fact that the water was running now along our descending path. My waterproof boots were soaked from above, but I didn't care a bit. But the big surprise came when, after about two hours since we left the hut, we arrived to the torrent Reuse de l'Amône. Without any exaggeration, we both remained stunned, unable to say a word. The debit of its waters, now turned dirty brown, was simply huge and, worse than that, the bridge was nowhere to be seen. We looked up and down along the broken loose torrent but it was obvious that we couldn't cross it. John took a quick decision, in fact the only one possible under the circumstances:

–"Even if the level of the water goes down to what it was before the storm, which could take a very long time, we cannot cross the torrent without using the former bridge, which obviously has been taken down by the powerful flow. We have to go back to Cabane de l'A Neuve and remain there during the night."

This being the only reasonable alternative open to us, we were back to Stages 2, 3, and 4 already done once in the morning. Somehow magically, I forgot about being tired. The perspective of spending a night outdoors was much less tempting. We split a few biscuits and a small chocolate tablet found, in a still eatable state, in the pockets of our anoraks, and drank half a bottle of mineral water remained in John's knapsack.

On our way up, when we arrived again at the base of the final moraine, the storm restarted with a renewed strength. Facing a strong wind from the west, north-west, we struggled to reach the hut, barely visible because of the dark clouds and the approach of the evening dusk. More difficult was to cross the final patch of snow that became very slippery under the heavy rain. Once on the other side of it, we used the mobile chains climbing on the wet rocks through the crevice of the promontory and finally arrived up there.

The hut proved to be an excellent shelter. Everybody was inside. The little dining wooden room was like an oasis for us and for stranded patrons. The lady keeper of the hut welcomed us and gave us two blankets, allowing us to remove the wet clothes and dry them near the open fire from the small but cozy kitchen. Outside, the storm intensified and the lightning and thunderbolts became somehow even more frightening once the dark of the night settled around. But we were inside a warm hut and a kind of gentle camaraderie between tourists caught together in a heavy storm was building up.

An excellent and consistent chicken soup, with generous chunks of meat in it, followed by a big slice of fruit pie and hot tea, restored my good mood in spite of the thunderstorm going on outside. The lightning became so frequent that we somehow were getting used to it. Gradually, people started to withdraw, one by one, or in groups, to the common dormitory of the hut. In the meantime, our clothes, socks, and boots had dried up and became reusable. We remained in a warm and comfortable coin of the dining room and decided to remain there for a while, just talking, while slowly sipping the hot tea from big cups that we took care to replenish ourselves, from time to time, from the big kettle boiling in the kitchen. With the noise made by the thunderstorm, showing no signs to ease, I couldn't sleep anyway.

Just when John noticed how lucky we were that the hut was built from pieces of solid rock, a dazzling flash of lightning, almost instanta- neously followed by a terrible thunderbolt, like having the sky cracking just above us, made the electric light from the hut go off. The lady keeper, with a flashlight in hand, tried to keep a brave face and offered to show us to the common dormitory. We politely refused and remained alone in our coin of the dining room, whose darkness was interrupted frequently by the outside lightning, revealing either fast moving clouds or the white snow of Mont Dolent during its instantaneous flashes.

−"This reminds me of the power outage during one of my lectures, I told you about when we met on Monday, when I couldn't continue writing on the blackboard and I started talking to my students about history of mathematics. So we can go on with our stories. No light or blackboard is needed. But maybe you are tired and want to take a nap. My brother, who is a physician, used to tell me, wisely of course, as the doctors always think they do, that even half an hour of sleep is better than no sleep at all."

−"No, really. Or, not yet. I find magic to listen about romantic mathematicians up in the clouds during a stormy night now that we are relatively safe. I shall tell you when to stop."

I found myself a good resting position, with my tired feet horizontally relaxed on a wooden bench. Only then I realized that my right knee wasn't all right and I felt a vague pain inside it. Due to panic and circumstances, I kneeled on different rocks several times during our last ascent, which is a no-no in hiking, as John told me. Then I asked:

−"I have read somewhere that in mathematics only young people could have new great ideas and major original contributions; anyway, younger than in other fields like physics, chemistry, or literature. Is this really so?"

−"It is difficult to say. In any of the fields mentioned by you, to which we may easily add some others, like music, for instance, there are examples of very young but also some very old major contributors. Obviously, we are much more impressed by a young genius who had a short and tragic life, and we lament about the unrealized full potential due to a premature death. Mozart and Chopin come up immediately to my mind and there are so many other examples."

−"Are there examples of mathematicians who made important discoveries in spite of having had a short life?"

– "Four of them are quite famous, namely, the Norwegian Niels Henrik Abel, the French Évariste Galois, the German Bernhard Riemann, and the Indian Srinivasa Ramanujan. Each of them brought a remarkable contribution to mathematics and had a tragic destiny and a very short, or relatively short life. Many pages have been written about them and it is very difficult to know the extent to which the romantic approach in narrating their lives has distorted reality."

– "None of these names rings any bell for me whereas almost anybody knows something about the lives of Mozart or Chopin. I still remember how impressed I was when I saw the movie *Amadeus* made by Milos Forman. My ex-girlfriend Linda even cried watching it and she wasn't the only one doing that. However, later on, some critics raised question marks about how Mozart had been presented in the movie, doubting the way in which Salieri's behaviour and Mozart's poverty and death had been described, for instance."

– "This applies perhaps to any movie, play, or novel about the lives of real people. It is much easier to deal with pure fiction then to the real stuff. However, it is just how a certain personality is presented in such a movie, play, or novel that remains imprinted in the conscience of ordinary people and not the real life. It is the old dilemma about whether art imitates life or vice versa.

As I already mentioned yesterday, I have a very good friend Marius, a Romanian mathematician who spent a year in Manchester, as a visiting research fellow. He told me many details about the greatest Romanian poet, Mihail Eminescu, who, by the way, had also a short and tragic life in the second half of the 19th century. His poetry is unbelievably beautiful and it is a pity that any translation in a different language cannot preserve its flavour. I don't know the Romanian language but I saw the English version of some of his poems translated by a very gifted teenager, Corneliu M. Popescu, who tragically died, together with his mother, during a powerful earthquake which shook Bucharest, in 1977, two months before his 19th birthday. Translating poetry is obviously extremely difficult, especially when the two languages are so different as Romanian, a Latin language, and English are. The only thing I remember is that the rough translation of the Romanian verses:

> 'When with tired eyelashes
> In evening I blow the candle,
> Only the clock is following
> The long time's path.'

were put by the young translator in the poetic form:

> 'When my eyes are weighed with sleep
> I quench the evening candle's glow,
> And leave the ticking clock alone
> Along the path of time to go.'

Except love lyrics, Eminescu wrote patriotic poems and among them, perhaps the most well-known was the so called *The Third Letter*, also known as *Satire III*, describing a battle between the little army of brave Romanian soldiers, conducted by the 'voievod', which means somebody less important than a king, Mircea 'the Old', defending their country against the big army of Turkish invaders, conducted by Baiazid Ildîrîm 'the Lightning', sometime at the end of the 14th century. Marius knew it by heart, in its entirety. It described an epic battle between good and evil, between the weak and the strong, between Mircea and Baiazid, and the invaders are defeated by those defending their land by cleverly using the environment known to them and the courage of somebody who has everything to lose if defeated. Marius explained to me that this poem has been taught in schools for many many years and is meant to inspire the patriotic feelings of the young generation. As a result, everybody is convinced that Mircea 'the Old' defeated the army of the powerful Ottoman Empire. According to the historians, however, Mircea 'the Old' won indeed that heroic battle with Baiazid but couldn't win the war and had to leave his country, crossing the mountains to go to Transylvania and get foreign help."

–"That was a nice story. What was so remarkable about the four mathematicians mentioned by you a couple of minutes ago?"

ABEL

–"Niels Henrik Abel was born at the beginning of the 19th century (1802) in a family of Norwegian pastors. Both his father and his father's father were pastors in remote villages. He was of delicate health. When he was thirteen years old he was sent to the Cathedral School in Oslo. The main subject in school was Latin with some added instruction in Greek, English, religion, history, geography, natural philosophy, and three hours a week of mathematics. Niels was characterized as being very good, orderly, and modest. He liked to be together with his friends and throughout his life the theater remained his greatest joy. He liked chess and earned money by playing cards. His marks deteriorated and he couldn't muster interest for any of his subjects. Fortunately, a young new professor, Bernt Holmboe, awakened and guided Abel's interest in mathematics, giving him special problems and his own textbooks from the university courses. Later, Niels began to read by himself the classics (Isaac Newton, Leonhard Euler, Jean Le Rond D'Alembert, Siméon-Denis Poisson, Carl Friedrich Gauss) and embarked upon serious original work.

The early death of his father put serious financial constraints on the young Abel who, however, made every effort to assist his brothers and sisters. Graduating from the Cathedral School, he passed the entrance examinations to the new university in Oslo with mediocre marks in all subjects except mathematics. The university had no money for fellowships but did assist needy students by providing free room, light, and firewood in the university dormitory. Niels got this kind of assistance and, due to his more and more recognized talent in mathematics, some professors, like Christopher Hansteen, Soren Rasmussen, and Niels Treschow among others, personally contributed money for a cash grant for him.

Everything seemed to go very well. In Oslo, it was well known that Abel was a genius, supported by his professors who expected a great future for him. This opened for him the doors to many prominent families in Norway's capital. I have seen only one portrait of Niels Abel, executed by some painter in Paris, when he was about 24 years old, which shows a delicate adolescent, with almost feminine beauty, interior calm, and intelligent eyes.

When he was 20 years old, Niels completed his preparatory examinations, again with the highest marks in theoretical physics and mathematics and mediocre results in the other subjects. He contributed with papers to the newly created *Magazine for the Natural Sciences* and took his first trip abroad, sailing through the Oslo fjord down to Copenhagen. During this trip, he met Christine Kemp, known as Crelly, a charming girl, poor, but of good family, who later became his faithful fiancée but the bad fate prevented them from ever getting married.

At that time, Niels Abel was already interested and did research on solving the algebraic equation of fifth degree by radicals, on the last Fermat's theorem, and on some strange integrals of square roots of algebraic expressions of third and fourth degree, called elliptic integrals because the lengths of arcs of ellipses are particular cases of such integrals."

−"You have mentioned research on solving equations of fifth degree by radicals. In high school we have been taught about how to solve a general quadratic equation by radicals and there is a relatively simple formula for getting its solutions. Why is the fifth degree so important and what happens with the equations of third and fourth degree?"

−"Well, polynomial equations have a lengthy history. To make the long story short, let me mention that it is said that around 1600 B.C. the Babylonians possessed methods for solving quadratic equations. The ancient Greeks solved such quadratic equations by geometrical constructions but there is no indication that they knew any algebraic formula for solving them. They had some methods, however, for solving even some cubic equations, or equations of third degree, by intersecting conics. The Arabs inherited the problem from the Greeks and were concerned about the cubic equations.

Making a huge jump in time, around the year 1500 A.D., the book *Summa di Arithmetica*, written by Luca Pacioli, ended up with the remark that the general solution of cubic equations was as impossible as squaring the circle. At that time, however, one of the Renaissance mathematicians at University of Bologna, Scipio, or Scipione del Ferro, found such a solution but preferred to keep his discovery secret. When del Ferro died, his secret was passed to his son-in-law Anibale della Nave and to one of his students, Antonio Fior, or Fiore. The last one made the mistake of publicly challenging the well-known algebraist Niccolo Fontana, nicknamed Tartaglia from Venice, in 1535, about the solution of the cubic equation. The legend says that a few days before the expiration of the time limit for the deposition of the solutions, Tartaglia independently found the rule and Fiore was defeated. Tartaglia showed his method in that public competition but refused to reveal the details.

After a while, for unknown reasons, Tartaglia divulged the details of his method of solving cubic equations by radicals to Girolamo Cardano from Milan, provided he would swear never to publish the secret, or communicate it to somebody. Ten years later, however, Cardano published the algebra book *Ars Magna* containing the full solution in radicals of the cubic equation, credited to del Ferro and rediscovered by Tartaglia. The book also contained the solution in radicals of the equation of fourth degree, called quartic equation, obtained by Ludovico Ferrari, who had been taken by Cardano into his house as a servant lad, a few years earlier, and mathematically educated by him. Tartaglia was appalled by the revelations from *Ars Magna*. He wrote his own book and denounced Cardano as being a dishonest individual. Ferrari jumped to the defense of his master, revealing that it was del Ferro who had made the first discovery of the solution in radicals of the cubic equation and his solution was provided to Cardano by del Ferro's son-in-law della Nave. The fiery confrontation between Tartaglia and Ferrari continued for a couple of more years and raised the troubling question whether it is justifiable or not to keep a scientific discovery secret.

When I was in high school, my mathematics teacher showed us the formula for solving a cubic equation by radicals and called it the Cardano-Tartaglia formula, as mentioned in some algebra textbooks, without ever mentioning del Ferro's name. But the history of mathematics is full of strange associations between proper names and famous theorems or formulas."

– "How does this formula look and why isn't it taught in high school?"

John switched on his flashlight and put it on the wooden table in front of us. Then, he took a pencil and a small notebook from his pocket and continued:

–"The formula doesn't look very nice. In fact, if we start from a general cubic equation, $y^3 + ay^2 + by + c = 0$, by making a transformation of variable $y = x - a/3$, we get a simpler cubic equation of the form $x^3 - px = q$. Cardano-Tartaglia-del Ferro solution of this last equation is: $x = (q/2 + A)^{1/3} + (q/2 - A)^{1/3}$, where I denoted by A the square root: $A = [(q/2)^2 - (p/3)^3]^{1/2}$."

–"It is not so bad. But what does 'solving an equation by radicals' really mean and what happened to the polynomial equation of fifth degree?"

–" A polynomial equation contains the sum of different terms consisting of given numerical coefficients that multiply different positive integer powers of the variable or variables involved. Thus, $x^3 - 2x^2 + 5x + 7$ is a polynomial of degree 3 in one variable x, but $y^4 + 3x^2y - 5x + 6y - 12$ is a polynomial of degree 4 in two variables x and y. The solutions, or the roots, are those values of the variable, or variables, for which the corresponding polynomial equation is equal to zero. To solve a polynomial equation by radicals means to express the solutions, or the roots of such an equation from the coefficients of the respective equation by repeated addition, subtraction, multiplication, division, and extraction of roots. As you know by now, the roots of an equation of second degree $ax^2 + bx + c = 0$ may be expressed by radicals, being $(-b \pm \sqrt{b^2 - 4ac})/(2a)$.

Once the polynomial equations in one variable of degrees up to four have proved to be soluble by radicals, many mathematicians tried unsuccessfully to solve the general equation of fifth degree, or the quintic equation, $ax^5 + bx^4 + cx^3 + dx^2 + ex + f = 0$. Even the great Leonhard Euler failed to solve the problem but found new methods for solving the quartic equation by radicals. But let me switch off the flashlight because the night is long and, maybe, we will need it later.

Around 1770, the French mathematician Joseph Louis Lagrange analyzed the different tricks used for solving equations of degree up to four and showed that they depended on finding functions of the roots of the equation which were unchanged by certain permutations of those roots. He also showed that such an approach doesn't work when tried on the quintic equations. Thus, mathematicians started to believe that a general equation of fifth degree cannot be solved by radicals. Around 1813, another Italian, Paolo Ruffini, attempted to prove this impossibility but, unfortunately, his paper appeared in a little known journal and, more than that, his proof had several gaps."

–"How did Abel come into this picture?"

–"At the beginning, Niels tried himself to solve the quintic equation by radicals. But, faithful to his belief that the best strategy is to read the masters, a surprisingly sound principle for such a young person, he intensively read Lagrange's papers. After his return from the trip to Copenhagen, he arrived to the conclusion that no solution in radicals for the general quintic equation could be found and focused on proving that."

–"You mentioned that he was also interested in solving Fermat's last theorem and in dealing with elliptic integrals."

–"Yesterday, we have discussed what happened with Fermat's last theorem and the name of Abel wasn't mentioned there. He, however, did work on it intensively. In the end, Abel didn't solve Fermat's last theorem but, as far as I know, his attempts at solving it show that if integer solutions of Fermat's equation exist, they must be of a tremendously large size. This result is mentioned nowadays in all treaties dealing with important intermediary, partial steps in proving Fermat's last theorem.

As far as the elliptic integrals are concerned, he changed the entire optics of the domain. Instead of analyzing these integrals themselves, he focused on inverting elliptic integrals, yielding to so-called elliptic functions, whose theory became a generalization of the classic trigonometry. Abel discovered analogies between the properties of the elliptic functions and the properties of the trigonometric functions like sine or cosine, but obtained also new properties for which no correspondents exist in the old trigonometry."

–"Did Abel succeed in proving the impossibility of solving the general equation of fifth degree by radicals?"

–"Yes, around 1824, Niels Abel rigorously proved that the general quintic equation was insoluble by radicals. Perhaps this was his major achievement in his very short life. The story, however, wasn't so simple. When Abel proved the impossibility of solving the quintic equation by radicals, normally, he wanted to make his result known to the mathematical community. As the new journal *Magazine for the Natural Sciences*, published in Oslo, was written in Norwegian and had a very limited audience, he wrote his paper in French and decided to have it printed at his own expense but, for limiting the publication cost, Abel wrote a very short version of it in a condensed style. This important result had no immediate impact on the great names in mathematics and it is said that Abel's paper was found uncut among other papers in Gauss's office after his death. But, don't ask me whether this was true or not."

–"You mentioned, however, that Abel already had a high reputation in Oslo for his unusual talent in mathematics. What did his professors do in order to help him become known abroad as well?"

–"They did help him indeed, but just this help proved to be very tricky in Abel's case. Due to the efforts made by some professors, the administration of the university, and some high authorities, a small group of promising young Norwegian intellectuals of different specialties, including the mathematician Niels Abel, who was 23 years old at that time, got a travel grant for taking a long trip abroad, meant to last about two years. Unfortunately, just during this trip, an academic position at the university in Oslo became open, a very rare opportunity then, and Abel was supposed to be the top candidate for the position. However, invoking a strange combination of reasons – Niels already had a two-year travel grant approved, he lacked teaching experience and lectured in a less accessible way and, alas, he would get an academic position later anyway – the university gave the position to Abel's former high school teacher Bernt Holmboe.

The trip, however, proved to be important for Niels. In Germany, he knew August Leopold Crelle, a rich construction engineer, fond of mathematics, who had an excellent mathematical library and founded a new *Journal für die reine und angewandte Mathematik*, known even today as *Crelle's Journal*. August Leopold Crelle quickly sensed Abel's unusual mathematical talent and became a fatherly friend for him. In all subsequent years, he helped him financially, unconditionally opened his journal to Niels's mathematical papers, and even tried to find an academic position for him in Germany, unfortunately when it was too late for Abel to accept it."

–"Did he travel only to Germany during this trip?"

–"No. He went to Paris as well, after a short trip to Switzerland. Apparently, he met some big names like Adrien-Marie Legendre, Peter Gustav Lejeune Dirichlet, and Augustin-Louis Cauchy, but overall, as mentioned in Abel's letters, he enjoyed more the time spent in Germany than in France. In Paris, he wrote a very long memoir on transcendental functions presented to the French Academy of Science. Jean-Baptiste Joseph Fourier, the secretary of the Academy, gave the paper to Cauchy to referee about. Unfortunately, Cauchy was very busy writing his own numerous papers and it appears that he laid Abel's memoir aside."

–"What happened after the long trip abroad?"

–"Not much. Abel was 25 years old when he returned to Oslo. He had serious financial problems and some debts to cover, accumulated during his long trip abroad. No permanent position at the university was in sight. He took some temporary jobs, teaching an introductory course on theoretical astronomy at the university and some general courses at the new military academy. His salary was acceptable for a bachelor, but he had to help financially some members of his family including his mother and a handicapped brother.

Then, a question of priority marred his life. Abel wasn't the only one working on elliptic integrals. In Germany, Carl Gustav Jacob Jacobi also worked on the subject. Both Abel and Jacobi went in their research beyond the first results on elliptic functions obtained earlier by Legendre. Jacobi sent for publication two notes on the transformation of elliptic integrals containing no proofs. The notes were sent to Gauss who gave his blessing but not before mentioning that the results obtained by Jacobi followed directly from his own, unpublished yet. Jacobi's notes were then published in the same month in which Abel's paper on this topic appeared. Legendre read Jacobi's notes and wrote to him that one of his results was already known and that Jacobi's general formula on the transformation of elliptic integrals was very important, but he doubted that Jacobi had a proof for it indeed. Anyway, Legendre publicly praised Jacobi for his achievement but only later he became acquainted with Abel's paper on the subject. In the following months Jacobi worked hard for getting a proof for his formula and the specialists claim that he probably succeeded in getting it by using the inverse elliptic functions instead of the elliptic integrals, an idea from Abel's paper. However, Jacobi's proof didn't mention Abel's contribution. We will never know for sure whether Jacobi deliberately omitted any reference to Abel's results or he may have found the proof independently. What is known, however, is that after publishing the proof of his formula, Jacobi, then 23 years old, received his appointment to a professorship in Germany, while Abel, 26 years old, was waiting in vain for a lectureship at the university in Oslo. For different reasons, at that time, Abel got less recognition for his original contributions to the theory of elliptic integrals.

Afterwards, his health rapidly deteriorated, with frequent attacks of cough and fever. After four months of illness, he died when he was only 27 years old. Many felt sorrow and guilt for his premature disappearance. Even Gauss mentioned the great loss for science and Jacobi was now very active in praising Abel's contribution. The French Academy of Science made inquires about the fate of Abel's ignored *Memoir* and finally decided to publish it posthumously. But the sudden death of Joseph Fourier, the secretary of the Academy, the forced eight-year exile of Augustin-Louis Cauchy, for political reasons, and the disappearance of the original manuscript for a very long period of time, postponed the publication of the famous *Memoir* for almost a century!

Not long after his death, Niels's friends erected a monument at his grave. In the Royal Park in Oslo there is a sophisticated statue of Abel. Frankly speaking, I didn't like it but an art critic explained to me that the symbolic statue represents the flight of his genius. I would have preferred a three-dimensional replica of his only authentic portrait, I talked about, painted in Paris.

Niels's name has become a famous adjective in modern mathematics and it is quite frequent to read and talk about Abelian groups or Abelian integrals."

–"What happened with Abel's fiancée?"

–"It was a romantic ending. Baltazar Mathias Keilhau, a professor of geology at the university in Oslo, the best friend of Abel, had never seen Christine Kemp, but a couple of months after Niels's death, he wrote her, asking her to consent to become his wife. This was his way of answering the concerns expressed to him by his best friend Niels Abel about the fate of his fiancée in the last days of his life. After a short engagement, they got married and, apparently, they had a happy life together."

GALOIS

–"That was very moving indeed. But let me understand it right. Therefore, any polynomial equation of second degree may be solved by radicals, and the formula is learned even in high-school but, as shown by Abel, no polynomial equation of fifth degree may be similarly solved."

–"Well, not quite. Abel proved that the general polynomial of fifth degree cannot be solved by radicals. This doesn't mean that any equation of fifth or higher degree cannot be solved by radicals. In fact Abel himself worked on finding conditions under which equations of order larger than four may be solved by radicals, but he had no time to get results in this direction. This problem was magnificently solved by another young and equally unfortunate genius, namely Évariste Galois. He had the revolutionary new idea to attach to any irreducible equation with rational coefficients the group of permutations of its roots, called today the 'Galois group' of an equation. He proved that the equation may be solved by radicals if and only if its Galois group has a special property, called solubility. Therefore, if the Galois group of an equation is not soluble, then it cannot be solved by radicals. Following this line, it was relatively easy to show that there are specific polynomial equations of degree 5, for instance, which cannot be solved by radicals.

But Galois theory had a more impressive impact than showing when an equation may be solved by radicals. Thus, it has been used both for solving problems involving ruler-and-compass constructions in an elegant way and for rigorously proving the fundamental theorem of algebra. The general group theory, inspired by Galois group of permutations, proved to be a very powerful tool in different domains of modern mathematics and generated the systematic study of the general algebraic structures like abstract rings, ideals, modules, fields, and vector spaces we talked about. The Galois theory of so-called finite fields proved to have surprising applications in coding theory. We could talk about it some other time.

Anyway, Évariste Galois is another great romantic of mathematics and I have always asked myself when finally somebody will make a movie or write a play about this fascinating character."

–"I never heard of him. What happened with him?"

–"Évariste Galois was born near Paris in 1811. His father was a Republican and the head of the village liberal party who, a little later, became mayor. His mother was the daughter of a jurisconsult and had a solid education in classics and religion. Évariste was first educated by his mother, who kept him home until he was 12 years old, when he entered the high-school Louis-le-Grand. He became interested in mathematics reading Adrien-Marie Legendre's book on geometry, but found very boring the other subjects taught in school. He didn't pay much attention to the form of his written work and liked to solve problems mentally. His negligence for details caused his failure to the examination for entrance to l'École Polytechnique, the best French institution for mathematical education at that time.

When he was about 17 years old, he entered l'École Normale, a second class institution as far as mathematics was concerned. One year later, he published his first paper, on continued fractions, and started doing very serious research on the polynomial equations. He submitted two memoirs about some of his results to the French Academy of Sciences. Both were rejected by Augustin-Louis Cauchy, chosen as referee, and the manuscripts were lost. To add to Évariste's despair, his father committed suicide after a political dispute with the village priest. And, as a tragedy does not come alone, Galois failed the second attempt to pass the examination for entrance to l'École Polytechnique, his last chance. The legend says that during the examination he lost his temper and threw an eraser or the chalk into the examiner's face. More probable is the version that he entered a mathematical controversy with his examiner who failed him.

Half an year later, he sent an ample memoir to the French Academy of Sciences in the competition for the Grand Prize of the Academy. The manuscript was taken home by Joseph Fourier, the secretary of the Academy, who died before reading it. Strangely enough, the memoir couldn't be found among Fourier's papers. Galois started to feel only intentional hostility against him from the academic milieu, in particular, and the unjust society, in general. Criticizing the director of l'École Normale in a note published in *Gazette des Écoles*, Galois was expelled.

Unsuccessfully, he tried to set up a private teaching of advanced algebra, and sent once more a memoir to the Academy of Sciences, dealing just with conditions of solubility of equations by radicals. The mathematicians Sylvestre-François Lacroix and Siméon-Denis Poisson were appointed as referees. Two months later, Galois inquired to the President of Academy about the fate of his memoir but got no reply."

–"This is absolutely awful. This young man had no joy in his life. Only a chain of tragedies and bad luck!"

–"Doing mathematics and getting the extraordinary results he discovered perhaps gave him a lot of internal joy, but the tragedies were far from over for him. He joined the artillery of the National Guard, which was a Republican organization at that time, soon dissolved by the king. During a banquet held in protest, Galois proposed a toast to the king Louis-Philippe, holding a knife in his hand. It is said, but I don't know whether this was really so, that the writer Alexandre Dumas, 'le fils', who was attending the banquet, jumped from the window, afraid of possible reprisals. Galois was arrested on the following day, but the jury acquitted him after a couple of weeks.

When he got out of jail, he finally received the report on his last memoir sent to the Academy of Sciences but the referee Poisson declared it as being incomprehensible and couldn't recommend its approval. After this new blow, on July 14, Évariste attended a Republican demonstration wearing the illegal uniform of the dissolved artillery, carrying a gun and a knife. He was arrested again but this time he was imprisoned for six months. He continued to do mathematics in the jail but, due to the cholera epidemic, he was transferred to a hospital and later put on parole.

Sentimentally involved with a mysterious and dubious mademoiselle, and apparently rejected by her, but ready to defend her honour, Évariste Galois was challenged to a duel. The heart-breaking fact is that, on the eve of the duel, he wrote his famous mathematical testament to his friend Auguste Chevalier. Mentioning several times 'I have no time!' in the margins, he summarized his revolutionary discoveries involving the relationship between groups and the field extensions associated to polynomial equations, stating the crucial result that an equation may be solved by radicals if its associated group of permutations of its roots is soluble, moving all the previous difficulties in solving equations by radicals to dealing with groups of transformations, and hoping that 'someday, some people will decipher all this mess and see the importance of these theorems'.

The duel, with pistols at 25 paces, occurred on 30th May 1832. Galois was hit in his stomach, left unattended, and carried to a hospital by a peasant passing by. To his brother, arrived to see him, he said: 'Please don't cry. I need all my courage to die at 21.' He died on the next day, after refusing the office of a priest. It was his way of leaving a hostile world. He was buried in the common ditch at the cemetery of Montparnasse."

I really don't know when and how but, at some point of the night, the fatigue overcame the noise of the storm and I fell asleep, wrapped in the warm blanket and with my head on the wooden table.

FOURTH DAY

RETURN TO LA FOULY

It was seven o'clock when I woke up on Friday morning. It was still relatively dark in the dining room. From the kitchen, I heard somebody handling dishes and a nice smell of fresh coffee came out of it. Three other people were already eating breakfast. John wasn't there. He came a little later from outside, accompanied by a huge shepherd dog who, irreverently, shook off the water from his fur, spreading it all around.

–"This is the dog of the hut," said John. "Very friendly. He asked to be let out and I was also anxious to see how was outside. Not too good. There are only dark clouds around us, the storm is still going on but the lightning and thunderbolts are farther away, whereas the rain is not as heavy as last night. It is also much colder than yesterday. A rather dull, grey, hopeless day. I am very surprised because I expected a glorious morning after the storm.

In fact, I feel quite guilty. I knew from past years that, around here, there is a relatively stable weather pattern: after a couple of nice days, when humidity gradually rises, you can expect a heavy rain to come. I wasn't supposed to suggest a trip up here yesterday morning. But still, I have never seen such a sudden change and a violent thunderstorm lasting so long. It is like having the clouds caught up here and they don't dissipate. I talked to the lady keeper of the hut, who by the way is called Mireille, and she cannot remember something so violent around La Fouly either. Electricity is still off. They use up here some solar batteries, installed on the roof, but the electric circuit was damaged by lightning. Fortunately, she can still cook because she uses gas from cylindrical containers, brought up here by helicopters. In fact, everything they need here is provided by helicopters, which come once or twice a week."

–"Nobody can predict weather with certainty. In Toronto there is a television channel specialized only in weather forecast, broadcast 24 hours a day. Generally they do a good job, because they rely on a lot of data available but still, they are proved wrong many times. Once, they couldn't predict a disastrous ice storm in the Montreal area which, among other damages, left people there without electricity for more than a week, or so."

–"It is true that we cannot predict almost anything with certainty. Somebody nicely said that we advance with our back towards the future and we don't have two opposite faces like Janus, the Roman god, to see what is going to happen. We can look backwards to the past, however, and learn something from it. But this time, I didn't apply what I learned from the past about the weather around La Fouly during summer time. I am really sorry."

–'Please, don't feel guilty. It was quite an experience and we are OK, have a solid roof above us, and I am looking forward to having a great breakfast."

I went outside to refresh myself and wash my face with the water from a trough filled by rain. It was cold outside and I felt happy when I went back into the dining room. After my breakfasts inside or in front of my tent, this one was infinitely better. We had bacon and eggs, gem on buttered bread, and hot coffee. What a treat! It couldn't be better.

–"I really enjoyed what you told me about Abel and Galois. The storm and, later, the dark made their lives seem even more dramatic."

–"In fact, I also started talking about Riemann too, but soon I realized that you had fallen asleep."

–"I am sorry. I was really tired, but I do remember that I heard the end of Galois's life story. I am afraid that a movie or a play about the life of Galois would be viewed as fiction because it is almost unbelievable that such a sad human destiny was really possible. Anyway, as we have nothing to do but wait for the weather to change for the better, I would be more than happy to listen what happened with Riemann and the other romantic mathematician mentioned by you. But, please, start from the beginning. Before you start, however, I should like to ask you to clarify something about solving algebraic equations. I understand that Abel was the first one who proved rigorously that a general polynomial equation, with rational coefficients, of degree 5 or more, cannot be solved by radicals. My first question is: why does the degree 5 play such an important role? The second question I want to ask you refers to Galois. You said that he showed that a polynomial equation can nevertheless be solved by radicals if a certain group of permutations of its zeros is solvable. Isn't it a contradiction between what Abel proved and what Galois claimed? At the same time, I understand, or I think I understand, what solving an equation by radicals means but I don't know what a soluble group of permutations is."

—"Very pertinent questions. I have to admit that you are really smart."

—"I am not! In fact, more often than not, I am very slow and I need a lot of time until I finally grasp what is significant. But I liked the story of solving algebraic equations told by you and I want to get it right."

GROUP THEORY

John cleaned the table in front of us while I brought the dirty stuff to the kitchen. He removed a couple of white pages from his notebook, took a blue pen out of his upper pocket, and started to answer my questions, speaking very slowly. It was still very grey outside but, however, we got enough daylight through the tiny windows to allow me to see what John was writing, without using the flashlight as we had done in the previous evening.

—"It is not very easy to explain briefly the essence of Galois's theory and I always tried to avoid the mathematical formalism as much as I could. But, as you are asking for details, some formulas are however needed.

Solving polynomial equations is a way of getting new kinds of numbers. Thus, if $\mathbf{Q}$ is the field of rational numbers, or fractions, then the roots of the quadratic equation $x^2 - 2 = 0$ are not rational numbers; they are irrational numbers $\pm\sqrt{2}$. The adjunction of the irrational number $\sqrt{2}$ to the field $\mathbf{Q}$ gives a larger field, denoted by $\mathbf{Q}(\sqrt{2})$, whose elements have the form $a + b\sqrt{2}$, where a and b are arbitrary rational numbers from $\mathbf{Q}$. The equation $x^2 - 2 = 0$ may be solved by radicals and we have $(\sqrt{2})^2 \in \mathbf{Q}$, where the symbol $\in$ means 'belongs to', or 'is an element of'. In general, if $\alpha_1, \alpha_2, \ldots, \alpha_n$ are the zeros of a polynomial equation of degree n with rational coefficients, then the corresponding equation may be solved by radicals if for each solution of the equation α_i there is a positive integer $m(i)$ such that $\alpha_i^{m(i)} \in \mathbf{Q}(\alpha_1, \ldots, \alpha_{i-1})$, which means that the solution α_i may be obtained by taking the radical of order $m(i)$ from an algebraic combination of the coefficients and other solutions of that equation. Using words, an equation may be solved by radicals if every solution of it may be obtained by applying arithmetic operations of addition, subtraction, multiplication, division, and taking radicals of different positive, integer orders on the coefficients and other solutions of the respective equation.

Let us go back now to the multiplicative group of transformations and let denote this group by $\mathbf{G}$. In such a group of transformations, like the group of translations or the group of rotations for instance: 1) The composition (or product) AB of two transformations A and B of the group is also a transformation of the group meaning: apply transformation A first, followed by the application of transformation B; 2) The identity (or unit) transformation E belongs to the group, where $AE = EA = A$ for every transformation A of the group, and where $=$ is equality between transformations; 3) If a transformation A belongs to the group, then the inverse transformation A^{-1} also belongs to the group, where $AA^{-1} = A^{-1}A = E$. Such a group of transformations being given, the 'commutator' (A, B) of two transformations A, B is the transformation $A^{-1}B^{-1}AB$. The subgroup of $\mathbf{G}$ generated by the commutators of all elements of $\mathbf{G}$ is called the derived group $\mathbf{G}'$ of the group $\mathbf{G}$. The derived group of $\mathbf{G}$ consists precisely of those transformations that can be represented in the form of products of commutators.

The derived group of the derived group $\mathbf{G'}$ is called the second derived group of $\mathbf{G}$ and is denoted by $\mathbf{G''}$. Repeating this, we can define the derived group of arbitrary order of a group $\mathbf{G}$. The derived group of an Abelian (commutative) group consists only of the identity transformation E because, from the commutativity property $AB = BA$, it follows that $(A, B) = E$. Thus, using the symbol $\subset$ for 'a subgroup of', we have $\mathbf{G'} \subset \mathbf{G}$, and if the group $\mathbf{G}$ is commutative, we have $\mathbf{G'} = \{E\}$. The concept of commutator was introduced by Arthur Cayley (1821-1895), if I remember well.

Historically, the first group of transformations studied by Évariste Galois was the permutation group $\mathbf{G}$ of the solutions $x_1, \ldots, x_n$ of a polynomial equation of degree n. This group of permutations is called the 'Galois group' of the respective equation. As the solutions of a polynomial equation satisfy different relations, there are some delicate points here that must be made very clear. Algebraic relations between $x_1, \ldots, x_n$ that are unchanged under all permutations of $x_1, \ldots, x_n$ are called symmetric relations. For example: $x_1 + \ldots + x_n$. The set of all $n!$ permutations of the solutions $x_1, \ldots, x_n$ is called the 'symmetric group' $\mathbf{S}_n$ of degree n. Let us consider now the expression:

$$\triangle = (x_2 - x_1)(x_3 - x_1) \ldots (x_n - x_1)(x_3 - x_2) \ldots (x_n - x_2) \ldots (x_n - x_{n-1}),$$

which is the product of all differences of the form $(x_j - x_i)$, with $i < j$. Every permutation of $x_1, \ldots, x_n$ either leaves the value of the expression $\triangle$ unchanged, in which case it is said to be 'even', or changes its sign only, in which case it is said to be 'odd'. The set of even permutations, denoted by $\mathbf{A}_n$, forms a subgroup of $\mathbf{S}_n$ containing $n!/2$ permutations. It is called the 'alternating group' of degree n. The funny thing is that the commutator of any two permutations is always an even permutation. For instance, if we take $n = 3$, and the odd permutations:

$$A = \begin{pmatrix} x_1 & x_2 & x_3 \\ x_2 & x_1 & x_3 \end{pmatrix}, \qquad A^{-1} = \begin{pmatrix} x_1 & x_2 & x_3 \\ x_2 & x_1 & x_3 \end{pmatrix},$$

$$B = \begin{pmatrix} x_1 & x_2 & x_3 \\ x_1 & x_3 & x_2 \end{pmatrix}, \qquad B^{-1} = \begin{pmatrix} x_1 & x_2 & x_3 \\ x_1 & x_3 & x_2 \end{pmatrix},$$

then, their commutator is the even permutation:

$$(A, B) = A^{-1}B^{-1}AB = \begin{pmatrix} x_1 & x_2 & x_3 \\ x_2 & x_3 & x_1 \end{pmatrix},$$

because it leaves the expression:

$$\triangle = (x_2 - x_1)(x_3 - x_1)(x_3 - x_2)$$

unchanged. The derived group of the symmetric group $\mathbf{S}_n$ is the alternating group $\mathbf{A}_n$.

Let $\mathbf{G}$ be a group of permutations of the solutions $x_1, \ldots, x_n$ of a polynomial equation of degree n. If among the derived groups of $\mathbf{G}$ at least one, hence all subsequent ones, consists of the identity transformation E only, where:

$$E = \begin{pmatrix} x_1 & x_2 & \ldots & x_n \\ x_1 & x_2 & \ldots & x_n \end{pmatrix},$$

then the group $\mathbf{G}$ is called soluble. As shown by Galois, solvability of the Galois group attached to a polynomial equation corresponds to solvability of the corresponding equation by radicals. This is the crucial point but the story isn't over yet.

I said before that the solutions $x_1, \ldots, x_n$ of a polynomial equation

$$x^n + a_1 x^{n-1} + a_2 x^{n-2} + \ldots + a_{n-1}x + a_n = 0$$

with rational coefficients satisfy some relations. Very long ago, François Viète noticed a very nice symmetric dependence between the coefficients and the solutions of such a general equation, namely:

$$x_1 + x_2 + \ldots + x_n = -a_1$$
$$x_1 x_2 + x_1 x_3 + \ldots + x_{n-1} x_n = a_2$$
$$\vdots$$
$$x_1 x_2 \ldots x_n = (-1)^n a_n,$$

where the first relation refers to the sum of all solutions, the second relation refers to the sum of all products of two solutions $x_i x_j$, with

$(i < j)$, ..., the last relation refers to the product of all n solutions. This is a generalization of what is learned in high school about a general quadratic equation $ax^2 + bx + c = 0$, where a, b, c are integers with $a \neq 0$. It may be written as $x^2 + (b/a)x + (c/a) = 0$. If x_1 and x_2 are its solutions, then Viète's relations between solutions and coefficients are: $x_1 + x_2 = -b/a$ and $x_1 x_2 = c/a$, respectively.

For a general polynomial equation of degree n, its solutions are independent and Viète's equalities just mentioned are the only relations satisfied by $x_1, \ldots, x_n$. As these relations are obviously symmetric, they are invariant with respect to any permutation of these n solutions. Therefore, the Galois group of the general equation of degree n is the symmetric group $\mathbf{S}_n$. The symmetric groups $\mathbf{S}_2$, $\mathbf{S}_3$ and $\mathbf{S}_4$ are solvable because their first, second, and third derived groups, respectively, are just the group containing only the identity permutation $\{E\}$. In contrast, the symmetric groups $\mathbf{S}_n$, with $n \geq 5$ are not solvable since it can be shown that their second derived group coincides with the first derived group and is different from the group containing only the identity permutation $\{E\}$. This is how we can justify today the fact that any polynomial equation of degree 2, 3, or 4 may be solved by radicals and Abel's famous result that the general polynomial equations of degree 5 or higher cannot be solved by radicals.

For particular kinds of equations, the solutions $x_1, \ldots, x_n$ of a polynomial equation of degree n could satisfy not only Viète's symmetric equalities but some other relations, as well, which are not necessarily symmetric. In such a case, the corresponding Galois group of the corresponding equation is different from the symmetric group $\mathbf{S}_n$ and contains only those permutations of the solutions $x_1, \ldots, x_n$ that keep these restrictions invariant. Thus, the equation $x^4 - 2 = 0$, for instance, whose solutions are:

$$x_1 = \sqrt[4]{2}, \quad x_2 = i\sqrt[4]{2}, \quad x_3 = -\sqrt[4]{2}, \quad x_4 = -i\sqrt[4]{2},$$

where $i = \sqrt{-1}$, satisfy the asymmetric relation $x_1 x_2 - x_3 x_4 = 0$. The corresponding Galois group $\mathbf{G}$ is generated by the permutations:

$$A = \begin{pmatrix} x_1 & x_2 & x_3 & x_4 \\ x_2 & x_3 & x_4 & x_1 \end{pmatrix} \qquad B = \begin{pmatrix} x_1 & x_2 & x_3 & x_4 \\ x_1 & x_4 & x_3 & x_2 \end{pmatrix},$$

and contains the following eight permutations:

$$\mathbf{G} = \{E, A, A^2, A^3, B, BA, BA^2, BA^3\},$$

while $\mathbf{S}_4$ contains 4!=24 permutations.

To summarize: 1) If $\mathbf{B} \supset \mathbf{C}$ means 'the set $\mathbf{B}$ includes the set $\mathbf{C}$', then if the Galois group $\mathbf{G}$ of a polynomial equation is the symmetric group $\mathbf{S}_n$, then it is solvable for $n \leq 4$, because:

$$\mathbf{S}_2 \supset \mathbf{A}_2 = \{E\}$$
$$\mathbf{S}_3 \supset \mathbf{A}_3 \supset \mathbf{A'}_3 = \{E\}$$
$$\mathbf{S}_4 \supset \mathbf{A}_4 \supset \mathbf{A'}_4 \supset \mathbf{A''}_4 = \{E\}.$$

2) If the Galois group $\mathbf{G}$ of a polynomial equation is the symmetric group $\mathbf{S}_n$, then it is not solvable for $n \geq 5$, because we have:

$$\mathbf{S}_n \supset \mathbf{A}_n = \mathbf{A}_n^{(k)} \supset \{E\},$$

and no k-th derived group of $\mathbf{A}_n$ contains only the identity permutation E.

3) If $\mathbf{G}$ is the Galois group of a polynomial equation, we always have:

$$\mathbf{G} \supset \mathbf{G'} \supset \mathbf{G''} \supset \ldots \supset \mathbf{G}^{(k)} \supset \ldots \supset \{E\}.$$

The corresponding equation may be solved by radicals if its Galois group is solvable, which means that there is a k-th derived group which contains only the identity permutation E, namely: $\mathbf{G}^{(k)} = \{E\}$. If $\mathbf{G}$ is not solvable, then the corresponding equation cannot be solved by radicals.

Let me say that, practically, it is very difficult to find the Galois group of an equation and to check whether it is solvable or not. In the end, the emergence of the general group theory, with so many applications in modern mathematics, theoretical physics, chemistry, and crystallography, is the major outcome of Èvariste Galois's brilliant efforts to solve equations by radicals."

–"I think that I had enough formulas for the day. Please give these pages to me, to attach them to my notes and let see what you have in store about the other two romantic mathematicians."

RIEMANN

–"Indeed, the next one to talk about should be Bernhard Riemann, a German mathematician who published very little but whose genius deeply changed a large part of modern mathematics, with profound reverberations in physics as well."

–"Did he work in algebra, like Abel and Galois?"

–"No, he could be classified as being mainly a geometer, but he had major contributions in many other domains of mathematics except algebra. His main quality was an amazing creative power based on an extraordinary intuition. He avoided long computations and was more interested in presenting his new ideas in a clear form than in insisting on an exaggerated rigour in his very condensed writings. Some mathematicians have complained about lack of rigour in some of his proofs, like the use of a variational principle, for instance, based on a minimizing function whose existence wasn't guaranteed. But his theorems are correct and it was left to others the task of bringing the right justifications for his results.

But let us start with his life first. There is a very rich literature about Riemann but I am going to tell you only what I remember now from what I read about him. He was born in 1826, near Hanover. He had four sisters and one brother. His father, a poor Lutheran minister, taught Bernhard until he was ten years old. Later, he continued his education in a local school, followed by the Lyceum in Hanover, where he lived with his grandmother, and the Gymnasium in Lüneburg, where he moved after his grandmother died.

He was a good but not outstanding pupil, but showed a particular interest in mathematics. It is said that when the director of the Gymnasium lent him Adrien-Marie Legendre's book on the theory of numbers, Bernhard read the 900-page book in six days, which is almost impossible to believe.

When he was 20 years old, Riemann enrolled at the Göttingen University, first in the theology faculty, but switched, with his father's permission, to the faculty of philosophy so that he could study mathematics. There, he took elementary mathematics courses from Carl Friedrich Gauss and physics courses from Wilhelm Weber. Then, he moved to Berlin University, an important mathematical center at the time, being influenced mainly by Peter Gustav Lejeune Dirichlet and Ferdinand Gotthold Eisenstein. Here he did his work on the general theory of complex variables.

After about two years spent in Berlin, Bernhard Riemann returned to Göttingen, where he finished his PhD thesis, under the supervision of Gauss, in 1851. In the meantime he acquired a solid background in theoretical physics. The doctoral thesis written by Riemann was characterized by Gauss as having 'a gloriously fertile originality'. It contained new ideas about the geometric properties of the special functions of complex variables represented by analytic functions and conformal mappings, which became later extremely important in the mechanics of fluids.

Recommended by Gauss, Riemann got an appointment in Göttingen and prepared his Habilitation, the title which would allow him to give lectures at the University. In his Habilitation dissertation he dealt with the integrability of functions and the representation of functions by trigonometric series. Except writing the dissertation, another requirement was to give a public lecture selected by the examination committee from a list of three lectures prepared by the candidate beforehand. Riemann prepared three lectures, two on electricity and one on geometry. Normally, the examination committee used to choose always the first title from the list provided by the candidate. This time, Gauss made a surprising exception and chose the lecture on geometry, taking Riemann by surprise. He had little time to prepare it in its final form. In the end, his lecture on the hypotheses that lie at the foundations of geometry became a mathematical jewel. Basically, he described the structure of curved n-dimensional spaces, called today Riemann spaces, whose curvature is defined by the local deviations from the theorem of Pythagoras which holds in the flat Euclidean spaces. Riemann's geometry, called also elliptical non-Euclidean geometry, fundamentally differs from Euclid's geometry as far as Euclid's second and fifth postulates are concerned. As it is well-known from the elementary geometry taught in schools, as discussed by us the other days, Euclid's fifth postulate says that through a point, not on a given line, there is only one line parallel to that line. Riemann's geometry states that there are no parallel lines at all. Also, the second Euclid's postulate says that a straight line has an infinite length and can be extended continuously indefinitely. In Riemann's geometry all straight lines have equal length and, as consequences, the sum of any triangle's angles is larger than two right angles and similar polygons with different areas don't exist."

–"But this seems very strange to me. Obviously, through an exterior point I can draw a parallel to a given straight line and a line may be extended, at least theoretically, indefinitely. I remember that when our math teacher told us that the parallel lines meet only at the infinite, one of my colleagues remarked that there must be a lot of noisy collisions far there. Riemann's geometry seems to be possible only from a logical point of view but perhaps it has no practical applications in the real world."

–"Our intuition heavily depends on what we know or have been taught at some point of time but it changes when new facts are found. Thus, our perception of space has dramatically changed when, discovering that the earth is round and not flat, we had to accept the idea that, at the opposite pole, our human brothers and sisters are walking upside down. And, in fact, the surface of a sphere offers an excellent model for Riemann's geometry if the lines are defined to be the big circles on the sphere."

–"What do you mean by a big circle?"

–"Come on, you know it. A big circle is obtained by intersecting the surface of the sphere with a plane passing through the center of the sphere. With this definition of the line on the surface of the sphere, it is easy to see that through an external point we cannot draw any parallel to a given 'line', which means that there is no big circle which doesn't intersect a given big circle, and that all the 'lines', namely big circles on the surface of the given sphere, have the same finite length."

–"What did people say about this new geometry?"

–"Gauss, the creator of the differential geometry on surfaces, understood immediately the importance of the new geometric ideas because, in fact, Riemann's geometry of an n-dimensional space is a curved variant of the Euclidean geometry of an n-dimensional space just like the general geometry of a surface which is a curved variant of the Euclidean geometry of a flat plane. But it took half of a century to mathematicians to grasp the importance of the Riemann spaces and Riemannian geometry for understanding the structure of our real space. Since 1905, when Albert Einstein created the special theory of relativity, which uses a simple mathematical formalism, he spent the next ten years to learn what Riemann did in geometry, until 1916, when the foundations of Einstein's sophisticated general relativity theory were published. Inside this revolutionary theory about the universe, the real space proved to be just a Riemann space whose curvature is determined by the presence of mass and whose 'lines', as the shortest paths, are the geodesics of the curved space."

–"Therefore, after getting his Habilitation, Riemann had the right to lecture at the University. What kind of lecturer was he?"

–"All I read about is that he had to overcome his shyness and that he had very few students attending his lectures. Fortunately, one of these students, Julius Wilhelm Richard Dedekind, later became an important mathematician and published some of Riemann's lectures. Anyway, Riemann was appointed as a full professor when he was 31 years old and, two years later, when Gustav Peter Lejeune Dirichlet – the successor of Gauss – died, he was appointed to the chair of mathematics at Göttingen and was elected a member of the Berlin Academy of Sciences. In the same year, 1859, he wrote a famous report, eight pages long, on the function $\pi(x)$, discussed by us already, denoting the number of primes less than or equal to the given real number x, whose properties have been studied by many great mathematicians like Euler, Legendre, Gauss, and many others. You remember that in dealing with this problem, Euler introduced the remarkable function $\zeta(s)$ which assigns to any real number s the sum, with respect to the natural number n, of the series whose general term is 1 divided by n at power s. Riemann replaced the real variable s from Euler's function by a complex variable z, having a real part and an imaginary part, and showed its usefulness in the study of the distribution of primes. To be more specific, Riemann's zeta function is:

$$\zeta(z) = 1 + \frac{1}{2^z} + \frac{1}{3^z} + \frac{1}{4^z} + \dots$$

In his famous paper, Riemann made six assumptions, or conjectures, and proved that if these assumptions are true, then they imply the famous 'prime number theorem', according to which $\pi(x)$ behaves like $x/\ln x$, for large values of x. In the meantime, five of his six conjectures have been proven true, but one of them, the so-called 'Riemann's conjecture' is still defying the efforts of many mathematicians who are trying hard to prove it true. This conjecture, also called 'Riemann's hypothesis', asserts that there are infinitely many nontrivial roots of the function $\zeta(s)$ that all have the real part equal to $1/2$. More intuitively, this means that all zeros of Riemann's function in the strip of the complex plane corresponding to the unit interval (0,1) lie on the central line, parallel to the imaginary axis, passing through the real number $1/2$. Riemann's hypothesis has remained unsolved until now, and many other difficult questions from mathematics would become answered in the affirmative if it were proved true.

When we talked about Gauss, I mentioned that his function $Li(x) = \int_2^x (1/\ln t)\, dt$ gives an excellent approximation for $\pi(x)$. In his paper from 1859, Bernhard Riemann remarked that Gauss's density $1/\ln x$ rather 'counts' not only the primes but also a half of the prime squares, a third of the prime cubes, a quarter of the prime fourth powers, etc. Thus, he arrived to the function:

$$R(x) = Li(x) + \sum_{n=2}^{\infty} \frac{\mu(n)}{n}\, Li(x^{1/n}),$$

which approximates even better $\pi(x)$, where Möbius's function $\mu(n)$ is equal to 0 if n is divisible by a prime square, to 1 if n is a product of an even number of distinct primes, and to -1 if n is a product of an odd number of distinct primes.

In a scribbled note, discovered after his death, Riemann mentioned that he had obtained some of his theorems in number theory by using an explicit alternative expression for his complex variant of Euler's function but he hadn't simplified it enough in order to be publishable. Nothing of the kind was found among his posthumous papers."

–"Until now, everything seems to be just fine with Riemann's life and career. What went wrong?"

–"First, he was very poor during his youth. Second, Riemann's family was marred by tragedies. His mother, his brother, and three of his sisters, all died young. When he was 36 years old, he married a friend of his living sister and they had a daughter together. Immediately after his marriage, Riemann, who was frail all his life, got tuberculosis and, looking for a milder climate, made three long travels to Italy. When he was 39 years old, he died on the shores of the beautiful Lake Maggiore, not very far from here, working until his last day on an unfinished paper."

RAMANUJAN

–"When somebody discovers something really important in mathematics, is this the result of a lot of work, based on a high mathematical education, or of a divine revelation, as being inspired by gods?"

–"I wish I knew the answer but I don't. Some people believe that mathematics is a science created by human beings, as the result of a logical thinking, rethinking, analyzing, trying, dissecting, recombining, particularizing, or generalizing results previously obtained by predecessors, or induced and ordered by problems from other natural sciences, like physics, chemistry, biology, or social sciences. Other people believe that the mathematical truths do exist, independently of human beings, and some mathematicians of genius have the power or chance to reveal some of them to the other mortals, from time to time. Obviously, it is much easier to adopt the first viewpoint, but sometime, some extraordinary facts are really puzzling and difficult to explain."

–"Like what?"

–"The first example coming to my mind is the case of the Indian mathematician Srinivasa Ramanujan. We can put him in the group of romantic mathematicians because he also had a dramatic and short life, but his way of doing mathematics was one of the most mysterious ones.

He was born in 1887 in a high but very poor Hindu caste. As a little boy, he was labelled as being quite out of ordinary. It is said that he independently rediscovered Euler's formula which shows the relationship between the exponential function with imaginary exponent and the complex combination between the trigonometric functions sine and cosine, namely $e^{i\alpha} = \cos\alpha + i\sin\alpha$, where $i = \sqrt{-1}$. He had no access to some really good mathematical textbooks and his 'bible' was the book *Synopsis of Elementary Results in Pure Mathematics* written by George Shoobridge Carr. It seems, however, that this book had less influence on Ramanujan's writings than it was claimed. Thus, the book contained a large part on geometry, a domain with little impact on Ramanujan, whose interest focused mainly on number theory, the theory of functions, and calculus.

Ramanujan started filling in some strange notebooks containing amazing good and false formulas, practically without any proofs. Three notebooks were written before 1913 and the originals are kept at the library of the University of Madras. A fourth 'lost notebook' is supposed to have been written during his last year; it has been 'found' in Cambridge only in 1965. He claimed that the goddess of Namakkal inspired him with the formulas in his dreams.

Since he was about 17 years old, he devoted all his time to doing mathematics, completely neglecting other disciplines. Consequently, he moved from one college to another, took time off, failed examinations, had no regular employment but got married, when he was 22 years old, with Janaki, who was 12 years younger than her husband. They had no children. Three years later, he finally became a clerk in the office of the Port Trust of Madras. In all these early years of his life, he continued to do mathematics by himself but didn't get any high education in mathematics. He succeeded, however, in publishing two very original mathematical papers which brought him a reasonably good scholarship from the University of Madras.

In 1913, he sent a letter and a paper to the well-known mathematician Godfrey Harold Hardy in Cambridge, England. This was the moment when the destinies of two very different men – Hardy, a sophisticated and highly educated English academic, a radical who had deep sympathy for the poor but lived like an aristocrat, and Ramanujan, the unlucky, modest, and undereducated Indian clerk – intertwined in an unexpected way. I remember that I read somewhere that when Hardy got the paper sent by Ramanujan, he looked at it and threw it in the garbage basket. Later in the day, at his club, he thought about the paper and suddenly realized that his author was either a madman or a genius. Going home, he reexamined the paper and decided to invite Ramanujan to come to Cambridge. It took one year, however, to bring him there. Among other difficulties, Ramanujan, a strictly observant Brahmin, wasn't allowed to cross the water and therefore go to England. His mother, however, claimed that, during a dream, some goddess gave her the needed blessing for the trip.

For three years, in Cambridge, Ramanujan worked hard, doing research together with Hardy and trying to improve his mathematical education. It is said that he was rarely seen in Cambridge, working for 24 hours and then sleeping for 20 hours. During his entire life, he remained a strict vegetarian, with a strong preference for spicy foods, cooking all his food himself, but only after changing into his pyjamas first. This diet didn't help him cope with the damp English climate and he fell ill, when he was 30 years old, with a regular rise of temperature every night but without lung trouble, complaining of severe pain in the stomach, wrongly diagnosed with a malignant growth, and later suspected of having tuberculosis. It is said that due to his illness and his solitary life while in Cambridge, Ramanujan had fits of depression and attempted suicide by falling in front of a train in an underground subway station in London but, miraculously, the train stopped in time to avoid the fatal accident. Anyway, he never really recovered from his illness until his death in 1920, one year after his return to India from England. Two years before his death, he became the first Indian elected a fellow of the Royal Society."

– "What did he do in mathematics?"

– "I am not the most qualified person to talk about Ramanujan's work. It has been characterized as profoundly original, as coming from nowhere. His notebooks, some of them recovered much later from his mother, are still being examined for clues. He published five papers before leaving for England and the majority of his papers after arriving in England. Some of his numerous theorems, almost never fully proved, are surprisingly difficult, new and correct, some are already known from other sources, and some are simply false or misleading. His formulas involving the sum of infinite series, surprising definite integrals, and continued fractions unseen before are very complicated but some reveal an amazing kind of inductive regularity. A continued fraction, for instance, is a fraction whose denominator is equal to a number plus a fraction whose denominator is equal to a number plus a fraction whose denominator is equal to a number plus a fraction whose denominator . . . , etc., etc., indefinitely. He gave beautiful continued fraction expansions of analytic functions. Ramanujan was a master of such strange mathematical objects and his results are given very often without details, apparently being obtained by using a heuristic procedure.

Ramanujan was very fond of elementary identities involving radicals and of finding the roots of cubic and quartic polynomials. His way of transforming infinite series and getting, by induction, general algebraic formulas from numerical examples was unique, especially in the modern times when the mathematicians prefer rather to deal with the formal reasoning than to generalize a computational approach, normally passed on to computers for a brute evaluation with some prescribed degrees of approximation.

All the mathematicians I know, including myself, are not good at all at doing arithmetic computations mentally. Ramanujan was fascinated by numbers and their properties. In one of his recollections about Ramanujan, Hardy wrote that one day he paid a visit to him in the hospital and mentioned that the taxicab which brought him there had the rather dull number 1729. 'Not at all,' Ramanujan, who was seriously ill, replied, 'it is the smallest number equal to the sum of two cubes in two different ways.' Indeed, 1729 is the sum of the cube of 10 and the cube of 9 but also the sum of the cube of 12 and the cube of 1.

It is not surprising that he was interested in the distribution of prime numbers, those positive numbers that may be divided exactly only by 1 and themselves, like 2, 3, 5, 7, 11, 13, etc. As I mentioned twice before, the number of primes less than a number x is approximately the ratio between x and the natural logarithm of x for large values of x. There are some equivalent forms of this result which is called the 'prime number theorem', empirically discovered by great mathematicians like Adrien-Marie Legendre, Carl Friedrich Gauss, and Gustav Peter Lejeune Dirichlet. Ramanujan found some ingenious forms of the 'prime number theorem' by himself, due to his powerful intuition and insight. This was a remarkable achievement. However, he didn't rigorously prove the theorem and number theory is full of conjectures that are true for a tremendously large number of integers but, yet, not for any integer. The 'prime number theorem', which had been conjectured by different great mathematicians for a long time, was rigorously proved independently by two French mathematicians, Jacques Hadamard and Charles Jean Gustave Nicolas de La Vallée-Poussin, who I believe has the longest name in the history of mathematics, at the end of the 19th century, using functions of a complex variable, as mentioned before.

A large part of the work done by Ramanujan in India consisted in independently rediscovering some results already known in Europe. The large majority of his published work was done in England, some in collaboration with Hardy, where he got somewhat used to what a rigorous proof meant, but he remained as original and unpredictable as before, not particularly willing to make use of some well-known results from the mathematical literature, now accessible to him."

–"How could two people with such different backgrounds collaborate and publish together?"

–"It is very difficult, in general, to know how any collaboration works. Nobody really knows how the Russian writers Ilf and Petrov, for instance, created the brilliant books signed by both. But, as Hardy himself mentioned that Ramanujan was showing him half a dozen new theorems almost every day, we can only speculate that Ramanujan brought in his intuition and imagination whereas Hardy was in charge with the critical reading, the details of proofs, the existing literature on the subject, and, perhaps, the actual writing.

Whatever their working habits were, the outcome was excellent. As far as I know, they published together a classic paper on how many prime factors may be expected to occur in a random, large positive integer, and remarkable results on the number of integers which are sums of two squares, on the representation of an integer n as the sum of a given number of k squared integers, and on the number of points with integral coordinates from the interior of an arbitrary circle.

To give an example about how the collaboration worked, let me mention that a partition of the integer n is a decomposition of n into any number of positive integer parts. Thus, for instance, the number 4 may be decomposed into 5 partitions, namely: 4 alone; 3 and 1; 2 and 2; 2 and 1 and 1; 1 and 1 and 1 and 1. We can say that there are 5 partitions involving 4 given elements, or 5 distinct decompositions in disjoint subsets of a set of 4 given elements. Ramanujan was the only mathematician who discovered new properties, mainly by observation, of the number of partitions of some types of numbers. Later, together with Hardy, they obtained new results involving bounds for the number of partitions corresponding to arbitrary or large positive integers.

Ramanujan also studied the very complicated hypergeometric infinite series and introduced a mysterious function, called Ramanujan's function in literature, which has remarkable properties but is still very imperfectly understood."

– "What would have happened if Ramanujan had had benefited from a solid mathematical education in his youth?"

– "When he came to England, he continued to focus on his own original way of doing research and also tried to improve his general mathematical knowledge, but had very little time to pursue a thorough mathematical education, as required by the English academic standards. For instance, it seems that he never became familiar with the theory of functions depending on a complex variable, which perhaps would have been a powerful tool in his research. But, as Hardy said in his recollections, if Ramanujan had had a standard mathematical education in his early years, perhaps he would have been less of a Ramanujan and more of a European mathematician and the loss would have been greater than the gain.

This reminds me of a discussion I had, a couple of years ago, with one of my friends, Donald. We discussed about many calculations performed by Gauss in the last period of his life when, using only a table of logarithms, he succeeded in discovering a new comet, and I asked, rhetorically, 'What would have Gauss achieved if he had had a modern electronic computer in his office?' To which Donald answered: 'Nothing, because he would have played games on the computer!' "

BOLYAI

After a while, referring to Cabane de l'A Neuve, which had proved to be a good shelter for us during the long and violent thunderstorm, John noticed that he had never seen a lodge or a hut in Switzerland built on such a strange site, where the final access to it is so difficult, using mobile chains through a narrow and long, vertical chimney.

−"This reminds me of a similarly strange castle, built on a huge rock, I visited in Transylvania a couple of years ago," he said.

−"When I hear the word Transylvania, I instantly think about Dracula and mysterious castles. Was any important mathematician born there?"

−"Marius, my Romanian friend was born in Transylvania. By the way, he heard about Dracula only during his trip to England, when he read Bram Stocker's book about the famous vampire. Historically, in the 15th century, there was a Romanian 'voievod', called Vlad the Impaler, whose real name was Vlad Dracul, where 'dracul' is the Romanian word for 'the devil', how Marius explained to me, who was a fierce and courageous fighter against the armies of the Ottoman Empire. He was also very cruel and used to literally impale thieves and beggars, letting them die in horrible pain. But nobody ever said that he was a vampire. It is possible that he was an inspiration for Stocker's character. I don't know.

Anyway, Transylvania is a large area, with not so high but beautiful mountains, dense forests, many rivers, and fertile land, where have lived mainly Romanians but also Hungarians and Germans. But, going back to mathematics, there was an important mathematician born there. His name is János Bolyai, a Hungarian, and he certainly could be put in the same group of 'romantic' mathematicians along with Abel,

Galois, Riemann, and Ramanujan. He lived longer than them, it's true, but also had a tragic life."

−"Having a longer tragic life is even worse!"

−"János Bolyai is one of the discoverers of a non-Euclidean geometry. There is a vast literature about this topic and things are relatively clear today, but it wasn't so at the beginning of the 19th century. For 2000 years, the Greek geometry was considered a monument of rigour and clarity. Their great discovery was the concept of rigorously proving. As we discussed during our first hiking day, Euclid's geometry started from some accepted simple truths, called postulates or axioms, and using the classic logic for manipulating sentences involving the logical operators 'or', for disjunction, 'and', for conjunction, and 'non', for negation, a sequence of theorems and corollaries are obtained step by step. The postulates are supposed to be noncontradictory, independent, and to form a complete system, allowing us to obtain all the known results of the geometry from them, using the classic logic as the deductive instrument.

Among these postulates of the Euclidean geometry, the fifth one, says that there is a line, and only one, passing through an arbitrary point, without intersecting a given line which doesn't contain the given point. Many geometers tried, unsuccessfully, to prove that this postulate about parallel lines is not independent and may be deduced from the other postulates of the Euclidean geometry.

By about 1820, János Bolyai had become convinced that a proof of Euclid's postulate about parallel lines, called the 'parallel postulate', was impossible and began instead to construct a new geometry which didn't depend upon the fifth Euclid's axiom. In this way, he created an absolute geometry of a space in which several different lines pass through an exterior point without intersecting a given line. He developed a formula relating the angle of parallelism of two lines with a term characterizing the given line. In this new geometry, the Euclidean space was simply a limiting case of the new space and Bolyai introduced his formula to express what later became known as the space constant. He was delighted by his discovery and used to say that he created a new and different world out of nothing. Replacing Euclid's fifth postulate with one of its possible negations, 'several parallels instead of only one', he obtained a new geometry rather than a contradiction of the Euclidean geometry.

In this new geometry, some consequences are very different from what we are used to. Thus, from the postulates of the Euclidean geometry, a consequence is that the sum of the angles of any triangle is equal to two right angles. In the so-called 'absolute' geometry created by Bolyai, the sum of the angles of any triangle is less than two right angles."

−"In high-school we have studied the Euclidean geometry and it seems to me that it is quite natural to assume that only one parallel may be drawn to a given line through an exterior point. After drawing the parallel, if I try to draw a second line passing through the exterior point it comes up inclined and not parallel to the given line."

−"You are right because you are doing your geometry on a flat piece of paper, which is an Euclidean space with which we are so well accustomed. Our daily experience deals mainly with the Euclidean space. The absolute geometry, however, is as logically legitimate as the Euclidean geometry.

It is possible, also, to give non-Euclidean models even inside the Euclidean geometry. Thus, let us take the plane, which is a two-dimensional Euclidean space, and the two rectangular axes of coordinates in it. We construct a new space, as the French mathematician Henri Poincaré did, consisting of the half-plane above the horizontal axis, where by line we understand either any semicircle centered on the horizontal axis or any half-line parallel to the positive vertical semiaxis. Two such 'lines' are parallel if they don't intersect. If two semicircles intersect at a point, the angle between these two 'lines' is the usual angle between the tangents at the two semicircles at the intersection point. A circle in the new plane is a usual circle contained in the upper half-plane. It follows immediately that, in Poincaré's plane, there are infinitely many non-Euclidean lines parallel to a non-Euclidean line, passing through a point not on the given line. Also, for any non-Euclidean triangle the sum of the angles of the triangle is less than two right angles. There are other strange things occurring in such a non-Euclidean space too. Thus, there are no rectangles because, if we take two arbitrary non-Euclidean parallel lines then, there is only one non-Euclidean line which is at the same time perpendicular to both of them."

–"What was tragic in Bolyai's life?"

–"Many things. First, he never had any academic position, of any kind, and, second, no financial resources either, which make his mathematical achievements even more impressive. But let me start with the beginning.

János Bolyai was born in the town Cluj, in the middle of Transylvania, in 1802. He was taught mathematics by his father, Farkas Bolyai, a college mathematics teacher in Târgu Mureş. It is interesting to mention that Farkas Bolyai, who worked hard himself on proving Euclid's parallel postulate, later tried to discourage his son from dealing with this postulate, prophetically telling him that such a fruitless, obsessive, and addictive work could only deprive him of all leisure, health, rest, and the whole happiness in life.

When János was 16 years old, he entered the Military Academy in Vienna. After graduating, he joined the army, carrying out special military engineering studies as a cadet. During the next ten years, he was gradually promoted lieutenant, main-lieutenant, and finally captain. In all these years he worked in Timişoara, Arad, Oradea, Szeged, and Olmütz. A brilliant young man, he worked on his mathematics, played violin, had a special talent for speaking many foreign languages, and was known as an excellent swordsman and dancer. Unfortunately, he was plagued with a frequent fever and, in 1833, to his request, he was pensioned.

In 1823, he presented his new absolute geometry in the paper *The absolute true science of space*. His father sent it to his friend and former colleague Carl Friedrich Gauss, in Göttingen, considered by many, as you know by now, to be the greatest mathematician of all times. Gauss replied that praising János would amount to praising himself because he himself had been thinking about non-Euclidean geometries all his life. In the end, János Bolyai's paper was printed in Latin, as an appendix of his father's book *Tentamen juventuten* in 1832. The answer from Gauss, the little attention received by the publication of his appendix, and the fact that he subsequently discovered that Russian Nikolai Ivanovich Lobachevsky, professor of mathematics at the University in Kazan, had published an independent account of a very similar geometry, called 'hyperbolic' geometry, in 1829, deeply depressed János Bolyai who, subsequently, tried more and more to live estranged from the world and from scientific life.

After his retirement from the army, he returned to his father to Târgu Mureş and, for ten years, moved to the family domain, to Dolmánd. He lived together with Rozália Orbán and had two daughters. He spent his time on doing research in mathematics; in addition to his work in non-Euclidean geometry, he worked on the geometric interpretation of the complex numbers, as ordered pairs of real numbers. He left thousands pages of manuscript of mathematical work. In 1857 he became ill, but I don't know what kind of illness he suffered from. Three years later, he died in Târgu Mureş and was buried in his army uniform. In 1911, his ashes were exhumed and laid into his father's tomb, and the two men, who quarreled so many times during their lives, are together in a statue erected in the town Târgu Mureş, in 1957, with Farkas sitting with a book on his lap and János standing up and melancholically looking ahead.

One University and at least one Mathematical Society were named after him, and there are some postage stamps in Hungary and Romania with his image on them. There is a Crater Bolyai on the moon but, with so many craters there, numerous mathematicians have craters named after them."

John stopped. I looked at my watch. Unbelievably, it was already half past one. For a long while we said nothing. I wasn't as hungry as I was when I woke up in the morning but I was all in favour of having lunch. There was more light outside and the clouds seemed to be less dense. There was no rain falling and I couldn't hear any thunderbolts either. Promising signs of a change for the better!

We had a light lunch consisting of a hot onion soup, pasta with tomato sauce on top, and the excellent fruit pie like yesterday evening. We drank mineral water. 'No alcohol during the daytime when we are up hiking in the mountains,' how John put it. We were just starting eating our fruit pie when the first rays of sun entered the dining room. People in there were simply ecstatic. When lunch was over, we went outside. The scenery was simply amazing. I could say, with my hand on my heart, that I have never ever seen something more beautiful. The dark clouds were all below us. It was like literarily stepping on clouds. Above us, a cloudless, shining, blue sky, more beautiful than ever. Around, at an altitude above 3500 meters, due to the lower temperature, the top of the high mountains were covered by fresh, white, clean, new snow. John was impressed too and only said:

–"There is always a blue sky above the dark clouds!"

We bought biscuits, bananas, chocolate, and mineral water, paid for the night, and said 'Good bye, thank you,' to Mireille, who was quite happy about the sales during the last two days but had a lot of work to do about the mess left behind by the customers, still with no electricity in the hut, and we left. The dog, who apparently developed a liking of John, insisted to accompany us in spite of our efforts to discourage him from doing so. He came with us down to the patch of snow heading to the moraine. Fortunately, Mireille, shouted something from the door of the hut, up there, and the dog decided to return, climbing with a tremendous speed and ease, obviously without using the mobile chains, through the crevice of the promontory.

Fortunately, the descent was uneventful. Still some running water along the path, a little mud here and there, but nothing really bad. We were worried, however, about crossing Reuse de l'Amône. To our relief, the waters of the torrent had receded to almost the normal level. The former bridge was still missing but somebody had come up here and put two long wooden thick poles across the torrent, approximately where the bridge had been. We carefully crossed the torrent, mounted and descended the high rock with chains, on the other side of the torrent, and we continued the descent witnessing the havoc and devastation made by the storm. Mud, rocks rolled over the place, logs brought down, branches of trees fallen down. Unbelievable! Down there, blocked by some big rocks on the border of the torrent, we saw the former bridge made a useless piece of iron. All this made our trip back to be longer than expected.

It was about six o'clock when we arrived at the camping site. The clouds were finally nowhere to be seen. The long storm was over. John insisted to come to Edelweiss for dinner but this time I refused firmly explaining that I just wanted to take a shower and have a good sleep. I didn't mention that I had a lot to write in my notebook in order to catch up with the events of the two days and the stories about romantic mathematicians still fresh in my mind. John succeeded, however, in convincing me to take with me the food we both bought at the hut, before our departure, remained untouched thus far.

I found the camping in a frenzy state. Tourists were busy cleaning up the mess. In some places the chaos was just depressing. I found my tent seriously damaged. Two logs hit it. One basic string was torn and another one in a shabby state. There was a lot of mud around. Fortunately, water didn't enter inside, which came as a big relief. My notebook was dry and safe. Nothing else was really important. I started cleaning and fixing. To my surprise, a young girl, who seemed to be about 16 years old, came to me offering to help me. She introduced herself as being Dutch and named Francine.

−"I was worried about you," she said, and seemed sincere when she said that. "When I noticed yesterday evening that you didn't come back to your tent, I was afraid that something wrong happened with you. We had a terrible night down here. The two torrents went crazy. Nobody could sleep. Not a bit. Little children were crying. People were afraid to stay inside the tents because of the flooding and outside it was heavily raining. At least three cars were seriously damaged. I don't know how these families will return home now. We had a lot of flooding and the lightning was simply awful. Some bulldozers came here, making some dams and barrages around the camping. They worked all night. Your tent doesn't look bad. You were very clever to put your tent on a hillock."

−"No, I wasn't clever. I was just lucky."

−"Where have you been these two days?"

−"I went with my older friend up to a beautiful hut called Cabane de l'A Neuve. We were stranded there for the night. It was tough up there but I realize that in fact it was much worse down here."

−"I am glad that you are all right. I am here with a group of Dutch people of all ages. We want to spend one more week here. Would you like to come with us tomorrow? We intend to go to Petit Col Ferret. I would like you to come."

−"Thank you for inviting me. It is very kind of you but I cannot. In fact, I was there on Wednesday and, for tomorrow and the day after tomorrow, I promised to go hiking with my friend. He is a mathematician I met here and has been an excellent companion for me. But on Monday, I will be free and glad to join you, if you wish."

−"See you then. It is a promise!"

She disappeared as fast as when she showed up. Is it really possible that a beautiful creature on this planet could be worried about my fate? Maybe John is right and there is, after all, some right balance in this universe.

I cleaned up my own mess, ate, took a hot shower, and returned to my tent to fill in pages and pages with everything kept in my mind and heart during the last two eventful days. When I finished writing and switched off the light, I completely forgot, however, about Abel, Galois, Riemann, Ramanujan, or Bolyai, and I thought about Francine instead. Life is great!

FIFTH DAY

LACS DE FENÊTRE

When I met John on Saturday morning, he came out of Edelweiss Hotel with *Le Matin* and *Tribune de Genève*, two newspapers popular in the French speaking part of Switzerland.

–"The thunderstorm is on the first pages," said John. "It touched a much larger area than Val Ferret. It wasn't just a local violent thunderstorm, which explains why it lasted so long."

Indeed, there were detailed comments and pictures about serious damages caused by the unusually violent thunderstorm that came a long way from the Pyrenees mountains. Nine people died and many were apparently lost in the mountains. Rescue teams were looking for them.

–"What are we going to do today?"

–"The weather seems to be excellent. Therefore, I think that we can go on the east side of Val Ferret, up to a plateau where there are three alpine lakes, two of them absolutely gorgeous, from where, if the weather remains as clear as it is now, we could admire the panorama of all the mountains from the west side of the valley."

Indeed, the weather couldn't have been better. After the thunderstorm that beat us for almost two days, there were no clouds on the sky, whose blue colour was made even more vivid by the fresh, dry, and cold air.

–"Let's go. I haven't seen a lake around here in the previous days. It would be a welcome change."

The signpost from our daily departure point, close to the hotel, showed the direction towards: Ferret 45 min, Alpage des Ars 1h 20 min, and Lacs de Fenêtre 3h 15 min.

Stage 1. The trail from La Fouly (1600 meters) to Les Ars (1795 meters), passing through the hamlet Ferret (1705 meters) along La Drance de Ferret flowing in the opposite direction towards north-north-west on our right-hand side, was a repeat of the first stage of Tuesday's hiking to Grand Col Ferret. Doing it again, we could really see how powerful the last thunderstorm had been and how much damage the flows of water generated by it could do. First, the debit of the torrent Drance de Ferret was still much higher than on last Tuesday, but more subdued than during the storm, as shown by the logs, pebbles, and rocks brought by its waters and thrown on its margins, indicating the high levels reached during the two days of incessant rain. Anyway, the paved road, still very wet due to several newly made brooks still collecting water from the slopes, was still all right, but not for long.

About 15 minutes after leaving Ferret, continuing our way to south-south-east along and against La Drance de Ferret, the main paved road was interrupted in several places by incredibly large mud slides. We lost time trying to find the best ways of crossing these large spots of still fresh mixture of earth, water, grass, branches, logs, and rocks. A former wooden bridge had been completely damaged and now several cars and two or three buses were blocked there, unable to advance. Several tractors and bulldozers were busy working on cleaning the road and building a new bridge. A helicopter was taking off towards the mountains, either looking for missing hikers or trying to reach some sheep folds, pens, cow-sheds, and huts that needed help. We saw another helicopter flying high, carrying a big cow, probably hurt, hanging from an attached cable. A state of agitation was visible, in contrast with the quiet first three hiking days.

–"Around the globe, Switzerland is generally regarded as being a beautiful, post-card country with a very high standard of living," said John. "It is less known, however, that Swiss people have to work hard not only in factories, on fields, in institutions, or offices, as anywhere else, but also for maintaining the roads, mountain cables and cabins, chair lifts, and the legendary perfect railway network in perfect shape, coping with the effects of thunderstorms, snowstorms, and the long winters that are much more violent and excessive in the high mountains. Think also how more difficult it is to get fodder, grapes, or raise animals on steep slopes than on flat plains."

We had started our trip at 9:00, but lingering, looking for the damage done by the thunderstorm, and finding ways for crossing the ford left without bridge and the patches of mud covering portions of the road, we arrived at Les Ars only at 10:30. The paved road ended there and, a little to the east, at Dessous, there was a small shepherd house and an empty sheep fold or cow-shed. Many cows and sheep could be seen relatively far away, spread here and there on the slopes of the left-hand side mountain and watched by some big guardian dogs.

Stage 2. We didn't stop at Les Ars and continued our walk along a narrower and unpaved road mounting slowly, in a very large serpentine, on the eastern side of Val Ferret, heading south-south-east. We left behind, to our right, the path crossing La Drance de Ferret, followed by us on Tuesday, on the way to Grand Col Ferret. Nothing was spectacular there and the strong odour of liquefied manure spread around for fertilizing the pasture made us speed up our ascent. Fortunately, after a while, the winding road started to cross some very fast brooks coming from the top of the mountain. It was a relief to wash my face with the cold refreshing water because the sun was shining and there were absolutely no trees around; only a couple of bushes at the beginning and nothing afterwards. Our road mounting gradually to the south-east, Val Ferret remained down to the right, the torrent La Drance de Ferret almost disappearing from sight in a narrow, rocky, and very green deep gorge. Not much later, the main Val Ferret suddenly turned west-south towards the impressive massif Grandes Jorasses, leaving only a short ramification of it to continue towards south-east, for a short while, up to its starting point located in a large, almost circular hollow, surrounded by high peaks apparently impossible to be crossed.

After about 50 minutes, at about 11:30, we arrived at the shepherd hut Plan de la Choux (2041 meters). Two dogs at the hut proved to pay no attention to tourists and I found nothing wrong with that. A small wooden plate mentioned that it was possible to buy milk and cheese there but nobody was around the hut at that time. A signpost informed us that we had to turn east for going to Lacs de Fenêtre (1h 10 min) and Fenêtre de Ferret (1 h 50 min).

Stage 3. The unpaved road was over and we had to follow a very narrow and steep path, marked with the same red strip bordered by white margins, climbing in a short, steep, and tiring serpentine followed by a longer and very exposed mountain ledge. Several times we had to overcome the effects of the previous storm that had damaged portions of the path, mainly at the crossings of some rocky, narrow, and very inclined valleys, having a lot of water running down as we went up towards the top of the mountain we were climbing. But everything around became more and more interesting, with more rocks and narrow streams in our way, along the winding path, telling us that we were again in the middle of a genuine alpine zone. Patches of snow showed up more and more often.

–"Mike, look behind you, to the west," John stopped me. "The top of Mont Blanc may be seen now from here."

Indeed, the white massif was there, justifying its name, like a huge snowy throne of gods, to the left of the gray rocky Grandes Jorasses which, being closer to us, seemed taller than Mont Blanc, the tallest mountain of Europe. I couldn't stop thinking that, a couple of days ago, I looked at the other side of Mont Blanc from Geneva, but very far from it. Now, it was much more visible, projected on the blue and cloudless sky and highlighted by the shining sun.

The path turned suddenly south through a rocky gorge, about 50 meters long, covered by snow. After crossing it, we arrived on a very large plateau, guarded to the east by a range of peaks, like the solid walls of a citadel, and just in front of us was the first Lac de Fenêtre, round, big, and just beautiful, at an altitude of 2456 meters. A signpost, close to the lake, pointed towards south, mentioning the possibility to go from there to the Fenêtre de Ferret in 40 min and, later, to the

Col du Grand-St.-Bernard in 1 h 40 min. Seeing the last name, John became nostalgic, remembering one of his past travels in the region, together with his wife.

–"A couple of years ago, we went there from Bourg-St.-Pierre, a village known from the 8th century, when a hospice run by monks was founded there. Another older hospice, founded by Saint Bernard in 1125, is up at the Grand-St.-Bernard pass, used very long ago by Romans to cross the Alps. Anyway, going to Col du Grand-St.-Bernard on the first day after arriving in Bourg-St.-Pierre for a seven-day stay wasn't a very clever decision because we had to walk about 20 kilometers on that day, and not on a flat level. But we wanted to follow the old route used by Napoleon's army from Bourg-St.Pierre to Col du Grand-St.-Bernard, when they crossed the Alps, with horses and heavy canons, to fight and conquer Northern Italy. The trip was tiring but interesting indeed. Just up, on the Col, there is the frontier between Switzerland and Italy, on the border of an alpine lake with a little island in the middle, having a big, simple cross on it. Beautiful St.Bernard dogs, a breed created by monks there in order to save people buried under snow after an avalanche, could be seen around. There is there even the statue of a famous dog, whose name I don't remember, who saved 27 lives but lost his own life during an avalanche. Anyway, on our way back, we got lost. We simply followed a shepherd path going nowhere. Then I learned that there could be paths in the mountains that just disappear. Before, I had always believed that every path had to go somewhere. We almost panicked and it was quite difficult to find the right path for going back. That was one of the very rare occasions when we returned to our hotel long after the sunset, finding the owners of the hotel, an old nice couple, very worried about us.

And because I mentioned the name of Napoleon Bonaparte, not very long ago, in a guide for skiers and mountain walkers about where to go in the large Chamonix-Zermatt area, including La Fouly and its surroundings, written by Peter Cliff (I have a very bad memory for proper names, but this one was a perfect name for somebody writing about mountains), I read that on his way to Italy, Napoleon and his brave soldiers stopped in the village Bourg-St.-Pierre and, obviously, ate a lot. Napoleon signed a bill but no payment was made. Many

many years later, anyway in our times, the community council of the village sent the bill to the French authorities, together with the interest rate accumulated after all those years. It is said that the French Ambassador came to the village, delivered a speech and presented a bronze plaque of Napoleon and this was all in order to settle the matter. But, again and again, who knows whether this story is really true!"

It was about 12 h 55 min and I was longing for a well-deserved lunch but John made a different suggestion:

–"It would be better to postpone having lunch until we arrive at the third lake. It is also beautiful and offers a better view of the entire range of mountains on the western side, especially today when we are having such a perfect visibility. We can take there a longer break."

Stage 4. After rearranging the knapsacks and our equipment, we continued our walk. We were not alone there. From place to place, along the margins of the lake, there were several groups of people, some of them with children, sitting, eating, talking, resting, or playing. There was enough room for all of us.

Indeed, from the first Lac de Fenêtre we couldn't see much because there was a big hill, like a huge camel's hunch, between the lake and the far western range of mountains. On the top of the hump there was a simple but big, wooden cross we had seen through John's binoculars on Tuesday afternoon on our way back from Grand Col Ferret, on the other side of Val Ferret.

We descended a little on the western side of the first Lac de Fenêtre, until the place where a small part of its waters disappeared, through a 'bottleneck', plunging down amidst big rocks.

–"Where is the lake's water coming from?" I asked.

–"I don't know. The lake is losing water every minute here at its western side and, on the other hand, the long and sharp top ridge of the eastern mountain La Chaux, from behind the lake, is neither taller than 2800 meters nor designed by nature to keep glaciers or snow on it and therefore cannot replenish the lake to compensate for the continual loss of water. And yet, the big lake is in a steady-state condition, with no sign of drying up. Fortunately! The other two lakes apparently have no output but no visible input either, keeping the level of their water relatively constant. I don't know what really happens below the lakes or whether there is a hidden source, or some kind of tunnel made by nature, allowing underground water to come from elsewhere. I also doubt that the amount of rain and snow falling are enough to maintain the surprisingly constant total amount of water in these three lakes."

After crossing the bottleneck of the lake on a short dam made of rocks and concrete, we followed the path going along, but a little above, the western side of the lake. From above, the dark blue waters of the lake revealed an impressive depth. After a short wile, we saw the second lake, much smaller and quite uninteresting. Leaving the marked path and descending a little to the west on a natural carpet of green grass and small yellow, red, and blue little flowers, we arrived at the third lake, at an altitude of 2495 meters, smaller than the first one but much larger than the second one. Almost round, it offered an incredible open view, a genuine panorama, like a window indeed, of the western mountains projected on the blue sky in the background, fully justifying its French name 'Lac de Fenêtre'. John remarked:

–"In fact, I don't understand why it wasn't called 'Lac Miroir' because its real charm consists in having the tops of some of those western mountains reflected in its waters, like in a wide, natural mirror, on a sunny day."

Summing up, in the wide and almost flat bottom of the hollow where we were now, at the end of our ascent, the landscape was rather bleak but the three lakes, surprisingly large and deep for such an altitude, just brought life into it. On a clear day, as the one we were having, its main attraction was the impressive view of the Mont Blanc massive in all its splendour, together with the panorama offered by the Pointe Walker, looking like a needle, the Grandes Jorasses, the Mont Dolent, and Tour Noir. We had our lunch sitting on the grass, just in front of the third Lac de Fenêtre, looking towards west, beyond the lake and on the other side of Val Ferret, to all those mountains that now agreed to fully reveal their beauty to the few crazy people who made the effort of coming up here, at about 2500 meters altitude, to contemplate the alpine scenery from above.

A little later, taking advantage of the fine weather, John took several pictures, from left to right, for covering the entire western range, from Mont Blanc to Tour Noir, with the intention to eventually paste them together in one long panoramic picture. For my part, I took several pictures of the lake, with the tops of Mont Blanc and Grandes Jorasses finely reflected in its water. One of them, probably taken in a moment of perfect calm, with no ripples on the lake's water, proved to be unexpectedly clear, showing a perfect symmetry between the real mountains and their reflections. I have never had the chance to take a more beautiful picture than that one. Never ever. A magnified copy of it still hangs on the wall of my bedroom.

In the previous days, we always had lunch after arriving at the end of our respective ascent. Now, I realized how wise had been such a strategy. Linearly, the distance from the third Lac de Fenêtre to Col Fenêtre de Ferret wasn't a big deal, but it proved to be very difficult to climb 200 more meters in altitude after eating, even if our lunch had been very light. The path was steadily mounting and the last portion was completely covered by a thick layer of slippery snow. Fenêtre de Ferret proved to be just another col, on the ridge which forms the winding boundary between Italy and Switzerland. Much narrower than the other two Cols reached on Tuesday and Wednesday, respectively, we couldn't spend too much time there because a very strong wind was blowing up from the Italian side of the mountain. That was the end point of our ascent for the day.

We returned to the third lake for a last look and we slowly descended following the same path, unpaved road, and main road, in reverse sense, down to La Fouly. Descending, I was again surprised by how much we had climbed during the first half of the day. Before arriving in the village, John was very categorical:

−"This is our last evening together because tomorrow, after our daily hiking, I have to catch the last bus, leaving from here at 18:44, and go to Geneva. Therefore, this is my last invitation to have dinner at Edelweiss Hotel. I do hope that you are not going to refuse my last invitation."

As this was going to be indeed John's last evening in La Fouly and I had almost no food stored in my tent, I graciously accepted. I went to the camping site, took a shower, changed my clothes, and I did some menial work in and around my tent, including cleaning, washing some clothes, and nursing two fingers, the right knee that had some scratches with a little stained blood on them, and a blister on the sole of my left foot. At seven o'clock sharp, I joined John at his table, near the big window facing Mont Dolent and Tour Noir, in the main dining room of Edelweiss Hotel.

After such a warm day, even hot at times, spent under a lot of sun, we chose to drink cold beer, 'de la région', and the menu, excellent again, consisted of two cheese caneloni, light soup (potage), fried trout with potato and green salad from different kinds of lettuce, ending with a cup of ice-cream mixed with banana slices and whip cream on top. It was a quiet and stable night, with fewer people in the restaurant, consequence of the powerful storm from the previous two days that perhaps had deterred new tourists from coming and spending the weekend up in the mountains. After dinner, we took a stroll along the main road of the village and, around half past nine, we parted our ways, John to his hotel, for his last night in La Fouly, and I to my tent, in the quiet camping that seemed to have forgotten the agitation from the last two stormy nights.

At the end of such a long and calm day, it was quite difficult for me to resume what John told and explained to me when we took a lunch break at the third Lac de Fenêtre, during our slow descent, in the restaurant, and after dinner, when we took a long stroll in the night. The best strategy seems to be by grouping the topics discussed in distinct sections.

BOURBAKI

After finding so many things about mathematicians who lived long ago, I asked John about more recent big names in mathematics. Without any hesitations he chose four names.

–"In modern times there were some great mathematicians who were also strange individuals, and lived relatively long lives. I am going to talk about three of them. Every great man has his own foibles, but it is a sound and fair strategy to speak about their qualities and major achievements, not about more or less plausible anecdotes about them. But before, let me tell you something about a great mathematician of the 20th century who didn't exist. His name is Nicolas Bourbaki."

–"So, he has a name but didn't exist! How could that be?"

–"You will find out soon but let me start with another name first. André Weil, born in France, was one of those mathematicians who traveled intensely (India, Russia, Brazil, the United States, England, Italy, Sweden, Norway, Germany, Switzerland). For failing to show up for the military service during the World War II, he spent time in jail where, by the way, he did good mathematics in confinement, away from the turmoil of the everyday life. Even if he reached an old age and was one of the founders of the famous 'Bourbaki group', he is not as well-known to the general public as his younger sister Simone Weil is, in spite of the fact that she died quite young. Coming from a well-to-do Parisian family, Simone was a school-mistress who later preferred to have a working-class life, tried to help the Republicans in the civil war in Spain, kept in touch with German and Russian dissidents who had fled their countries, wrote beautiful essays, and later, during the World War II, she worked for the General Charles de Gaulle in London, unsuccessfully asked to be parachuted in the occupied part of France, nursed wounded soldiers, and finally died in a sanatorium when she was only 34 years old.

To my knowledge, André Weil and Jean Dieudonné, are the only members of the original 'Bourbaki group' who, towards the end of their mathematical careers, made public disclosures about the 'birth' and 'life' of Nicolas Bourbaki. Jean Dieudonné, by the way, has written many specialized books under his own name. One of them, with a beautiful title, *Mathematics – the Music of Reason*, was meant for a large audience but, in my opinion, can be understood only by professional mathematicians."

−"Who are the members of this Bourbaki group and why is this group famous?"

−"Perhaps you have heard some speculations about the works of Homer's, in ancient times, and Shakespeare's, in the 16th century, as having been written by a collective group of people or by somebody else. No strong evidence has been provided in support of these speculations. The collective pen-name Nicolas Bourbaki, however, is a real example, and the only one in modern times, as far as I know, of a fictitious author of a series of extremely important mathematics books, written in fact by a group of eminent French mathematicians who preferred to remain anonymous, at least for a very long period of time. This was something very unusual because mathematicians, as the majority of poets, writers, or scholars, are very sensitive to see their names on papers or books, in a pursuit for public appreciation and fame. Towards the end of 1934, this group of young mathematicians, realizing that with so many and extremely specialized mathematical results, published in too many journals and books, the real danger was to fail to see the forest because of the trees, decided to sit down and start writing, collectively, a series of books in order to underline the general ideas and the basic structures of the modern mathematics. They decided to make Nicolas Bourbaki the author of these books. The Bourbaki group planned to finish the treatise in three years. Around 1970, however, they still worked on the 34th volume while many topics of modern mathematics were not even touched, like geometry, optimization, probability theory, mathematical statistics, or operations research, for instance. Bourbaki's objective was to provide mathematical work tools, and to bring maximum rigour in presenting the basic results in mathematics, not to list open problems."

−"Why did they choose this name which, by the way, doesn't sound to me to be French?"

−"When three members of the group entered the famous l'École Normale Supérieure in Paris, older students, respecting the bizarre initiation tradition of the School, played the following prank on the fresh students. The newcomers received an official notification that a professor with some Scandinavian name would be giving an important lecture.

On that day, an older student, with a false beard and heavy foreign accent, delivered an elaborate, pompous, and incomprehensible talk, culminating with a fabulous and amazing 'Bourbaki's theorem', the proper name chosen being that of a general associated with Napoleon III. This happened sometime in the early 1920s. About ten years later, remembering the prank, Bourbaki's name was selected as the author of the new books. The given name, Nicolas, was chosen by the wife of one member of the group. The funny thing is that much later, after some of Bourbaki's books had been published and already well-known, a distinguished Greek diplomat, Nicolaides Bourbaki, tried to get in touch with French mathematicians in Paris, puzzled by the fact that, to his knowledge, nobody in his family tree has ever been a mathematician and, obviously, was anxious to meet and find out details about such a famous relative.

In order to make things even more mysterious, let me mention that the first volumes signed by Nicolas Bourbaki appeared in the Collection of Publications of Nancago University. The problem is that there was no such a university either. For a fictitious author, the editor of the volumes, Enrique Freymann, created an equally fictitious university, Nancago, which in spite of its Japanese sounding, was simply a combination of the beginning of Nancy and the ending of Chicago, two cities where members of the Bourbaki group used to work alternatively."

−"Are the names of the members of this group of mathematicians known today?"

−"For almost fifty years, there were only speculations about such names. Now, after seventy years, it is known that the founding members of the Bourbaki team were Henri Cartan, Claude Chevalley, Jean Delsarte, Jean Dieudonné, and André Weil. They were active members of the Bourbaki group until they reached fifty, the age of retirement they had agreed upon. Gradually, other younger mathematicians were elected as members of the group and Nicolas Bourbaki has chances to survive for many years to come even if his productivity has become less book-oriented, focusing on very specialized seminar talks.

Details about Bourbaki's way of working and writing have become known more recently, after Jean Dieudonné published recollections about his membership to the team and André Weil wrote his autobiography entitled *The Apprenticeship of a Mathematician*, or something like that. A couple of years ago, talking to a physicist who was teaching in a French university, close to Paris, I was surprised to see that he knew absolutely nothing about Bourbaki. It is true that he knew nothing about François Truffaut's movies either, which is even less understandable. But, however, he was very good in his own field, which really matters in the end."

−"I find quite difficult to understand how a book may be written by several authors. The novels generally have only one author."

−"This is true. In literature normally the books have only one author but there are some exceptions. Besides the Russian novelists Ilia Arnoldovich Ilf and Evgeni Petrovich Petrov, that have already been mentioned in our discussions, there are the brothers Jacob and Wilhelm Grimm who delighted generations of children, including myself, with their fairy tales. Each of these two couples signed their books together but nobody could find out how they worked together and who did more of the proper writing. It is said that even when there are several authors, the book is good when only one of them writes it. In Bourbaki's case, it seems that Jean Dieudonné was the writer most of the time. His own treatise, *Foundations of Modern Mathematics*, and even the more elementary book *Mathematics − The Music of Reason*, I have just mentioned, resemble Bourbaki's style and notations. In fact, the members of the 'Bourbaki group' were free to publish their own research results under their own names, as anybody else. Only the work on Bourbaki's series of volumes was supposed to be collective and remain anonymous.

In his recollections on the work of Nicolas Bourbaki, Jean Dieudonné mentioned that, normally, a member of the group was designated to write a first draft of a chapter. It was later read aloud, the proofs closely examined and pitilessly criticized in meetings, resembling gatherings of madmen, held two or three times a year. Then, a new variant of the respective chapter was written down and the history repeated itself up to ten times. When, finally, everybody was sick of it and an unanimous vote was taken, the chapter was sent to press. On average, eight to twelve years were necessary for working on a chapter. Even so, sometimes they detected mistakes in an already printed chapter to be corrected in subsequent editions. Each member of the group had the right to veto any chapter and each chapter needed unanimity to get the final approval. They also decided that every member had to retire when he was 50 years old, not because a mathematician cannot be productive at that age but because it is less probable for such an individual to adapt to the new ideas."

GÖDEL

–"As little as I know," I said, "mathematics seems to be so precise, with no ambiguities. Our math teacher used to tell us that other sciences reach maturity only to the extent to which they employ some kind of mathematics to solve their problems. I am not sure that all physicists or chemists do agree with that."

–"This is true to a great extent, but mathematics has its own limitations and the man who rang the alarm bell was also quite a strange individual. His name is Kurt Gödel and was born towards the beginning of the 20th century, in 1906 if I remember well, in a German-speaking Lutheran family, in Brünn from Austria-Hungary, which is now the big city Brno in the Czech Republic. His father, a textile factory worker, wanted to see both his sons getting high education and made all necessary sacrifices for achieving this objective.

When he was 24 years old, Kurt got a doctorate in mathematics from the University of Vienna and, remarkably enough, in the same year, he gave a talk at a conference in Königsberg, published a year later, basically proving that in any axiomatic system there is a proposition whose truth or falsehood cannot be decided inside that system. This was the famous 'incompleteness theorem', which shocked and changed the old belief that everything was crystal clear in mathematics. This result ended David Hilbert's hope to put all mathematics on axiomatic basis, as a huge formal system without any kind of intuition to be used inside it. Gödel showed that in any axiomatic system there are propositions which cannot be proved inside that system, by using the axioms and the rules of the respective system. Bringing in other axioms and other rules, we obtain another axiomatic system that will contain its own unprovable statements. And so on."

−"How can somebody prove that something cannot be proved. This seems weird to me."

−"I don't know what Gödel had in mind, but traces of his method can be found going back to:

1. Contradictory concepts generating logical paradoxes, as Bertrand Russell's paradox about the set R of all sets that are not elements of themselves. There are sets that don't belong to themselves or are not elements of themselves. Thus, the set of apples is not an apple itself. But there are also sets that are elements of themselves like the set of nonapples. Anything which is not an apple, like a horse, book, song, or dream, is an element of this huge set. Obviously, such a set is not an apple and , therefore, belongs to itself. Is Russell's set R an element of itself or not? It turns out that R is an element of itself if and only if it is not an element of itself. It is a paradox somehow similar to the barber of the regiment, we have already talked about.

2. The 'diagonal procedure' used by Georg Cantor when he proved that there are more real numbers in the unit interval $[0, 1]$ than rational numbers. As we discussed on Tuesday, Cantor showed that if we assume that the real numbers from the unit interval form a countable set and, therefore, may be arranged in a sequence, then we can construct a real number from the unit interval which does not belong to this sequence which shows that, in fact, the set of real numbers from the unit interval is uncountable.

Kurt Gödel applied similar ideas at a grandiose level, referring to a general axiomatic system, like the entire arithmetics, for instance. In an ingenious way, he attached numbers to all mathematical and logical symbols and operators, and eventually to all equalities, axioms, theorems, and proofs which may be viewed as sequences of such mathematical and logical symbols inside the given axiomatic system. To give you a very simplified gist of the basic idea behind what he did, assume that I assign the numbers 1, 2, 3, and 4 to the numbers 1, 2, and the symbols $=$ and $+$, respectively. Then, the equality $2 = 1 + 1$, which may be viewed as a sequence of five symbols 2, $=$, 1, $+$, and 1, gets the

'Gödel number' obtained by taking the product of the first five primes, 2, 3, 5, 7, 11, raised at the powers given by the integers assigned to the symbols 1, 2, =, and +, respectively, namely: $2^2 \times 3^3 \times 5^1 \times 7^4 \times 11^1$ which is equal to 14 261 940. Forget about the big integer numbers we obtain this way. What really matters is that each sequence of mathematical and logical symbols and operators gets an integer number, like 14 261 940 just obtained. I said that his 'numbering' is very ingenious because, conversely, as the factorization of integers is unique, when the number 14261940 is given, we can uniquely decompose it in prime factors, $2^2 \times 3^3 \times 5^1 \times 7^4 \times 11^1$, and we can state, unambiguously, that it corresponds to the mathematical statement: $2 = 1 + 1$. Consequently, we can attach 'Gödel numbers' to axioms, theorems, and proofs. In fact, a proof is nothing more than a sequence of successive statements implied by previous statements. Using his numerical coding, Cantor's constructive diagonal procedure, and the general idea behind logical paradoxes of Russell's type, Kurt Gödel found something like 'This theorem cannot be proved in this system,' which was improvable, which means neither true nor false inside the respective system.

The result was so impressive that Gödel was invited to join the famous Institute for Advanced Study in Princeton, perhaps the first institute in the United States where its members had no teaching at all to do and could use all their time for doing research, in a peaceful ambience and without worrying about financial problems."

–"Wow, that was an incredible idea! To be paid for doing only what you want and when you want! I like that."

–"Yes, it was a great idea and many first class scientists spent a great time in Princeton. But, however, not all of them were happy there, at least not all the time. Thus, Richard Feynman, the famous physicist, wrote somewhere that he felt uncomfortable surrounded by geniuses in Princeton, where people expected him to come up with brilliant new ideas on a daily basis. As one of my professors said, 'Even exceptional scientists have the right to display and enjoy their own moments of stupidity!' It is said that even Einstein preferred to be paid in Princeton for teaching at the University and not for doing only research at the Institute."

–"I am sorry for interrupting. Let's go back to Gödel. Why was he a strange individual?"

–"Right. Periodically, he returned to Austria for lecturing. During this period he had some nervous breakdowns. Otherwise, he was a hypochondriac, obsessed about a potential poisoning and an imaginary heart disease, trying to avoid people and controversy.

In 1938, he married a former dancer Adele, he knew in Vienna. They had no children. Then, in 1939, when the World War II started and Kurt was on the point of becoming a conscript, he and Adele emigrated to the United States, using a long route via Russia and Japan, and settled in Princeton for good, getting a permanent appointment at the Institute for Advanced Study. It took him, however, about 13 years to become a full professor of mathematics there. His best friend in Princeton was Albert Einstein and he got even interested in some physics problems. Thus, he proved that the travel towards the past is allowed by the equations of the general relativity. I saw a picture of him, showing a slim, typically spectacled, insignificant math prof. He became more and more paranoid about selecting his food and reduced eating to a minimum.

He got many awards and honorary degrees, including the American National Medal of Science, but it is said that, in his final years, he had doubts about the importance of his own work. In 1976, Adele became handicapped by a cerebral accident. Gödel devoted himself to taking care of her but became depressed and almost stopped eating. In hospital, he refused treatment and food and three weeks later, at the beginning of 1978, he died. After his death, a huge amount of unanswered letters and not mailed answers have been found among his papers. Apparently, he was very religious during his entire life and it is well-known that he tried to prove mathematically the existence of God."

–"That was cool. I like the mathematicians who are eccentric human beings, anyway, different from normal individuals. Do you have another example of this kind?"

ERDÖS

– "Well, this brings us to Paul Erdös, who was one of the most prolific mathematicians of the 20th century if not the most prolific, and he was, definitely, a very eccentric character. He lived for mathematics and did only mathematics, even during his numerous journeys around the world. He simplified his life to the maximum in order to do mathematics practically all the time.

He was born in Budapest of parents who were Jewish intellectuals. His mother, who previously lost two daughters due to scarlet fever, shielded him almost completely from the everyday problems of life. Paul Erdös liked to say that he never had to tie his own shoelaces until he was 14 years old, and never buttered his own toast until he was 21 years old in Cambridge, England.

When he was only 20 years old, he gave a simple proof for the Bertrand's conjecture that there is a prime number between any positive integer and its double, which had been previously proved in a very complicate way. About one year later, he got his PhD from the University in Budapest. Afterwards, he became a traveling mathematician for the rest of his life, without a steady job or a fixed address. He was famous for moving from place to place, carrying almost no luggage, dropping unannounced at the front door of the house of some mathematician friend, and he had many such friends who had no choice but letting him in. Sometimes, he let other people deal with his knotty financial problems."

– "How could he survive without a steady job or income source?"

– "Again, it is difficult to know for sure how he managed financially. People prefer to see him as an individual doing mathematics in poverty. Perhaps this was true for some periods of his life but certainly not for his entire life. After becoming famous, he was invited to lecture in different places with very generous honoraria. He was also given some temporary appointments in some universities or research institutes. As far as I know, Notre Dame University, in the United States, offered him a permanent position but he declined it, jokingly saying that there were too many pluses there. When he became a member of the Hungarian Academy of Sciences, which like other similar institutions in socialist countries had a generous budget for a small elite of scientists, he benefited of the material advantages automatically offered by such a membership. I remember that I saw a picture of Erdös and his mother relaxing somewhere in country-side, at a guest house run by the Hungarian Academy of Sciences. Anyway, it seems that sometimes he had no money indeed and relied on other people, but sometimes he had money, in which cases he generously gave them away to poor fellows or as mathematical prizes for solving easy problems (small prizes) or difficult problems (bigger prizes)."

– "What did he do in mathematics?"

– "I read somewhere that he wrote or co-authored 1475 academic papers. He was a pure mathematician, uninterested in any kind of applications, but fascinated mainly by the beauty of number theory, especially the primes, which is not so surprising if we take into account the fact that he was born in 1913, which has no other divisors but 1 and itself, being therefore a prime number. But he went much beyond the naive and empirical approach in dealing with numbers and used modern tools involving analytical functions of real variables and results from the general measure theory and probability theory. He liked concrete, specific problems not general theories. Writing books and using powerful computers were not among his priorities. He was an unexhausted source of specific, well-defined, concrete problems he used to spread around to anybody willing to listen to him. Erdös attended thousands of conferences and meetings, talked to thousands of people of all ages, wrote thousands of letters, made thousands of distant telephone calls, at all possible hours of day and night, just to connect to those interested in thinking about mathematical problems formulated by him. He definitely was what is called a problem poser.

He was very generous in spreading out his ideas but he was also involved in a priority dispute concerning an elementary proof of the 'prime number theorem', which states that, asymptotically, the number $\pi(x)$ of primes smaller than or equal to the real number x behaves like $x/\ln x$, as we discussed twice before. Erdös was very fond of his proof, which wasn't simple at all but was called 'elementary' because it didn't use results involving functions of complex variables, as Jacques Hadamard and Charles de La Vallée Poussin previously did, but only real analysis.

Independently, a young Norwegian, Atle Selberg, also obtained an 'elementary' proof of the 'prime number theorem'. Erdös spread around the news that he and Selberg had obtained the elementary proof of this important theorem. But Erdös was well-known to the specialists in number theory while very few, if any, had heard about the Norwegian. Thus, when the news went back to Selberg, his name was obscured and it appeared to him that Erdös had claimed priority about their achievement. At this point, I don't know what really happened. One version is that they both agreed to publish their work in back-to-back papers, in the same journal, but Selberg, feeling slighted by his colleagues due to the renown enjoyed by Erdös, changed his mind and published his own proof. According to another version, the animosity between them continued even after they published a joint paper and, later, Selberg published another elementary proof of his own and got many honours, including a permanent appointment at the prestigious Institute for Advanced Study in Princeton and a Fields Medal. Erdös didn't get something similar for his contribution."

–"What kind of hobbies had he?"

–"Erdös lived for mathematics and did only mathematics. He had no time left for art, fiction, television, movies, or romantic involvement and physical intimacy. He was very careful and selective about what to eat or drink, liked to wash his hands all the time, and was terrified about picking up germs. His clothes fit into a small suitcase and he used to say that private property is a nuisance. He was perhaps the most one-sided person who ever lived, but this side was mathematics.

I met him only twice but I didn't speak to him. It wasn't only a gap of age but also a big professional distance between us. The first time was in the sixties, when I attended an International Conference on Information Theory in Debrecen, Hungary, organized by the distinguished probabilist Alfred Rényi. I was surprised to see Paul Erdös among the participants because he wasn't known to be interested in information theory. He attended all the sessions of the Conference and seemed to work on his own problems, apparently quite detached from what was happening around him. From time to time, however, he made suddenly very pertinent comments at the end of some talks, showing that he had a very distributive mind.

The second meeting was many years later, sometime in the eighties, when I saw him at the airport in Vancouver. He was waiting for his flight, covering page after page with formulas in a shabby notebook. He looked absent-minded and very frail. I am sure that after boarding his plane, he continued his work during the long flight to another continent."

– "What happened with his family if he was so busy traveling or doing mathematics full time?"

– "For him, his family consisted of only one person, his mother Anna. All his life he remained his mother's son. She protected him, took care of him, and looked up at him with unbounded admiration. Even when she was old, she used to accompany him in some of his trips and to attend talks, totally incomprehensible for her, but given by her beloved son. Otherwise, as I have said, Erdös renounced material possessions and physical pleasure for an ascetic life entirely dedicated to mathematics. It is not sure at all whether or not he believed in God, probably not, but he did believe that there is a transcendental Book where the big mathematical truths are written and he tried hard to reveal at least some of them for us, the mortals.

It is difficult to say what are the major contributions of Paul Erdös. When somebody writes 1475 papers, a lot of time is needed to discern what is really important and durable in these papers and, certainly, I am not qualified and willing to do that. A book written about him was entitled *The Man Who Loved Only Numbers*. I would add 'and his mother' to the title. Without any doubt, however, he will be remembered for his results in number theory, combinatorics, which is the scholarly way of counting, and graph theory, which deals with the structure and properties of complex networks involving nodes, branches, and sometimes flows going through.

A heart condition made the last year of his life to be particularly rough, and Paul Erdös died from a heart attack at a conference in

Warsaw, in 1996. The legend says that, not long before his death, he attended a conference in Boca Raton, Florida, and going to write something on the blackboard he suddenly fell down. The participants were nervous and scared but Erdös, temporarily regaining consciousness, asked them not to leave because he had two more problems to tell them about."

GROTHENDIECK

−"I have always believed that eccentric scientists don't exist in the real world and the stories, anecdotes, and jokes about them have simply been invented. But what you have just told me shows that there have been some very original characters among prominent mathematicians. Do you have another name in store?"

−"Yes, I have. Alexandre Grothendieck was born in 1928 in Berlin. He is considered to be a German French mathematician. He kept the name of his mother, Hanka Grothendieck, who wrote a huge biography of more than 2000 pages, describing her meeting with and eventual marriage to Alexandre's father, Sasha Shapiro, who belonged to different anarchist movements. Between 1928 and 1939, living in the anarchist circles of Berlin, Hanka was very poor, hounded by the police, without any fixed address, and wrote for the anarchist journal *Der Prager*. Together with his mother, Alexandre moved to France and, during the German occupation, got shelter and protection in the village of Le Chambon.

After studies at the University of Montpellier, in France, and a year at the famous l'École Normale Supérieure in Paris, he received his doctorate from the University of Nancy in 1953. Soon he became famous for his research in the category theory and algebraic geometry. These are methatheories where the primary objects or elements are already entire classes of sophisticated spaces with given structures and the relationship between them. The representations of one such class of structured spaces by another kind of class of structured spaces are described by very general correspondences called general morphisms, or functors. It is like when somebody who knows and dominates from above, everything which has been done by now in functional analysis, abstract algebra, and abstract geometry, can see analogies and relationships between big mathematical theories and structures. He was mainly interested in unifying topics from geometry, number theory, topology, and complex analysis, by creating the theory of schemes and the theory of topological vector spaces, while mastering the modern functional analysis and the general category theory whose objects are abstract spaces and functors between them. He raised the art of mathematically generalizing to heights never achieved by somebody else in our recent times. But his extraordinary intuition and capacity to generalize were doubled by his ingeniousness in creating supple mathematical tools for solving problems in these general frames. Grothendieck's theory of schemes is considered to be the ultimate generalization of the concepts of curve and algebraic surface.

These are fields very far from my background and mathematical interest. I still remember, however, that during the sixties and seventies, reading Grothendieck's papers was a must for anybody working in these domains. As a researcher in the most prestigious French mathematical research institute, l'Institut de Hautes Études Scientifiques, he became a star of the new generation of pure mathematicians, the charismatic leader of a world center of algebraic geometry and, as far as I know, he joined the rejuvenated Bourbaki group.

For his major contributions, Grothendieck was awarded the Fields Medal, the closest equivalent in mathematics to a Nobel Prize, and was expected to get the Medal and to deliver a major invited talk at the International Congress of Mathematicians held in Moscow in the summer of 1966. I remember that all numerous participants, including myself, were excited about finally seeing and listening to Alexandre Grothendieck. But he didn't show up, for political reasons.

My Romanian friend Marius told me that, once, Grothendieck paid a short visit to the Faculty of Mathematics of the University in Bucharest. He gave a wonderful talk but, to the surprise of many, he came in shorts, with a shaven head, and preferred to eat the simplest food, namely cheese and bread, instead of an opulent dinner prepared especially for him when he was invited to the house of the Dean of the Faculty.

In 1970, he left l'Institut de Hautes Études Scientifiques apparently for campaigning for peace and against the military built-up in the world and, around 1976, he practically stopped doing mathematics, refused some prizes, and soon started quarreling with colleagues and people around him. He also retired from the Bourbaki group and became a recluse, devoting his time to meditation and ecology. Later, he wrote a sour and very critical memoir or autobiography entitled *Récoltes et semailles*. I tried to read it but I couldn't find it because, apparently, nobody wanted to publish it. Therefore, I really don't know what he complained about. Apparently, the memoir circulated from hand to hand and fragments of it were available on the internet. I don't know for sure and I didn't see such excerpts.

Then, he simply disappeared. News about his real or invented whereabouts were few and contradictory. An editor, who visited him in the summer of 1988, claimed that despite his much advertised rejection of human society, Grothendieck actually appeared very lonely and seemed to appreciate if anyone just came to say hello. Around 1993, he disappeared from the little village in the Vaucluse region, in the Southern France, where he has been hiding out, to an unknown location.

Apparently, Grothendieck is now living somewhere in the Pyrenees. Although direct communication with him is practically impossible, due to his very restricted self-imposed visitor's list, his neighbours in the village where he resides look after him. He is known as somebody who has strange ideas like living only on dandelion soup. An anecdote says that a former student had the rare chance of having lunch with Grothendieck in a small and remote restaurant. Nobody said anything during the lunch but, towards the end of it, the owner of the restaurant asked the most famous living mathematician to write a mathematical formula on a napkin, as a substitute for the lunch payment. In a very small writing, Grothendieck scratched some mathematical symbols, as requested. When the owner of the restaurant asked for a signature as well, Grothendieck said: 'Don't push your luck, old man. I paid for lunch but I don't want to buy your restaurant as well.' As with many anecdotes about famous people, this story perhaps never happened."

−"I have heard and read about pure mathematics and applied mathematics. Isn't mathematics a unique science? Can somebody have important contributions in both? I would be happy to see my own results applied to something useful."

PURE AND APPLIED MATHEMATICS

−"Every science is divided into different distinct domains but the basic division between pure and applied is the most common. Mathematics makes no exception. Apparently, long long ago, some practical problems, like counting in general, or dealing with money in financial transactions, calculating the cost and interest, in Babylon, or remeasuring the areas of the lands after every flooding of Nile, in the ancient Egypt, were incentives for developing arithmetics, algebra, and geometry, respectively. Later, practical problems or questions raised in other disciplines have continued to be a source of inspiration for the development of many branches of mathematics. Thus, the study of mechanical motion has generated calculus. Games of chance have formulated problems requiring the elaboration of a theory of probabilities. The study of mortality tables gave birth to statistical inference. Thermodynamics and the study of molecular motion have given a serious impulse to the theory of random motion and stochastic processes. Communication problems in engineering have led to the apparition of information theory. I could continue with many other examples. These impulses from outside, taken together, form only one cause of the development of mathematics.

Once different domains of mathematics are born, new results are obtained due to internal problems and the application of logical reasoning inside them. This is the so called internal cause of the progress of mathematics. A real miracle is that results obtained due to the internal evolution of mathematics itself prove later to be suited for solving practical problems. It is like paying back to the real world for inspiring the creation of new branches and tools in mathematics itself. Many mathematicians believe, however, that mathematics is a creation of the human spirit without any connection with any kind of practical problems. Other mathematicians are not very much concerned about who inspired what, but think that they have to deal only with the internal development of mathematics, ignoring any further application to the real world. These last categories of mathematicians consider themselves to be pure mathematicians. By contrast, those who start from an open practical problem or are interested in developing and using parts of mathematics that can or could solve problems from other sciences or from the real world are applied mathematicians.

The relationship between pure and applied mathematicians is not simple. Very often it is a peaceful coexistence which doesn't mean mutual admiration. Paul Halmos, a very good mathematician who wrote excellent text books on set theory, measure theory, and functional analysis, once published a paper entitled 'Applied mathematics is bad mathematics'. Obviously, there are good and bad papers and books both in pure mathematics and in applied mathematics. Often the source of discontent resides in the fact that sometimes it is perhaps a little easier to obtain research grants and academic jobs for topics that claim to be applicable to real life problems. Also, some academic people claiming to be involved in applications of mathematical modeling to problems of large interest as SARS, AIDS, cancer, mad cow disease, or avian flu, get not only huge financial support from different governmental and nongovernmental organizations but also appear on TV shows or in newspapers. There are many examples showing that good pure mathematics can have unexpected applications sometime later and that many domains of good applied mathematics require a lot of knowledge and skills from pure mathematics."

OPTIMIZATION AND LINEAR PROGRAMMING

−"In high school we have been taught basic topics from pure mathematics like algebra, geometry, or calculus. Which chapters do belong to applied mathematics?"

−"Operations research, or operational research as it is called in Great Britain, for instance, is a relatively young domain of applied mathematics. It is intimately related to optimization or, more exactly, to applied optimization. During the World War II, high military headquarters were interested in optimizing objective functions subject to limited resources. Later, it became obvious that such problems were of interest in management, in general.

The first models were linear: maximize or minimize a linear objective function subject to a finite number of linear inequalities involving the unknowns, called decision variables. This is how linear programming was born. It seems to be a simple problem to solve but it is not. The objective function could be the production cost, and we want to minimize it, or could be the profit, and we want to maximize it. The variables involved could represent the levels of several activities, namely how much to produce in each activity. The inequality constraints refer to lower or upper bounds for the levels of demands for the outcomes of some activities and for the amounts of resources needed for accomplishing these activities, respectively. The inequality constraints define a so-called feasible space, containing those values of the variables that satisfy these constraints. When the constraints are linear inequalities, the feasible space is a domain similar to the interior of a polygon in a multidimensional space. Generally, there are infinitely many feasible solutions, namely systems of values of the decision variables satisfying all the inequality constraints. We want to select those solutions for which the objective function is optimized, which means maximized if the objective function is the profit or minimized if the objective function represents the cost. Such special feasible solutions are called optimal or optimum solutions."

–"What you are telling seems to be very intuitive. Are there many applications of linear programming?"

–"Many different optimization problems may be reduced to solving a linear program. To give an example, in a network, which consists of nodes, representing localities, for instance, and branches, connecting some of these nodes and having some lengths or transportation costs assigned to them, we can be interested in finding the shortest path, or the least cost path, from a given node, called source, to a given node, called destination. Or, we can look for the maximum flow of some commodity from a source to a destination in a given network whose every branch is assigned some maximum capacity for the amount of commodity allowed to go through it."

–"Could you show me the simplest linear program possible?"

–"Assume that a certain small factory manufactures two kinds of products, called product A and product B. There is an unlimited demand for the two kinds of products on the market, but due to inherent limitations induced by the capacity and resources available, the maximum number of items that can be manufactured every week is 100 for product A and 120 for product B. Manufacturing an item of product B requires twice the amount of time required for manufacturing an item of product A. There are 240 work hours available per week. The profit per item is $100 for product A and $150 for product B. How many items of product A and product B have to be manufactured per week in order to maximize the total weekly profit?"

−"It sounds like a problem in arithmetics and I could be tempted to find the solution by simply trying different possibilities."

−"Yes, you could do this because the problem has only two decision variables and three simple constraints. But no trial and error search for solution is possible when we have hundreds of such decision variables and hundreds of constraints. Thus, we have to switch from arithmetics to an optimization problem in linear algebra. Denoting by x the number of items of product A and by y the number of items of product B manufactured during a week, we have to maximize the total weekly profit $100\,x + 150\,y$, subject to the factory capacity and resources constraints $x \leq 100$, $y \leq 150$, and the time constraint $x + 2y \leq 240$. As we have only two decision variables, the problem can be solved by using the graphical method. The feasible space is the set of all points (x, y), in the first quadrant $x \geq 0$, $y \geq 0$ of the plane, that satisfy, simultaneously, the three constraints. It proves to be the interior and the boundary of a polygon. The objective function, $z = 100\,x + 150\,y$ is a line. In the feasible space, we move this line up, keeping its slope constant, until we obtain the largest value of z for which the objective function still intersects the feasible space. This happens in a corner point of the polygon representing the feasible space. The coordinates (x^*, y^*) of this corner point are the optimum values of the decision variables, and the corresponding value of the objective function, namely the optimum profit, is: $z^* = 100\,x^* + 150\,y^*$. In our simple case, we have the optimum values: $x^* = 100$, $y^* = 70$, and $z^* = \$20\,500$."

−"How can be a linear program solved if there are more than two decision variables?"

–"Solving linear programs, namely finding the optimal solutions of a linear program, could be very cumbersome when the number of decision variables involved is large. A popular algorithm for solving a linear program is the so-called Simplex algorithm. As the optimum solutions are corner points of the polygonal feasible space, according to the Simplex algorithm, we start our search for optimum from a corner point. It is optimum if, moving to neighbouring corner points, the value of the objective function cannot be improved. If a better corner point of the feasible space is found, we move to it and check for its optimality, investigating again what happens with the value of the objective function at its neighbouring corner points. Thus, Simplex algorithm starts from a corner point and successively jumps, by small jumps, to better corner points until the optimum solution is found."

–"But this way of solving seems to depend very much on how the starting point is chosen. And it is a very cautious approach, always moving to neighbouring corner points. Who proposed this algorithm?"

–"I really don't know who proposed it for the first time. Simplex algorithm is so popular and so widely used that the name of its creator has been lost in the mist of the past and forgotten. I think, however, that the first mathematician who formulated it was George Dantzig."

–"Is this the best way of looking for an optimum solution?"

–"Doing the computations by hand, the Simplex algorithm is applicable only for solving simple linear programs with few iterations. It is so popular and intensively used because today there are many computer programs that implement it, like LINDO, LINGO, and SAS-OR, for instance. As many new computer packages, their use is very simple. We are told how to enter the data set, how to ask for the optimum solution, and what kind of output we get. But the details of the computer programs used for solving problems according to the indications of the Simplex algorithm are hidden. It is like a new kind of religion: believe and don't ask why. Obviously, this is not good for teaching or for doing research. It is perfect only for those who are interested in practical daily applications without being bothered by a deep understanding of the mathematical details and the justification of the procedures used.

I prefer to give my students open, detailed computer programs that may be used for solving different topics from operations research but few of them are really interested in following the steps of such computer programs. They are more interested in knowing how to use the software packages available on the market and routinely bought by different companies that hire graduates with degrees in mathematics. The paradox is that the simpler the use of such software packages the more sophisticated computer programs are hidden to the user. It is like replacing the details about how to prepare a chicken soup from old fashioned cooking books, for instance, with a simple command like 'Give me a chicken soup' in a new vending machine. Simpler, but less personal and definitely much less creative. This only creates the illusion of being powerful but in fact you entirely depend on the machine providing the soup."

−"If so many things are hidden in the existing computer software packages available on the market and there is no control on what is hidden how could we know whether they solve correctly our problems?"

−"The reality is that, properly speaking, we actually don't know. Common sense tells us to try a new software computer program for solving simpler problems first, that can be also solved by hand, for testing what the computer is doing in such cases when the final results are already known to us. If everything is OK, our degree of belief increases but still there are no guarantees that the computer could properly solve all cases mainly when the number of variables is very large and the degree of complexity of the problem is very high. Very often, we buy or use a computer software if it is recommended by friends or if it is issued by reliable companies. By contrast, if the computer program is written by yourself, you don't only have all the steps under control but, also, can change some essential parameters like the number of iterations, the number of variables and constraints, or the degree of approximation allowed."

–"Did it happen to you to detect a faulty computer software?"

–"In fact, it did happen and in a funny way. A new edition of a textbook in operations research came accompanied by a diskette for computer applications. An assignment asked the students to solve some linear programs by hand and some by using the new diskette. To my surprise, the students obtained different kinds of results for the solution of one problem supposed to be solved both by hand and by using the respective diskette. It took me a relatively long time to realize that the students made no mistakes but, in the hidden computer programs from the diskette, the small number of iterations was fixed and the computer stopped looking for better solutions when the respective number of iterations involved in the search process was reached."

–"You didn't answer my question about whether or not the Simplex algorithm is the best search strategy for an optimum solution in linear programming."

–"I am sorry, Sir! I forgot about your question. As far as I know, nobody has proved that the Simplex algorithm is optimum, which would mean that it is the simplest and fastest way for solving linear programs. Somebody published a big monograph claiming that, on average, which means after solving a lot of linear programs, the strategy of the Simplex algorithm seems to be the optimum way to follow. I confess, however, that I didn't understand the details and what that 'best on average' really meant in that context. But this could be my fault, a consequence of my own limitations. Anyway, many algorithms in operations research are not necessarily optimum, which would mean to be the best way of solving the respective problems. They are used, very often, because they are simple and user friendly.

If an algorithm, however, is not proved to be the best in order to get the solution of the problem in the fastest way, then there is always hope that somebody, someday, will find a better algorithm. And this is just what happened in linear programming when N. Karmarkar had the idea of moving towards the optimum corner point inside the feasible space, instead of jumping from a corner point to another corner point on the frontier of the polygonal feasible space as the Simplex algorithm does. According to Karmarkar's strategy, the starting point of the search is well-defined and, at each step of the search process, it tells us how to correct and adjust the direction of the advancement towards the optimum solution."

–"This run for finding the optimum point reminds me of a well-known joke about how to catch a lion in Sahara desert. A mathematician would draw a square containing Sahara desert. Dividing this big square into four disjoint and equal squares, by drawing a big cross in the middle, the lion should belong to only one of these smaller squares. Taking this square and dividing it into four disjoint and equal squares, the lion should belong to only one of them. Select this square and continue the division process. As the sides of the selected squares become smaller and smaller, each having the side equal to half of the side of the previous square, we stop splitting when the side of the selected square becomes smaller than the side of the cage available. Arranging now the cage on the last selected square, we catch the lion.

Instead of such a systematic search procedure used by the mathematician, a physicist would put Sahara desert into a huge sieve, shaking it well. The sand will pass through the little holes of the sieve and the lion will remain inside the sieve."

SIMULATION

–"I heard this somehow differently, but your variant is better," said John. "You have forgotten to mention, however, that the mathematician's solution assumes that the lion doesn't move. If it does, the search procedure described cannot be applied. The funny thing is that what happens these days in solving optimization problems by using simulation procedures resembles rather the physicist's way of catching a lion in Sahara desert than mathematician's approach."

–"Simulation is a funny word. A soccer player can simulate a fall in order to get a penalty kick for his team. Switching to more serious matters, I heard about using simulation for training pilots or cosmonauts. But I can hardly see any connection between simulation, which for me is closer to roughly approximating what really happens, and mathematics, which signifies precision and rigour."

–"Many domains of modern mathematics are indeed precise and rigorous. In fact, looking back into the history of mathematics, some periods were characterized by less rigour and more new ideas or new results, whereas in some other periods the focus was put on rigour, trying to classify the results previously obtained, separating what was good from what was wrong, and putting the missing bricks in the incomplete edifice of some proofs. There are, however, domains of mathematics, like probability theory and mathematical statistics, which deal with uncertain events and aim at introducing a rigorous approach of uncertainty in general. But I don't want to touch the topic of uncertainty, not now anyway, because it is a fascinating subject that deserves a special discussion about. Another time, maybe.

But let me go back to simulation in mathematics. When I start teaching about simulation, as a distinct chapter of an operations research course, I use to tell my students that simulation means going back to common sense and using a lot of random numbers. It is said that simulation in mathematics started very long ago, in the eighteen century, when Georges Louis Leclerc Comte de Buffon (1707-1788), a renowned French naturalist, performed a simple experiment, called today 'Buffon's needle'. This simple experiment allowed him to get a good approximation of the mysterious transcendental number π by simply tossing a needle. He did this experiment when he was very very old, contradicting the common opinion that senior people cannot have new, original ideas in mathematics. By the way, as a young 32 years old, he became the keeper of Jardin du Roi, and was elected to the Academy when he was 46 years old. He pleaded in favour of the popular study of natural history and published a vast treatise on *Natural History* in 44 volumes. A very interesting character, indeed."

–"Approximating the number π means approximating the area of a circle because the area of a circle is obtained by multiplying π with the square of its radius."

–"Absolutely. In fact this is what Buffon did. One variant of the legend says that Buffon went to a palace and had to wait before meet-

ing the busy owner of the palace. The floor of the waiting room had
a regular geometric pattern consisting of equal circles inscribed into
equal squares. Buffon focused on one such square and started tossing a
little needle counting the ratio between the number of times when the
needle fell into the circle and the total number of tosses of the needle on
the respective square. As the square is a very simple geometric figure
whose area is the product of its side by itself, Buffon approximated the
area of the inscribed circle by multiplying the area of the square with
the ratio explained before. The radius of the inscribed circle was obviously equal to half of the side of the square. Once the area of the circle
was approximated this way, dividing it by the squared radius of the
circle, Buffon obtained an approximation of the transcendental number
π. This was the first time when a random experiment, tossing a needle,
was used for approximating a strictly deterministic entity, the number
π in this case. But this experiment remained rather a curiosity. Closer
to our times, more exactly during the World War II, in Los Alamos,
where a group of brilliant brains were brought together working on the
construction of the first atomic bomb, Stan Ulam, inspired or not by
Buffon's experiment, had the idea of using random numbers for approximating definite integrals, which apparently had nothing to do with any
kind of randomness. He called this approach the Monte Carlo method."

–"Why Monte Carlo which, if I am right, is in Europe, whereas Los
Alamos is in the United States?"

–"Monte Carlo, a beautiful place to visit on the Mediterranean coast
between France and Italy, is famous for gambling, like Las Vegas in the
United States. As the outcomes of playing roulette are random and
the random numbers proved to be essential in simulation, Stan Ulam
chose Monte Carlo as the name for the methodology of using random
numbers in order to approximate strictly deterministic entities. Instead
of approximating a multiple definite integral of a certain function by
taking a regular network of equidistant points forming equal cells in the
domain of integration, and calculate the sum of the values of the function to be integrated at a point of each cell multiplied by the volume of
the respective cell, for all the cells, investigating what happens asymptotically when the network becomes finer and finer, Ulam's idea was

to cover such domains with random points and take the average of the random sample provided by the values of the function that has to be integrated at these random points. Random points instead of regular partitions, random sampling instead of taking limits. I remember that, in an interview, Ulam mentioned with modesty that, intellectually, it wasn't big deal. I think that it really was."

–"To be honest, I don't understand this at all."

–"Well, let's go back to Buffon's approach for approximating the area of a circle. If the radius of a circle is a certain number, let's say 5, we can inscribe this circle into a square of side equal to the diameter of the circle, which is 10. The square and the inscribed circle have the same center. In simulation, as the name itself says, we don't really perform the experiment but generate its possible outcomes. Thus, instead of randomly tossing the needle inside the square, we cover the square with random points, as uniformly as possible, and then count how many of them have fallen inside or on the inscribed circle."

–"How can random points be generated in order to cover uniformly a square?"

–"This is very simple to do these days due to the tremendous proliferation of all sorts of computer softwares. But let me explain first what a random number is.

The real numbers between 0 and 1 form the so-called unit interval, denoted by $[0, 1]$. An arbitrary interval with endpoints a and b is denoted by $[a, b]$. The rational numbers from $[0, 1]$ are the numbers that have the integer part 0 and a finite number of decimals or infinitely many decimals with a set of consecutive digits that repeats itself indefinitely, like a periodic pattern. The irrational numbers from the unit interval have the integer part 0 as well but infinitely many decimals with no set of consecutive digits repeating itself indefinitely. An irrational number cannot be expressed as the ratio, or quotient, of two integers. The rational numbers form a dense subset because for any irrational number there are rational numbers as close to it as we want. Indeed, if an irrational number is given, taking more and more of its decimals into account, we obtain rational numbers closer and closer to it. Mathematically, a 'random number' is a continuous random variable whose possible values are uniformly distributed on the unit interval. In the current language, we use the words random numbers to denote arbitrary possible values from the unit interval having the same uniform probability to be chosen.

There are tables, widely available, containing rational numbers, randomly selected in order to cover uniformly the unit interval. These tables are just enough to generate random numbers uniformly distributed in any finite interval. Indeed, if the random numbers R cover uniformly the unit interval, then the numbers $\tilde{R} = a + (b-a)R$ cover uniformly the interval $[a, b]$. There are also a lot of computer programs that generate as many random numbers as we want from any given interval.

Going back to the approximation of the area of a circle, when the square is given, then each of the two coordinates of an arbitrary point (x, y) belonging to the square takes values from a certain interval. Thus, if we have a circle of radius 5 centered at the point of coordinates $(1, 2)$, then it is inscribed into a square of side 10 and the first coordinate x of an arbitrary point (x, y) of the square is a number between -4 and 6, whereas its second coordinate y is a number between -3 and 7. In such a case, to generate random points uniformly distributed in the given square, it is sufficient to take pairs of random numbers (R_1, R_2) uniformly distributed in the intervals $[-4, 6]$ and $[-3, 7]$, respectively. Thus, we don't toss any needle on the square circumscribing the circle on the floor pattern, as Buffon effectively did, but we can easily cover uniformly the square with random points.

If we generate n random points uniformly distributed in the given square, we count how many such point fall inside or on the circle. Let us say that this number is m. Then, the area of the circle is approximated by the proportion of the points falling inside or on the circle, namely the ratio m/n, multiplied by the area of the square which is 100. This is what happens in one so-called run of the simulation. Thus, after one run, we get the approximation $A_1 = (m/n)(100)$ for the area of the circle. We repeat several times, say N times, what happened in the first run described above. In each subsequent run we obtain another number as an approximation of the area of the circle. In N runs we obtain a sample of size N formed by the corresponding approximations $A_1, \ldots, A_N$. Taking the average $\overline{A} = (A_1 + \ldots + A_N)/N$, we obtain a more reliable approximation $\overline{A}$ of the true area of our circle. Using a little statistical inference, we can be even more cautious and get a confidence interval for the true area of a circle instead of using only one number, namely $\overline{A}$, as an approximation for this area. A $100(1-\alpha)\%$ confidence interval, where the significance level α is a small positive number, like $\alpha = 0.05$ for instance, is an interval centered at the mean sample value $\overline{A}$, whose length is small if the sample standard deviation is small and/or the sample size N is large. Mathematically, this confidence interval is:

$$\left(\overline{A} - t_{N-1, \alpha/2} \, \frac{s}{\sqrt{N}}, \; \overline{A} + t_{N-1, \alpha/2} \, \frac{s}{\sqrt{N}} \right),$$

where $t_{N-1, \alpha/2}$ is the critical point of the t-distribution with $N-1$ degrees of freedom and significance level α, a positive number obtainable from statistical tables, and s is the sample standard deviation. In the end, we use to say that we are $100(1-\alpha)\%$ confident that the true value of the exact area of the circle is located in the corresponding confidence interval."

– "What is the sample standard deviation in this context?"

– "The sample standard deviation is the positive square root of the sample variance $[(A_1 - \overline{A})^2 + \ldots + (A_N - \overline{A})^2]/(N-1)$. It measures the deviation of the sample values $A_1, \ldots, A_N$ from the sample mean $\overline{A}$. If the standard deviation is small, the true value is closer to the sample mean with probability $1 - \alpha$. Also, if the number n of random points used in one run and the number N of runs are larger, the approximation obtained for the area of the circle is better and better. And the computer helps us to do it with a tremendous speed.

Simulation without computers was rather a curiosity or exotic topic. With the computers we have today, simulation is a very representative domain of what can be called experimental mathematics.

The same methodology may be applied when we want to approximate multiple definite integrals on different domains. Thus, if we want to approximate the value of the integral of a function $f(x)$ on an interval $[a, b]$, in one run we take n random numbers uniformly distributed in $[a, b]$, we calculate the values of the function at these points multiplied by the length of the interval $(b - a)$, and we take the average of these n values obtained. Then, we take a number N of such runs and calculate the average, or mean value, of the sample consisting of the N approximations obtained in all the runs, like a mean of the means. This is a better approximation of our integral but, again, instead of an approximation expressed by a numerical value, we can write a confidence interval, centered at the sample mean, whose length depends on the sample standard deviation, and the true value of the definite integral does belong to this confidence interval with a high credibility level."

–"This means that we can approximate the value of a definite integral using only elementary arithmetical operations, without using calculus. Could you write down the formula for the corresponding confidence interval. I should like to keep it."

–"Assume that N is the number of runs and n is the number of random numbers from $[a, b]$ taken in each run. If $R_{1,j}, \ldots, R_{n,j}$ are n random numbers from $[a, b]$ used in the j-th run, we calculate the sample:

$$F_j = (b - a) \sum_{i=1}^{n} f(R_{i,j}), \qquad (j = 1, \ldots, N),$$

and the corresponding sample mean and sample variance:

$$\overline{F} = \frac{1}{N} \sum_{j=1}^{N} F_j, \quad s^2 = \frac{1}{N-1} \sum_{j=1}^{N} (F_j - \overline{F})^2.$$

And now, a $100(1 - \alpha)\%$ confidence interval for our definite integral is obtained in the same way we used when we dealt with the approximation of the area of a circle, namely:

$$\overline{F} - t_{N-1, \alpha/2} \frac{s}{\sqrt{N}} < \int_a^b f(x)\, dx < \overline{F} + t_{N-1, \alpha/2} \frac{s}{\sqrt{N}},$$

but, of course, if n and N are larger integers, which means that we use a lot of random numbers in our simulation in order to make the approximation better, we need a computer to do these simple but numerous computations."

–"Going back to 'Buffon's needle' experiment, if I understand correctly, no formula for the area of the circle has been used in what you have been saying but, on the other hand, only an approximation for the area of the circle has been obtained this way."

–"No formula has been used, indeed, and this is the main advantage in simulation. As I said, simulation means back to common sense using a lot of random numbers. As far as the approximation is concerned, the funny thing is that even when the well-known formula for the area of a circle is used, which is the product between π and the squared radius, as the number π is irrational, nobody ever could know with infinite accuracy the area of any circle and we have to resign to using only approximations. The letter π is only a symbol for something never accessible to us in an absolute way. God only knows the exact value of π. We, the mortals, have to resign to knowing only a rough approximation of it. The most powerful computers can make this approximation considerably better, but it still remains an approximation."

–"It is very depressing to know that reality depends on numbers, like π for instance, that cannot and will not be known with absolute precision by anybody ever."

–"In fact, the same is true in dealing with any irrational number. Long ago, in ancient times, the disciples of the Greek philosopher and mathematician Pythagoras were convinced that the integer numbers and their ratios were the only numbers needed to explain anything in our world. It was very stressing for them to discover that the diagonal of a square with the side equal to 1 is not a rational number but the square root of 2, which is irrational. Indeed, assuming that the length of such a diagonal is a rational number results in a contradiction. I don't remember whether I told you or not but the legend has it that each member of their group had to swear to tell nobody about the existence of such an embarrassing new type of numbers. One member of them, however, didn't respect the requested secrecy and it is said that he was killed by the congregation. And the square root of 2 wasn't an exception. Keep in mind that although the infinite set of rational numbers is infinite and dense in any numerical interval, which means that there are rational numbers arbitrarily close to any irrational number, there are many more irrational numbers than rational numbers in that interval. As somebody said, intuitively, the rational numbers are the raisins scattered in the pound cake of the irrational numbers."

−"Therefore, we have here an infinite set which is 'bigger' than another infinite set?"

−"Yes, indeed. As we discussed when we referred to Georg Cantor, there are different types of infinite sets. The set of rational numbers can be counted, which means that its elements could be arranged in a sequence. This is why it is called a countable set. By contrast, the set of irrational numbers is larger because it is uncountable; its elements cannot be put in a sequence, which means that we cannot count its elements. Infinite sets have properties that contradict our intuition which has been formed in dealing mainly with finite sets. Thus, we are used to say that a part is smaller than the whole; there are fewer students in a certain class than in the entire school. This is not necessarily true when we deal with infinite sets. Thus, the set of positive integers is a subset of the set of positive rational numbers but it is not 'smaller' because both are countable and, therefore, may be put in a one-to-one correspondence."

−"From what you are saying, simulation is like a new kind of mathematics, whose objective is to get a good approximation instead of running after an illusory absolute precision."

−"Frankly speaking, I couldn't have said it better. Except getting good approximations, simulation has another objective, as well, which is sampling, or getting representative samples, from probability distributions of interest. In simulation, random numbers form the primary clay from which we can mold samples coming from different probability distributions of interest. The probability distributions, except the uniform one, are not chaotic. They have some kind of probabilistic regularity. Sampling in simulation goes on according to the following scheme: The random numbers, representing pure chaos, are introduced into the random regularity constraints induced by the respective probability distribution and the output gives a representative sample from the respective probability distribution. Thus, from chaos we get something structured in a probabilistic way. For instance, if we want to get a sample of size N, $z_1, \ldots, z_N$, from the standard normal probability distribution $N(0, 1)$, we can use the simple formula:

$$ z_j = \left(\sum_{i=1}^{n} R_{i,j} - \frac{n}{2} \right) \bigg/ \sqrt{\frac{n}{12}}, \qquad (j = 1, \ldots, N), $$

where $R_{i,j}$, $(i = 1, \ldots, n; j = 1, \ldots, N)$ are random numbers from $[0, 1]$ and $n \geq 12$.

This general scheme is just opposite to the model from the communication theory where a source transmits regular messages through a noisy channel and, as a consequence, the receiver gets the corresponding perturbed messages. Thus, from order we get something less structured. Claude Shannon's entropy is used for measuring the amount of information to be transmitted and the amount of information which is lost because of the random perturbations on the communication channel. Information theory teaches us that by basically making the messages we want to transmit longer and more structured, it is possible to counteract the destructive effect of the random perturbations and the reception can decipher the original messages sent to it. Coding theory shows how to use algebraic structures, notably algebraic fields, for writing our messages, for protecting what we transmit from the alterations caused by the noise on the communication channel."

−"I obviously feel that I couldn't understand just everything you have explained to me but, you know what, I am quite comfortable with simulation. Do you have another application of it I could understand?"

−"I could add one more and it doesn't take much time. You have seen how many great mathematicians were heavily involved in trying to solve algebraic equations. Del Ferro, Tartaglia, Euler, Lagrange, Abel, and Galois, among them. We spent some time talking about Fermat's last theorem whose content is so negative: The equation $x^n + y^n = z^n$

has no solution in distinct positive integers if the degree n is larger than 2. As I said before, for an applied mathematician, however, this is not a real tragedy because an approximation of the solution using rational numbers may be obtained with any practical degree of precision.

Thus, let me take Fermat's equation of degree 5, namely $x^5 + y^5 = z^5$, where $0 < x < y < z$. If we divide by z^5, the equation becomes $p^5 + q^5 = 1$. According to Fermat's last theorem, we cannot find two fractions p and q, where $0 < p < 1$ and $0 < q < 1$, that satisfy this equation. I find this to be amazing indeed, but very sad also. However, simulation could be used in order to find two rational numbers for which the last equation is satisfied with a very small approximation error. For doing that, we go back again to common sense, using a lot of random numbers. Using random numbers R_1 and R_2, covering uniformly the unit interval $[0, 1]$, where both p and q should belong, we calculate the expression $R_1^5 + R_2^5 - 1$ and we keep those pairs of random numbers (R_1, R_2), as approximations for p and q, for which the corresponding values of this expression are between $-\epsilon$ and $+\epsilon$, where ϵ is a small positive number, representing the degree of approximation, or the approximation error how it is also called."

At this point John looked into the minuscule notebook hidden in one of the numerous pockets of his anorak and, somewhere in it, he found what he wanted:

"Using 2000 random pairs (R_1, R_2), the computer found the rational approximations $p \approx 0.793760$ and $q \approx 0.827096$, for which $p^5 + q^5 - 1 = -0.0000094$, which means that this is a solution of Fermat's equation of degree 5, within an approximation error $\epsilon = 0.00001$. Andrew Wiles spent many good years of his active life to prove that there are no distinct positive rational numbers p and q from the unit interval $[0, 1]$ which satisfy Fermat's equation $p^5 + q^5 = 1$. Using simulation, the computer found an excellent approximation for the solution, with an approximation error of $\epsilon = 0.00001$, in a couple of seconds.

Simulation does contribute, substantially, to the gradual creation of a new kind of experimental mathematics. Often, we have to give up running after a beautiful but illusory perfection and be happy to find methods and techniques for building an approximate model, getting results which are humanly accessible. I am sure that many pure mathematicians, looking for the absolute mathematical truth, often hidden forever, disagree with such a viewpoint, but an applied mathematician could accept a relative approximation of this truth when such an approximation could give a better understanding, as imperfect as it is, of what happens in the domain for which a mathematical model is being built. "

CONFERENCES AND CONGRESSES

I think that, at that point, John realized that I had enough mathematics for the day. We talked for a while about sports, mainly about soccer, we both seemed to enjoy. But our preferences were quite different. I liked British teams, in general, and Manchester United, in particular, whereas John went for Spanish teams, in general, and Real Madrid, and Brazilian players, playing in European teams, in particular. After a while, however, I turned to mathematics, but in a rather nontechnical way:

–"You have attended several conferences and congresses. How are they?"

–"As they deal with different topics and are organized in different countries and places, it is difficult to compare them. The first International Congress of Mathematicians was held in 1897 in Zürich. The second, in Paris in 1900, the third, in 1904 in Heidelberg, followed by other such Congresses organized every four years, except during the World War II. Generally, they have sections covering the entire mathematics and are attended by a lot of participants. It is extremely difficult to organize such congresses. They cost a lot of money and involve an overwhelming amount of work from the part of the hosts. Only big countries could afford to organize such big congresses.

I attended such an International Congress of Mathematicians in Moscow in August, 1966. It was my first trip abroad. I took an airplane with two propellers and the entire flight took place in the clouds and not above them as it happens today with the supersonic jets. According to the officials, about 5000 mathematicians attended the Congress which was held in the huge Lomonosov university. As always, there were plenary sessions with one-hour invited talks, given by big names, and parallel sessions organized for different sections and consisting of 30-minute invited talks and 20-minute regular communications. In the first days, the lecture halls were almost fully packed, but as the Congress advanced, the number of participants in attendance was drastically diminishing, the mathematicians being also interested in seeing more of Moscow, which is a vastly spread city but, fortunately, with an excellent subway system.

I had my communication scheduled just in the first day in the section dealing with statistical mechanics. I gave my talk and I would have felt more comfortable if there had been fewer people in the huge lecture hall. Anyway, the government, anxious to create a good impression to the foreign participants, gave a fabulous reception in Kremlin, and it was interesting to see a hungry crowd of 5000 mathematicians devouring, in a record time, the abundant and excellent food provided. By contrast, the restaurants in Moscow were very modest and in one of them, just in the center of the city, they had only one kind of cake on the menu, called 'tort', and, when I asked for it, there was no piece available. Otherwise, Russian people proved to be very friendly and disciplined. I attended some excellent lectures given by famous mathematicians but I had serious difficulties understanding not only the full contents of their talks but also the language used by many of them. I was anxious to see and listen to Andrei Nikolaevich Kolmogorov, one of the big stars of Russian mathematics, who first put probability theory on a rigorous measure theoretical basis. Unfortunately, at that time, he was interested in mathematical education, a topic which, at that time, didn't interest me at all.

Except discussing with some participants, not too many anyway, who asked for reprints and details after my talk, my biggest success was to be the goalkeeper of the erratic soccer team of 'the rest of the world', made ad hoc, in a match against the well trained team of the Russian mathematicians, on the beautiful playfield of the famous 'Dynamo Moscow' soccer club. Honestly, I played acceptably well in the first half but I wanted to quit at the break because the small size borrowed soccer shoes were killing me. The captain of our team, a Yugoslav mathematician, didn't want to replace me. In the second part of the match, I was an almost total wreck. In the end, the Russians won by 6-3. I regret even today that, by accident, I left behind in Moscow both the festive badge, commemorating the 'historic' match, and the comments published about it, with the explicit names of the players of the two teams, in the official Russian newspaper of large, national circulation *Sovietsckii Sport.*"

−"What is the difference between a congress and a conference?"

−"A conference, or a colloquium, focuses on one specific topic, or a couple of narrow topics. It is much more specialized than a congress, has considerably fewer participants, costs much less to organize, and is more profitable for the participants who could easier discuss their problems with other people working in the same field. The future of the big international congresses is in doubt, whereas more and more conferences and colloquia are being organized. Also, a big congress generally is held in big cities, whereas small conferences could be organized in small but picturesque locations, in the mountains or seaside resorts.

One such conference was organized, many years ago, in Varna, at the Black Sea, in Bulgaria. All mornings were reserved for going to the beach, swimming, and enjoying the sun. The talks were scheduled late in the day, followed by discussions in an excellent restaurant. Everybody was really in a good mood.

More difficult is when, at a conference, you are the chair of a section on a certain day. Then you have to examine in advance the respective room and the necessary technical installations, like screens, overhead projectors, slides, computers equipped with power-point programs, etc., to learn how to pronounce correctly the names of the speakers and, mainly, to keep the session under control because, more often than not, people tend to talk too much and, sometimes, some participants could engage themselves in unpleasant disputes. It is not always easy to do all this stuff properly. I shall always remember a chair of a session who came with a big alarm clock, which probably belonged to his grandmother, settled to ring up after every 15 minutes. When the alarm clock started ringing, he would rise from his seat, interrupting the speaker in the middle of his or her sentence, bluntly saying: 'Thank you for your interesting talk. The next speaker is . . . .' Brutal but efficient.

Mathematicians are human beings and, therefore, they are as different as all the other people. Some have an oversized ego and believe that only what they are doing is really important. I have seen mathematicians who were working hard to destroy or spoil the reputation of others, good friends and collaborators becoming fierce enemies, bitter fights for priority, or some individuals who thought necessary to ask questions and make comments after almost every talk presented at a conference or colloquium. I remember that, at an international conference, a young star from the host country, arrogantly interrupted every talk with questions and remarks. It became almost unbearable and nobody could do anything about it, in the name of the freedom of expressing scientific opinions, which in fact prevented the freedom of respective speakers to use the limited amount of time allotted to them. I have to confess that I was very happy when this ambitious fellow fell on the ground from the back of an impetuous horse he was riding when the participants to the conference visited a farm nearby.

But in this not so large community of professional mathematicians, I have also seen a lot of respect, noblesse, generosity, altruism, lasting friendship, and disinterested help offered by some. When I was a young student, one of my professors told us what happened to him when he attended his first conference abroad. Enthusiastic and full of himself, he announced a new theorem in algebraic topology, proving that its main condition was necessary but claiming that its sufficiency cannot be proved. In general, a necessary and sufficient condition for something to be true is always important because it becomes an equivalent definition of this something, and this equivalency is formulated as an 'if and only if condition', or an 'iff condition' how it is called in the mathematical jargon. After his talk, during a break when the participants generally drink fruit juice or coffee and eat biscuits or cookies free of charge, but in fact covered by high registration fees, a famous topologist came to my young professor telling him that the theorem was known, where and when it was published, and that not only the necessity but also sufficiency of its condition were proved there. But he kindly encouraged him to continue his research in such a difficult field. Instead of elegantly telling all this in a private personal conversation, the renowned topologist would have humiliate a young mathematician and spoil his reputation if he had made all those remarks in front of the large audience during the official discussion period after the respective talk. Not long after that conference, my professor published some important papers in topology, moved to Paris but, unfortunately, he died of a stomach cancer, shortly after, when he was only 38 years old."

It was about 11 o'clock when I finally stopped writing. I had a difficult time to put some order and coherence in so many different topics John talked about on that day. I am not sure at all that I did a really good job. But at least I tried and, for me, it was worth doing. Then I switched off the light but I couldn't go to sleep instantly, as I normally do. A lot of thoughts were still mingling in my head. Obviously, there has been life in mathematics, with a lot of achievements, but many dramas, failures, and uncertainty as well. And then I started asking questions to myself. Did Euler ever look at Mount Dolent? Why did he settle down in St. Petersburg and Berlin when Switzerland, his native country, is so beautiful? He spent his life doing mathematics, raising a big family, and witnessing the premature death of many of his children. But he left behind something durable, like the magic formula $e^{i\alpha} = \cos\alpha + i\sin\alpha$, where $i = \sqrt{-1}$, for instance, which is meant for eternity. There is something tragic in this effort of discovering the truth. Did the humans invent, or rather discover what is called truth or the truth was revealed to them as a reward for their efforts? If there is another civilization somewhere in another solar system, is their mathematics the same as ours? Did they discover Pythagoras's theorem? And if yes, before Pythagoras or after him? Who was the first? But, my God, I have to stop asking so many questions if I don't want to have Gödel's fate. But, unlike him, at least I like to eat and I still enjoy good food. The dinner this evening was really great. Now, I have to go to sleep not only because I am physically dead tired but also because I have to let my subconscious work on and put some order in the stuff I listened to today. I think, however, that my written notes are more reliable than what my subconscious is capable of doing. Maybe my brain and nervous system are not willing to do any subconscious work and need a rest too. In fact, before falling asleep, I always try to empty my head of any kind of thoughts and, perhaps, this is not such a good idea. But it is definitely healthier. During the night I don't think and I still exist. What would Descartes say about this?

SIXTH DAY

COL DU BASSET

–"Today, our last hiking day will be a premier for myself," said John when we met on Sunday, on a beautiful morning, at 8:00, the earliest departure time we had agreed upon. "I haven't been to Col Basset ever before. In fact, according to the information I got, the path up there has been marked and taken care of, to some extent, only recently. Some maps don't even mention it and very few people go there. Not even the landlord of the hotel who, by the way, is a very energetic young man who is not only the charming owner of Edelweiss, with his angelic young wife who is doing the book-keeping, but is also the main chef. They have three beautiful children. A really picture perfect family you can see only in some good old movies."

–"Where is Basset? To the west or to the east?"

–"To the east, but not as far as Lacs de Fenêtre. In fact it is just up there, to the east, above La Fouly. But we have to climb more than 1000 meters in altitude to go there."

–"It seems to be a very high altitude, up there, but there are no rocks in sight and the steep slope seems to be very open and bleak, except grass, of course. Everything is very green there."

–"Yes, the mountains from the eastern side of Val Ferret are indeed very different from the rocky mountains on the western side, but, up there, there are also some rocky portions as well, that could hide some surprises, as you saw yesterday when we suddenly discovered the three lakes in a very rugged alpine area. Let's start. Are you OK?"

–"Yes, Sir! I had a good sleep last night and the fine weather makes me very optimistic. In fact, the second hiking day was more difficult for me because I had some discomfort in my legs after the long trip to Grand Col Ferret, due to lack of any physical exercise in the previous week. Now, I feel myself to be in good shape."

The signpost from the middle of the village, at which we used to look every morning before starting, mentioned: Le Barfay 45 min, Le Basset 3h 30 min (Combe de l'A).

Stage 1. We started going to east-east-north, following the paved road perpendicular to the main road on which we had gone in the afternoon of the day of my arrival in La Fouly. At its end, at 1696 meters altitude, we caught a narrow path, brusquely turning south, and we went, for about 15 minutes, through a rugged forest with tall fir trees and a lot of shade, until we met the ski lift going straight up. A couple of minutes later, getting out of the forest, we arrived at Le Barfay (1820 meters), where both the shepherd hut and an adjacent sheepfold were empty.

Stage 2. From Le Barfay, the path followed a very steep and long serpentine, rather like an angular zigzag, winding up a little to the right hand side of the ski lift, and basically climbing to the east along what is called Alpage de la Fouly. Due to the severe gradient of the slope, looking back, it was like flying over the village and the camping site, both remained down there and seeming smaller and smaller as we went up. The end of the serpentine coincided with the terminus of the ski lift. A little later, we met a relatively senior Swiss couple, apparently husband and wife, who, after riding the ski lift, were going to Col du Basset as well. They introduced themselves as Martha and Christophe. I was happy when they joined us because four people could cope better with potential dogs than only John and I. They spoke a very clear French, seemed to be well experienced in hiking, and proved to be very pleasant companions. Martha didn't say much but Christophe talked most of the time, proving to be an incorrigibly optimistic 'bon vivant'. Or, at least, this is what he made us believe.

We had to climb along another serpentine, but with shorter turnings, in a green pasture, in the middle of a sea of edelweiss flowers, bilberry plants, and rhododendrons. John and our two companions admitted that they had never seen before such a huge colony of edelweiss. I took some pictures of this delicate, white, velvety flower, justifiably considered to be the queen of all alpine flowers. The old gentleman explained to us that edelweiss flowers only from July to August and is found on high meadows or on stony, sunny slopes, often on thin, dry, limestone-rich soil. This flower is almost the symbol of the Alps.

We continued our ascent together and, after a while, we arrived at a large closure full of sheep guarded by two huge, white shepherd dogs and, tragically, with no shepherds around. One of the dogs didn't do anything but the other one, seeing us, started barking, running aggressively in our direction. The small wired fence of the closure prevented the sheep from getting out but for such a big dog it would have been a joke to jump over if he had wanted to. Fortunately, it didn't, once he realized somehow that we were not predators. Relieved, we went along the fence, as peacefully as possible, showing a lot of respect for the two guardians. Then, the path turned left and, after about 10 minutes, we had to pass just through another shepherd hut which, luckily for us, was empty. Heading east again, we reached the beginning of an open ridge.

Stage 3. Advancing along the mounting edge, on our left-hand side we were up there just above the rugged, wild, short but abrupt valley where we had stopped our stroll in the afternoon of the last Monday. From above, we could see the bleak upper part of that valley, with no trees, bushes, or grass, full of debris from gray and dark rock plates and slates, in deep contrast with the steep but green pastures on the right-hand side of the ridge. At one moment, during our climbing along the ridge, we saw a big chamois, skillfully jumping on the unstable plates of the debris from the left-hand side, and eventually disappearing somehow somewhere. Shortly afterwards, our path climbed amidst boulders and rocks. Later, it went through a gorge with chains on some portions.

Weather was still good and stable, but some white clouds showed up here and there. A couple of times, we were above some of them, which made me feel very powerful, on my way to heaven. And, suddenly, we turned a little to the right and realized that we were on another ridge, with a man-made pyramid of stones marking Col du Basset (2765 meters), our final destination for the day.

A very nice place indeed. Looking to the east, we had Val Ferret and the range of western mountains at our back, a long, green, smooth, and peaceful valley, at the feet of the long but not extremely high mountain Combe de l'A, in front of us, and two high and rugged mountains at our two sides, namely Mount de la Fouly (2870 meters), on the left-hand side, and La Tsavre, or Mont Ferret (2977 meters), on the right-hand side. It wasn't so easy to come up here but it was worth doing.

We stopped just there and had lunch, all four of us, chatting in French. I didn't open my mouth too often but, when I did, I do believe that I managed to make conversation in quite an acceptable way. Christophe told many jokes. Some of them I didn't understand, due to my imperfect colloquial French, and those I understood I don't remember. With one exception, however. Thus, sensing my fear of dogs, Christophe advised me never to pet a dog. Not that I ever had such an intention! And he continued:

–"I learned this lesson myself when, one day, at a bus stop, I saw a young lady and a dog standing by. I asked whether her dog bites and she said to me that her dog was very friendly and didn't bite anyone. Then, I petted the dog who bit my thumb. So, I screamed at the young lady: 'You said that your dog doesn't bite!' 'Yes, but this is not my dog!' she answered back."

I am almost sure that he made this up but it was nice to see somebody irradiating a good sense of humour. He also advised me that life is not as short as to panic about but not too long to waste its good moments either. He also told me that there is no reason to worry about your heart as long as it works, a remark in deep contrast with 'Watch your cholesterol, young man!' I was told so many times in Toronto.

Immediately after lunch, the Swiss couple said good bye, descending towards east, on a long but easy path to the village Liddes on Val d'Entremont, a parallel valley to Val Ferret, where a car was waiting for them. From the pyramid of stones, looking east, we watched them slowly descending towards the wonderfully secluded green valley, guarded to the south by the long range Combe de l'A.

As it was only one o'clock, John and I remained on the Col du Basset for more than an hour, looking around, breathing the fresh air of the heights, and talking. Only during our descent, we fully realized how steep the mounting path really was. Anyway, we had no problems with the shepherd dogs because two young men were now there, working on something inside the sheepfold.

BEING A PROFESSIONAL MATHEMATICIAN

Compared to the previous days when he talked more about mathematics, in general, and different mathematicians, in particular, John's considerations made in our last hiking day were more personal. It is true that I was the instigator when I made the following remark:

–"You told me so many things about great names in mathematics but nothing about your own work."

–"I didn't because it would be a sacrilege to put myself among them. I belong to a much much lower and modest class."

–"I can find many other details about these great names in history of mathematics books but, as you told me, it is almost impossible to be absolutely sure that what is written there represents the absolute and complete truth because these books represent a second and indirect source of information. But about your own career and work you are the prime source and I really would like to know facts about your own experience as a professional mathematician."

–"Well, I could be not only the first source but also the only source about my own life because there will be no second or third source ever about it. My achievements will not be recorded in any history book for sure."

–"You are too modest, I believe."

–"No, it is not modesty, but realism. You know, being a mathematician working in a university or research institute is a good job these days. Many great mathematicians had a hard time, in unstable, temporary, and underpaid jobs, often unrelated with mathematics itself, for having a relatively decent life or, sometimes, even for surviving. But, due to their contribution, civilized societies have gradually learned that mathematics is important and mathematicians deserve consideration and good salaries. Now, we are the beneficiary of such an attitude change. In majority of universities, at least in all I am aware of, after a couple of years, going through several stages of research, teaching, and service evaluations, that could take up to seven or ten years, but sometimes much less, a mathematician working in an academic environment can get tenure. This is important because, subsequently, the tenured person could focus on his work without being worried about the future. Living under stress is not good for anybody.

There is, however, a catch here. Sometimes, getting a tenured position, as lecturer, associate professor, or full professor, could slow or even cease further real efforts for continuing doing research or learning. Cases of tenured academics who become incompetent, if they increase in number, could compromise the concept of tenure itself. Abandoning tenure could be a serious step backwards for those who really deserve it. Tenure has been a great achievement for academic people.

The symbiosis between teaching and research is also good in my opinion and I am certainly not alone in saying this. Doing research is exciting but the moments of advancement, progress, or success are considerably rarer than the many unsuccessful attempts for solving a certain open problem the researcher is working on. Whereas teaching forces you to rethink and reorganize the stuff which is already known and introduces a regular schedule in your life. It is true, however, that marking hundreds of tests and final exam papers is not quite the most exciting kind of activity we can do.

Switching on a lighter tone, I read somewhere that a young mathematician, newly appointed in an university, was asked by the hostile chair of the respective department to report back to him, on every Friday, what research she did during the week. After the first week, she handed him a sheet with the following sentences: 'Monday: tried to prove a theorem. Tuesday: tried to prove the same theorem. Wednesday: tried to prove the same theorem. Thursday: tried to prove the same theorem. Friday: the theorem is false.' It is not clear whether the chair was vexed or had a good laugh about."

–"What happens if somebody publishes a theorem or a certain mathematical result which proves to be wrong?"

–"Nothing. It is simply ignored or forgotten. In mathematics is not like in experimental sciences where you don't have always the possibility to check whether a certain result is correct or not. Nobody accepts something in mathematics until each step of the proof is verified. This is the power of proving. My own students could discover a mistake I could make in proving a theorem in class. I find this simply extraordinary. But there are mistakes and mistakes. For the well-known, classic, standard material, the mistakes are unacceptable. But in doing research in a new field, even great mathematicians have made mistakes. Somebody else comes later and makes the necessary corrections if possible. I read somewhere that a master is somebody who is admired for his achievements by his disciples while he cannot forget his own past mistakes.

A good friend of mine, an eminent mathematician, once noticed that very often, an imperfect research paper which has some good ideas inside it, in spite of some mistakes here and there, could be a better source of inspiration, and may be continued by other mathematicians, than an absolutely perfect paper to which nothing can be added and in which everything is done in a final perfect form. A paper like this last one has to be studied and learned but cannot be improved. But such absolutely perfect papers are rare in mathematics today and mathematicians cannot afford to polish an original result during a long period of time. You have to report results obtained in doing research for getting grants, for giving talks to conferences, for having travel expenses paid either by your university or by those who invited you, or for competing for sponsorship or even prizes. 'Publish or perish' is a familiar cliché but it is still true. Submitting a new paper for publication is a stimulant for working even harder and for getting new results, but it is also a source of headaches, high blood pressure, and stress."

–"You are saying that mathematicians have good salaries. I am sure that by saying so you don't compare them with hockey, basketball, or soccer players."

–"Certainly not. What happens today in the entertainment business is totally out of control and says a lot about how we are wasting our time, energy, and money these days. When I was in high school, I had no television, no telephone, and, obviously, no car. The only entertainment was reading books, listening to radio, which couldn't catch too many stations without interfering noise anyway, or going to a movie theater once a week and to a soccer match every other Sunday. We had to go to school every day, six times a week. The moments of happiness were only on Saturdays when, in evening, I could relax reading second and third hand detective novels, which very often had missing pages at the beginning and even at the end of them, leaving you uncertain about who the murderer really was. And look now how much time is spent with watching hundreds of television channels, listening to sophisticated audio equipment, browsing the internet, talking on the cellular telephones, going to expensive sports arenas and stadiums, or driving fast cars. I don't want to sound like a moralist, because now I spend a lot of time in front of the small screen myself, but there is little time left for reading books and especially for thinking. It is a major problem, mainly for young people, and somebody needs a powerful will to avoid being taken by the general flow.

This doesn't mean, however, that what is going on now is entirely detrimental to the individual. It is impressive to see how much information we have today about what happens everywhere in the world and how many people are concerned about what to do for fixing the wrongs and for choosing better ways of solving the problems of humanity as a whole. All this makes me think that maybe Theilard de Chardin was somehow right at least in one of his predictions."

THEILARD DE CHARDIN

–"Who is he? I never heard about him."

–"I am not a religious person even if, two days ago, during the terrible thunderstorm we faced up in the mountains, I would have said something different, but I like to visit churches wherever I go and especially when there is no religious service going on in there. Churches, either small ones or big cathedrals, and monasteries, are ideal places to spend some time and meditate mainly when there is nobody around you.

Once, in Liverpool, I entered the new and modern cathedral they built there not so long ago. On a table, close to the main entrance, I saw a couple of books, among which several were written by Pierre Theilard de Chardin. As I knew nothing about that name and the prices of the books were unusually low, I bought a copy of some of them. Theilard de Chardin was a French Jesuit father who was also a scientist of world renown, interested in paleontology. He traveled a lot and, if I remember well, he was involved in the discovery of the old Pekin Man in China. His books are not really religious books but rather collections of comments, essays, and confessions that have a special flavour, being written by a priest who was primarily a scientist. Back in Manchester, I read *The Phenomenon of Man* in three days. The book was written around 1940 and is focused on humanity as a whole, as a big system that is still in expansion but soon is going to enter a phase of involution, characterized by an increase in complexity, evolving towards the apparition of a global conscience of all humans, acting as essential parts of a unique, global, planetary entity. Being very much familiar with the pessimistic views propagated by physicists about more disorder and thermic death of the universe induced by the law of increasing global entropy, it was refreshing to see that somebody looked at the positive evolution towards more order and complexity, at least in a small part of the universe where we live.

If we look at the last 50 years, we can see that many extraordinary things have happened on this line. We know much much more about what is going on elsewhere, due to the tremendous progress in global communication, we travel more, are more concerned about injustice, abuse, or tragedies, are more willing to help those in need, and are more and more involved in global organizations, agreements, and events. Things are not simple, however, and this process of involution towards the creation of a unique, global human conscience is not smooth at all.

Remarkably, Theilard de Chardin wasn't afraid to deal with the

place and part of evil in a world in evolution. I have said remarkably because the origin and presence of evil has been a very delicate
topic in any religious doctrine. Theilard de Chardin didn't ignore the
presence of evil in this world and looked at it from a systemic view.
If I remember well, he mentioned the evil of disorder and failure, the
evil of decomposition, the evil of solitude and anxiety, and the evil of
growth. *The Phenomenon of Man* conveys a very rare refreshing optimism about the evolution of humanity as a whole, in contrast with so
many very pessimistic predictions about the future.

For instance, many years ago, Dennis L. Meadows, Donella Meadows, and Jorgen Randers published a very pessimistic book entitled
The Limits to Growth, which, as the title obviously suggests, reminded
us that the population of our planet increases much more rapidly than
the resources needed to sustain it. Sadly enough, almost everybody
is afraid that this is indeed so. This is why I was delighted when,
about ten years later, a little booklet written by James Botkin, Mahdi
Elmandjra, and Mircea Malitza, tried also to remind us, as its well-
chosen title says, that there are *No Limits to Learning.*

As a teacher, I am obviously happy when somebody highlights the
importance of learning. It is interesting that just where the forecast
is more pessimistic, we often could expect a major breakthrough, that
solves unexpectedly the respective dilemma. Thus, long long ago, before the trains were invented, taking into account the increase in the
number of roads and travellers who used coaches, the future looked
bleak due to the insufficient number of horses needed to cope with such
an increase in transportation needs. Who is using horses for public
transportation today?

In more recent times, I remember that when I was still a student
and the first computers started to be built, taking a lot of room space,
the predictions about building even more powerful computers were very
dark, based on the general belief, at that time, that the more powerful
a computer is the bigger it should be. And look at the light and tiny
laptop computers of today, incomparably more powerful, that can be
carried easier than an attaché case."

– "Some colleagues of mine had such laptop computers. I couldn't
buy one because they are still too expensive for me but even my pro-

grammable pocket calculator does a lot of things and I don't really know how it works."

COMPUTERS

−"In a couple of months the price of the laptop computers will go down. The positive result of the fierce competition between companies manufacturing such computers is that better and better types of computers come up, at more affordable prices. The negative result is that the old software is replaced by new software requiring to be installed only on new types of computers. This new software becomes also available in new forms, switching from large format disks to small diskettes and now to CDs. In this way you are forced to buy new types of computers more often than it should be. Now, a certain type of computer becomes obsolete in about ten years. I find this terrible. We are indirectly forced to throw away computers that are not out of order but simply obsolete and unfitted for the new software available which also requires more and more memory. Consequently, we have to spend more and more time learning how to use new computers and new software packages instead of focusing on solving our mathematical problems. It is a vicious circle or, better said, a vicious ascending spiral.

But the progress is not related only to getting faster and more powerful computers. The software has also evolved dramatically. At the beginning, the computers did only numerical computations. Later, they became useful for drawing graphs or plotting in one, two, or three dimensions. Now, it is possible to do symbolic mathematics on the computer as well. Due to ingenious software packages, like *Mathematica*, created in the United States by Stephen Wolfram, or *Maple*, created in your country Canada, for instance, you can manipulate algebraic formalism, use expressions and functions in analytical form, calculate derivatives, integrals, optimize functions without or with constraints, solve or approximate systems of equations, solve differential equations, and apply statistical techniques for getting confidence intervals or testing statistical hypotheses. It is something nobody could even dream about, twenty years ago.

I frequently have used in my own research the computer package *Mathematica* and once, when I wrote a letter to the Wolfram Institute, who created it, asking for a new version of the package, I expressed my admiration about what can be done with this computer software saying that 'I really don't know whether it was created by God or Devil'. A lady working for Wolfram Institute promptly answered back saying 'Let us say that it was created by God'.

More than that, the entire printing industry has also dramatically changed. There are computer packages allowing to type and print in any imaginable form, colour, and font any kind of text and to insert pictures and graphics wherever we want. I believe that the creation of the package *TeX* by Donald Knuth and its variant *LaTeX*, ideal for printing mathematical texts of any degree of sophistication, is the most major accomplishment in the printing industry after the great discovery made by Johann Gutenberg (1400-1468), the inventor of printing from metal movable types in Germany, very long ago. I remember that, when I was a little child, I used to visit an old man, in the basement of a small printing house, and look how he patiently arranged small leaden characters, one by one, for assembling the hard pages of some books to be printed. I was fascinated by his work and sometimes he gave me even something to work on, like printing numbers on some standard notebooks and receipt forms, giving me the possibility to earn some money for doing that. I still remember the heavy machines around there and the smell of lead and ink everywhere. Now, I printed three mathematical books of mine, in my own office, using *LaTeX*, my computer, and my own laser printer. The publisher simply bounded them artistically, added nice hard covers, made copies, and distributed them. But I am still thinking of the old man from the basement of the small printing house who was so happy to be the first one to read the pages of a new book still smelling of fresh ink.

Speaking about computers, the big danger is that the new, user friendly computer softwares containing easier and easier to use packages for solving specific problems, numerically or symbolically, create the illusion that we are more and more powerful. We are more powerful indeed but, more often than not, we don't know much about what they really do. For instance, for solving an optimization problem, we are told how to put data in and what commands to use for getting the answer to our problem. But the main programs and files, which in fact solve the problem itself, are hidden and we have no direct control on them. As I mentioned yesterday, it is like a new religion, 'believe it and don't ask why'. I like to repeat that, before, we were instructed with the details about how to prepare a chicken soup. Now, we are not given any details about how to do it and we are told that it is enough to use only one command, 'Give me a chicken soup', and it is given to you. Much simpler, of course, but we know nothing about how to do it. This is obviously useful for people who use a computer software in doing their routine work but, certainly, is not good for teaching and doing research when, more often than not, you have to write your own programs for solving new problems that are not standard ones. In my own applied mathematics courses, I try to keep the balance between using the existing computer packages, because it would be stupid to ignore their availability for solving standard problems, and teaching my students detailed rules and languages for writing their own programs in dealing with nonstandard types of problems.

The main topics in mathematics, at least those chapters that are taught in class, don't change as fast as the computers do. New types of hardware and software come up as many as the mushrooms after rain. All the time! Among the academic people I know, computer scientists are the ones who get more major bouts of depression or, sometimes, simply give up. It is hard to keep track of new developments. Worse than that, each software company upgrades its versions at a terrifying pace. An unwritten law requires that each new version should include the commands from previous versions or at least explain by what they have been replaced if abandoned. But more and more software companies don't do this, making old programs obsolete and forcing you to buy the new stuff.

Recently, dealing with a new version, the 14th, of a computer package popular in operations research and statistics, when I used an important command 'store', present in previous versions of the same package and very useful for creating subprograms inside the main program, I got the message: 'Unknown command'. When, mischievously, I used an arbitrary word instead, like 'orange' for instance, which had nothing to do with that software, the message from the computer was the same: 'Unknown command'. Once the old important command 'store' had been replaced, for whatever reasons, it would have been not only normal, but professionally ethical, to mention something like: 'This command is no longer available in this version. It could be replaced by doing this or that, whatever.' I called the company by telephone, to politely raise this problem. 'Press 1', 'Press 2', 'Press 1' again, and finally I had to leave a message. They didn't call back, of course. I sent an e-mail with the same content, but I got no answer either. Perhaps I was too polite. The funny thing is that the competition between different companies, on one side, and the market needs, on the other side, make the new computers and software packages better, with some exceptions, however. But for the users, this permanent change makes life miserable."

–"What does happen with the old computers when they become obsolete?"

–"It is sad to see how they are simply thrown away like any piece of garbage. There are cases, however, when an old computer can still be better than a new one!"

–"This is hard to believe."

–"I know, but I can give you such an example. I have a very nice software for playing chess against the computer. Installed and used on a new computer, everything goes so fast that it is impossible to clearly see the computer's responses to your own moves. It is really very annoying, if not even impossible, to play a normal chess game. On the contrary, installed and run on my first computer, bought a quarter of a century ago, both my moves and computer's moves are done at a slow pace and, therefore, are clearly visible on the screen. This is why I am still keeping my old computer, which hasn't even a hard disk, and perhaps only a museum would be interested in acquiring it. But I need it for playing chess, mainly after my future retirement."

Abandoning the discussion about computer hardware and software, we descended to the village and this time it was finally my turn to invite John to stop at the small Coffee Shop, on the main road, and he graciously accepted, reminding me that: 'It has been often said that mathematics is a collection of theorems and proofs written with coffee.'

With only three other customers in the shop, two very young wait-resses were more than willing to serve us. We chose a table under a huge umbrella on the narrow terrace and focused on a big cappuccino with chocolate on top and a dessert consisting of a huge home made apple pie with cream on top, for each of us.

John, who was obviously more talkative than ever before, told some good jokes. Unfortunately, I remember only one of them because, un-less the serious stuff, I didn't write them down in my precious notebook at the end of the day. The joke was about a young fellow who arrived at the house of Niels Bohr, the famous Danish physicist in Copenhagen, and noticed that, on the doorstep, there was a nailed horseshoe. He then said 'How is it possible that you, a renown scientist, still believe that a horseshoe brings good luck to the owner of the house?' 'Of course that I don't believe it,' said Bohr, 'but people say that it brings luck even to those who don't believe it.'

WILL EDUCATION

After a while, I remembered something said by John that really in-terested me:

−"You have said that a young person needs a powerful will in order to resist the temptations of the modern life and focus on what really matters. I think that any student has felt the terrible discrepancy be-tween the desire to work hard and the frequent state of weakness and lack of energy, preventing him or her to do this. How is it possible to have such a strong will power for overcoming a state of laziness and indecision?"

−"It is very difficult to give a general advice. Each human being is unique and something that proves to be useful for somebody doesn't work for somebody else.

Speaking about myself, I have to go back to my father. He was around 40 years old when I was born. Due to the age difference and his very reserved way of being, always listening but speaking very little, I could barely cover one page with what I know about him and his life. I am very grateful to him for at least two things. First, contrary to the pressure put on me by other members of my family to get a diploma in engineering, he simply said to me: 'Do what you want to do. I have never been happy with what I did in my life.' Then I decided to become a mathematician even if this would normally imply to become a high school teacher, a very demanding but very poorly paid job back then. I have never regretted my decision and I never became a high school teacher either, even if I have always had a tremendous respect for this noble profession. Second, one day, when I was about fifteen years old, my father gave me a book written by a French author, Jules Payot, entitled *Will Education*. He never ever asked me about that book which, in the meantime, has become my bible. For many years, I used to read two pages from it, every day, and think about their content. Even now, I have it on my desk and I look from time to time into its pages that have become yellow with the passage of time.

Such a book cannot be summarized. It has to be read, reread, and thought about it. I warmly recommend it to you. It is written in an informal way and explains the relationship between ideas, sentiments, and actions. We have power on our ideas coming from outside or from inside, but their power on us is very weak. It is very easy to say 'Tomorrow, I will start a new life', or 'Tomorrow, I will give up smoking', which are noble ideas, but in fact nothing really changes. On the other hand, sentiments have a tremendous power on us but our power on them is negligible. The book analyzes carefully the difference between the sentiments favourable and the sentiments unfavourable to our willpower. Time is our great liberator. The only successful strategy for intelligence is to associate itself with time and, through a persevering strategy, to use the favourable sentiments and cope against unfavourable sentiments in order to acquire durable good habits which allow the ideas to transform themselves into actions. In order to make the association between ideas and actions strong and durable it must be forged at the warmth of the affective feelings. The book discusses the important role played by the personal meditation in getting a close insight into what we have to do, about our failures and usual mistakes, and about the best ways for achieving our goals. In order to be effective, the reflexive meditation has to be specific and concrete, replacing the words by images viewed in the slightest details. We have to see, smell, and hear our thoughts. In intellectual realm we have to think permanently on the topics and problems we work on. Contrary, in coping with sentimental dreaming, for instance, success is achieved if you never think about, leaving unfavourable sentiments to die of hunger, as to speak, or, if they are too persistent, you have to analyze critically the reasons and ideas they are based upon.

I am afraid that I am talking now in a somewhat schematic way but the book contains many examples from its author's personal experience. It is much more than a reminder of well-known motherly or fatherly advices like 'Don't postpone for tomorrow what you can do today', or 'Very often we waste our time simply because we didn't decide beforehand what to do on the next day', or 'Be aware of the usual occasions when you are wasting your time and try to avoid them'. It thoroughly discusses the mechanism of getting more control on your personal life.

I got a lot of energy from reading the book. The two extreme opinions about human character are Immanuel Kant's and Arthur Schopenhauer's theories that the character is inherited when we are born and remains so whatever we do, on one side, and the so called theory of 'free will', according to which we can change our character by simply deciding to do so. Jules Payot's book considers that the truth is somewhere in the middle: the human character may be changed but not by a simple decision as the adepts of the free will theory are claiming. It needs time, perseverance, and the use of the association between ideas and actions at the warmth of the favourable sentiments. Time uses, against us or in our favour, the dominant law of psychology, which is the law of association, for destroying old habits, bad or good, or for creating new habits, good or bad. Time is our precious friend when we allow it to use the law of association for creating good habits and for destroying bad habits. Time could be our great liberator. In its struggle against the blind and forceful sentiments, the personal intelligence, conscious of its limited powers, will try to associate with time and, by a patient but persevering tactics in using time for creating good living and working habits, will succeed to win more often and even conquer the dominant role over the sentiments."

–"Wow, I am going to look for this book! When was it published?"

−"The first edition of the book was published in France at the beginning of the twentieth century but it has been reprinted many times and translated in many languages. There will be no problem at all for you to find it in Toronto, I am sure. I do recommend it to you."

TEACHING MATHEMATICS

−"You haven't told me yet about your personal work as a professional mathematician."

−"I hoped that you would forget about this request. Nobody really likes to talk about himself. Anyway, I don't. If you insist, however, to find something about my own experience, I could say that now, approaching the retirement age and looking back at all those past years, I could say that I was a better teacher than researcher. I have always liked to teach. I have been helped by the old type of academic education when, as a student, I had to pass oral exams not only written ones. Strangely enough, in more and more universities today, a student could graduate without ever writing on the blackboard or ever talking to his or her professors. I write on the blackboard everything, trying to be as systematic as possible, proving everything in front of the students without looking into textbooks and without using notes, except for some numerical examples scratched on a minuscule piece of paper when needed. I have learned this from my violin teacher, a great little man who studied music in Vienna, and who always insisted that concerts have to be played from the heart and not looking into written scores."

−"So, you are also a violinist. I am very impressed because I don't know how to play any musical instrument but I like listening to music even more than watching movies."

−"Oh, no. I have been a very mediocre violinist. In fact, as I already told you before, I think, I always wanted to be a second rate pianist playing background improvisations in a third rate bar or restaurant, but I had no piano back then. Now, I have a small electronic organ and sometimes, rarely in fact, I play on it in the basement of my house, only for myself, and only as an amateur who never really studied how to play on a keyboard instrument. Violin is a very pretentious instrument because you have to create the sounds and it could be mastered only after a lot of daily exercise. All my violinist colleagues had a little lump under their chin, as a result of playing at least four hours every day. My chin was smooth and clean, reflecting how little work I put in playing my violin. A piano has all the sounds ready available and also the advantage of allowing more sounds to be played simultaneously, resulting in more harmony and self accompaniment. It certainly has, however, less 'soul' than a violin.

But let me go back to my teaching mathematics. The students have a tremendous respect when they see a teacher who can lecture without looking into written notes, without projecting transparencies prepared in advance for an overhead projector, or without using the computer power-point system for public presentations on a big screen. I do believe that everything has to be elaborated right there, on the blackboard, in front of the students, using only a piece of chalk, as in the old times, without any display of materials previously prepared. I use also many comments and stories about the history of mathematics and I give about 120 typed pages with problems, hints, and solutions for individual homework.

All these being said, am I an excellent teacher? Objectively speaking, the answer is no. Not because of some kind of modesty from my part but because lecturing only is not the best way of teaching. When you write everything on the blackboard and explain the smallest details for a good understanding, this is indeed a good teaching strategy. I use to tell my students that in mathematics we cannot understand everything in class, like in some other disciplines. They are supposed to go home, take a piece of paper and a pencil, and go again through all the topics taught in class. And for doing this, they need good lecture notes taken in class. Lecturing, however, is not the ideal way of teaching. The students should be actively involved in the teaching process itself. Instead of taking notes passively and asking sporadically some questions, they should come themselves to the blackboard and participate, along myself, in the elaboration of the lecture itself, debating and arguing with other colleagues. But, with so many students enrolled in the mathematics courses these days, this participatory way of teaching is practically impossible. Also, such an active way of teaching presupposes that the students come to class always prepared about what was previously taught and discussed. This is also something which simply doesn't happen. The tremendous majority of students study only a couple of days before a test or exam. Perhaps a tutorial with small groups of students could work better but, more often than not, the appointed tutors or teaching assistants don't put much effort in this kind of teaching activity, being more concerned about their own research and career prospects.

I have been lucky enough to teach mainly applied courses for third year and fourth year undergraduate students and some more specialized courses for graduate students. It is much more difficult to teach courses in big lecture halls filled with first year or second year students. Marking tests and exam papers is also a big nuisance. I always mark the tests and final exams myself. Perhaps I ought to trust more my teaching assistants, allowing them to mark at least some tests, but marking myself is the best way of getting a feedback from my students about what they have or haven't understood. Marking takes a lot of time, it is true, but not so much if the tests and exam papers are well prepared, with short, clear, and independent questions.

I generally assign ten marks for a correct answer to a question and gradually less, using integers, if there are mistakes or omissions, down to zero if there is absolutely nothing there. Once, a student wrote me a poem instead of the answer to a question and I obviously had to give him a zero for it, to my regret because the poem was nice. Different colleagues have very different philosophies about marking. The most radical one used to give to each answer either all the marks assigned to the respective question or nothing at all, saying that in mathematics something is either correct or not, refusing to give any partial marks. A little less radical colleague used only three marks, namely, 0 for nothing, 1 for attempt, and 2 for a correct answer, regardless of how long or difficult the respective answer was supposed to be. At the other side of the marking scheme, another colleague used to assign a total number of 3627 or 4823 marks for a test containing about six problems, willing to give marks for partial answers to the problems. I have never understood how could she make a distinction between an answer worth 747 marks and another one worth 741 marks? Somebody else, regardless of the marking scheme, systematically used to give very few marks from the maximum allowed, severely penalizing the slightest mistake or omission, even the spelling or grammar errors. At the end of the academic year, however, before deciding about the final grades, he automatically gave extra 20% marks to each of the relatively few students who still remained in his class. Many weird things happen in different departments and who really knows whose philosophy is better?"

–"Have you had PhD students as well?"

–"Yes. Ten of them finished and got the PhD degree and six of those have academic positions right now. I have to admit, however, that I didn't help them too much. It is true that to some of them I suggested the topic of their future PhD theses and I gave them references and some personal opinion, but nothing more. I tried, however, to solve all administrative burdens and help my PhD students meet all the required norms and deadlines of the PhD program. I am also proud that I never added my own signature on a paper written by a PhD student of mine. I have seen too many examples in which such a thing was done as a mater-of-fact. I believe that it is a risky responsibility to direct a young mind along a certain direction. Something that you think to be important maybe is not, or not suited for the aptitudes and tastes of a young mind at the beginning of a career in mathematics.

I know an old professor who, every time when a young mathematician came to see him about starting a doctorate with him, used to ask: 'Have you written your PhD thesis?' As, obviously, the answer of the candidate was: 'No, professor. I just want to start working on a PhD under your supervision,' the professor continued unbent: 'Go home young man, work hard, following your own ideas, if you have them, and when you finish your PhD thesis, come to see me and let me have a look at it.' We can smile about it but there was something serious in what the old professor demanded. A genuine PhD thesis in mathematics must be an original contribution, not only a compilation of known things or the result of the accumulation of data collected on the field or in a laboratory, no matter how much effort such a collecting and assembling work would require. And any spark of originality has more chances to arise when it comes from a question or problem asked by yourself and not given to you by somebody else. If after five years of undergraduate and graduate courses, in bachelor and master's programs, you couldn't find some topic which really appeals to you, feel comfortable with, and detect an open problem that would really interest you, then perhaps going for a PhD in mathematics is not a good idea to pursue."

–"What specific courses have you taught?"

–"I have taught probability theory, statistics, information theory, and, in the last 25 years, operations research."

–"This sounds Chinese to me. They seem to be very different from algebra, geometry, or calculus."

PROBABILITY THEORY

–"Yes and no. They deal with specific problems but, all of them, use algebra, calculus, and even geometry as prerequisites. Thus, probability theory is not so young. It started with a dialog between Blaise Pascal and Pierre de Fermat on how to deal mathematically with the games of chance. It is said that towards the middle of the 17th century, Blaise Pascal met le Chevalier de Méré, during a travel, who asked two questions about games of chance. The first question was about tossing two dice simultaneously: what is the minimum number of such repeated tosses for having a probability larger than 0.5 of getting 6 on both dice at least once? The second question referred to two players who play repeatedly a game of chance in which each of them has equal chances of winning. At the beginning, both players put the same amount of money in a bank. The total amount is going to be taken by the first player who wins a certain number of games, let's say 25. The problem is how to divide the total amount of money from the bank if, for whatever reasons, they stop playing after fewer number of games have been completed, let's say 13, and neither player has reached the number of games required; let's say that the players have won 5 and 8 games out of 13, respectively. Pascal informed Fermat about these problems and they exchanged several letters about the games of chance and this was how the calculus of probabilities started.

The first models were simple but still challenging and, gradually, the probability theory was being built. An important moment was the publication of the book *La théorie analytique de la probabilité*, written by Pierre Simon de Laplace around 1812, perhaps the first modern book on probability theory, introducing a formalism and notations that are used even now.

Today, probability theory is presented in the general framework of measure theory, due to a seminal book written by Andrei Nikolaevich Kolmogorov in 1933. Basically, to define a probability space means to give a set of elementary events, a class of events, and a probability measure on this class of events. An event is a set of possible elementary events. Logical operations on events, like the nonexclusive disjunction 'or', which describes the union, or alternative occurrence of events, the conjunction 'and', which describes the intersection, or simultaneous occurrence of events, and the negation 'non', which describes the complementary event, give events belonging to the same class of events. The impossible event, denoted with the same symbol as the empty set $\emptyset$, also belongs to the given class of events.

The probability of an event is a real number between 0 and 1. The probability space assigned to the probabilistic experiment 'rolling a fair die' has the occurrence of 1, 2, 3, 4, 5, or 6 as elementary events, any subset of elementary events is an event, like 'getting an even number' which corresponds to the subset consisting of the elementary events $\{2, 4, 6\}$, for instance. The six elementary events are equally likely when the die is fair, and the probability of any event is the sum of the probabilities of the elementary events making up the respective event. Thus, the probability of the event 'getting an even number', which consists of the elementary events 2, 4, and 6, has the probability $1/2$.

Getting randomly a hand of five cards from a well shuffled standard deck of 52 cards offers a much more interesting probability space and we can calculate the probability of getting any combination of five cards, like the probability of getting a royal flush, for instance.

The set of elementary events is not necessarily finite, but could be infinite and countable, like the set of positive integers, for instance, or even infinite and uncountable, like the points of an interval on the real line. The events could occur independently, or could be dependent in which case conditional probabilities are defined and used. The conditional probability of an event A given another event B, which means the probability of A if the event B occurs, denoted by $P(A \mid B)$ is equal to the probability of the event 'A and B', denoted by $P(A \cap B)$, divided by the probability of B, denoted by $P(B)$.

Probability theory deals with rules for calculating the probability of compound events and with the probability distributions induced by random variables. In general, a random variable assigns a well defined real number to each elementary event. What makes it different from a function studied in calculus is that it takes on some numerical values with some probabilities. For instance, we can talk about a finite discrete random variable X which takes on the values $-2.5, 1.2, 3.2$ with the probabilities $0.3, 0.2, 0.5$, respectively. The set of possible values of a continuous random variable X could be the set of all real numbers, or the set of all real numbers larger than a certain real number, smaller than a certain real number, or in between two real numbers. In such a case, a probability density $f(x)$ is assigned to the random variable X, which is a nonnegative function, whose integral on the set of all possible values of X is equal to 1. The probability that X takes values between two real numbers $a < b$ is $P(a < X \leq b) = \int_a^b f(x)\,dx$.

If X is a discrete or continuous random variable, its cumulative probability distribution function F, defined on the real line, gives the probability that the respective random variable is smaller than or equal to any real number, namely $F(x) = P(X \leq x)$. For different types of probability distributions, there are tables with the values taken on by the corresponding cumulative probability distribution functions. They are also provided by many computer software packages available today. When the cumulative probability distribution function F is known, we can always approximate the probability that the corresponding random variable X takes on values in between any real numbers $a < b$, because $P(a < X \leq b) = F(b) - F(a)$.

Even when the set of elementary events is an uncountable infinite set, a random variable defined on it could have a finite number of possible values, an infinite but countable set of possible values, or an infinite uncountable set of possible values. Consequently, a random variable is said to be discrete and finite, discrete and countable, and continuous, respectively.

To any random variable X we assign its mean value, denoted by μ, or more generically $E(X)$, called also its expectation, reflecting the trend, or probabilistic average, of the possible values of that random variable. It is equal to the sum, or series, $\mu = \sum_x x\, P(X = x)$, in the discrete finite, or discrete countable case, respectively, or the integral $\mu = \int_D x\, f(x)\, dx$, in the continuous case on the domain D, involving the product between the possible values of the random variable and their corresponding probabilities or probability density of these values.

The variance of a random variable X, denoted by σ^2, or generically by $V(X)$, reflects the mean squared deviations of its values from the mean value, which is the mean value of $(X - \mu)^2$, namely $V(X) = E((X - \mu)^2)$. The square root of the variance is called the standard deviation σ of the random variable X."

−"I assume that the notions of random variables, cumulative probability distribution, mean value, and standard deviation are the same as the ones mentioned by you when you talked about simulation. As I got lost, can you explain again, please, how the cumulative probability distribution, the mean, and the variance are defined?"

−"Yes, they are basically the same fundamental concepts that are used in simulation, probability theory, and statistics. But I am afraid that I wasn't explicit enough. Therefore, let me elaborate again about them, but slower this time.

If a probabilistic experiment consists of rolling a pair of fair dice, the elementary events are the 36 pairs (1,1), (1,2),..., (6,6) showing up on the two dice. If we assign to each such pair the sum of the two numbers, we obtain a finite discrete random variable X whose possible values are 2, 3,... 12, with corresponding probabilities 1/36, 2/36, 3/36, 4/36, 5/36, 6/36, 7/36, 6/36, 5/36, 4/36, 3/36, 2/36, 1/36, because the possible value 3, for instance, occurs when the elementary event, or outcome of the probabilistic experiment, is either (1,2) or (2,1).

The set of possible values of the random variable together with their corresponding probabilities form, together, the probability distribution of that random variable. For a discrete random variable, the corresponding probability distribution is described by a table listing the possible values of the random variable in one row and their corresponding probabilities in a second row.

For a continuous random variable, the corresponding probability distribution is defined by a curve, called probability density function, over the set of elementary events which could be either an interval on the real line, or the nonnegative real line, or the entire real line. As I said before, the mean value μ, or $E(X)$, of a discrete random variable X is obtained by multiplying each possible value of X with its corresponding probability and summing up all the values thus obtained. If X is a continuous random variable, its mean value $E(X)$ is obtained by integrating the product between a possible value x of the random variable X and the probability distribution density function of X at x, on the set of elementary events. The variance $V(X)$ of the random variable X, discrete or continuous, is obtained by calculating the mean value of the squared differences between the possible values of X and its mean value $E(X)$.

To each random variable, be it discrete or continuous, we attach the so called cumulative probability distribution function, defined on the entire real line and having values between 0 and 1. It does what its name says, namely, it cumulates the probabilities of the corresponding probability distribution. The value of the corresponding cumulative probability distribution function at the real number x is the probability that the respective random variable doesn't exceed the value x. For a discrete random variable, the cumulative probability distribution function is a non-decreasing step function, like mounting stairs, taking different increasing discrete values, going up from 0 to 1. In our last example, the values of the cumulative probability distribution function of X at 1, 3, 7.5, and 13 are equal to 0, 3/36, 21/36, and 1, respectively. For a continuous random variable X, the value of its cumulative probability distribution function at the real number x is obtained by integrating its probability density function on the set of real numbers less than or equal to x.

Different kinds of probability distribution functions have been studied. One of the most important continuous probability distributions met in applications is the so called normal distribution $N(\mu, \sigma^2)$, already mentioned when we discussed about simulation, whose probability density function is a symmetric, bell-shaped function defined on the entire real line, centered at the mean value μ of the respective random variable, having two inflexion points at a distance $+\sigma$ and $-\sigma$ from the mean value μ, where σ is the standard deviation, and tending asymptotically to zero when the possible values of X increase or decrease indefinitely. The probability density of a normal distribution resembles Napoleon's hat, a comparison I like to make frequently. The so-called standard normal probability distribution $N(0,1)$ has the mean value equal to 0 and the variance, and standard deviation too, equal to 1. The corresponding probability density function is a bell-shaped function centered at the origin, having the inflexion points at -1 and $+1$, tending asymptotically to 0 when the possible values x of X increase or decrease indefinitely.

It is not the right moment and place to give details about what kind of specific results are proved in probability theory. Many such results belong to the so called 'law of large numbers', that shows that in spite of randomness, there is some kind of surprising regularity if we take into account many similar cases or occurrences. I want to mention only one such result, known as the 'central limit theorem', which is somehow mystic indeed.

In general, we standardize a random variable if we subtract its mean value from its possible values and divide everything by its standard deviation. A standardized random variable has the mean equal to 0 and the standard deviation equal to 1. According to the 'central limit theorem', the standardized sum of n arbitrary independent random variables, identically distributed, behaves like the standard normal variable when n is large. There are many many possible probability distributions, but whatever it is, the standardized sum of independent random variables distributed this way, has a bell-shaped probability distribution centered at the origin with standard deviation equal to 1. Practically, a rule of thumb says that the sum has to contain more than 100 terms. This general result shows that, somehow, the standard normal probability distribution reflects a general law in this world. This result is essentially used in statistical inference based on random sampling.

Probability theory is continued by the theory of stochastic processes. Here time becomes an essential variable. Roughly speaking, a stochastic process is a family of random variables $X(t)$, one at each time instant t of a certain time domain T. This time domain could be a finite interval $[t_0, t_1]$, or an infinite interval $[t_0, +\infty)$. Thus, a stochastic process describes a random evolution in time. The random variables $X(t)$ are dependent, and could have different kinds of joint probability distributions. The main objective is to study the family of possible trajectories of the stochastic process and its asymptotic behaviour describing what happens when time goes on, increasing indefinitely. The mean trajectory is the curve $E(X(t))$, as a function of time t. The variances $V(X(t))$ measure the mean fluctuations around the mean trajectory. The dependence between the state of the process at time t_1 and the state of the process at time t_2 is measured by the so-called covariance, $C(t_1, t_2)$, which is the expected value of the product of the deviations of $X(t_1)$ and $X(t_2)$ from their mean values, with respect to the joint probability distribution of the pair of random variables $(X(t_1), X(t_2))$ of the stochastic process. A stochastic process is like a random kind of motion, very far from the strictly deterministic Newton's mechanics. The stock market can be interpreted only as a stochastic process, for instance."

–"I have an old uncle who every time I visit him is asking me: 'What did you learn in school about winning the lottery?' If I decide to study mathematics and take a probability theory course, perhaps I shall be able to give my uncle some useful advice about this."

–"I am afraid that after taking such a course you could tell him only three things. First, that the probability of getting 6 winning numbers out of 49, as the biggest win at Lotto 6/49 requires, is extremely small. In general, the number of subsets containing k distinct objects out of a set of n objects is given by the number of combinations of n objects taken k at a time, which is $n!/(k!(n-k)!)$, where $n!$ is the product of all positive integers from 1 to n. Therefore, the number of subsets of 6 distinct numbers from the set containing the first 49 positive integers is the number of combinations of 49 objects taken 6 at a time, which is equal to $49!/(6!43!) = 13983816$. Obviously, only one of this subsets will be the winner. Thus, if you buy one lottery ticket, the probability of getting the winning combination is $1/13983816 = 0.00000007151$. Second, if your uncle really wants to give fate a chance to help him win Lotto 6/49, tell him to buy only one ticket, because if he buys two tickets, the probability of winning will be 0.00000014302 which is almost as small as the previous one. As calculus teaches us, if ε is a very small positive number, $\varepsilon + \varepsilon$ is practically ε as well. Third, your uncle can win with certainty if he buys all 13983816 distinct tickets of 6 numbers, where two tickets are distinct if they differ by at least one number; but, doing this, there are also chances of sharing the big win with other winning players, which could dramatically diminish the prize money your uncle would actually win."

STATISTICS

–"I am sure that my uncle, who lives on a modest pension, cannot afford to put down the amount of money needed for buying all the tickets. But I want to ask you something else. What is the difference between probability theory and statistics? I have heard more about the last one from looking into the business section of the newspaper *Globe and Mail*, in Toronto."

–"During my stay in Canada, I noticed that statistics is very important in the curriculum of North American Universities. Also, many students need knowledge in statistics in order to get jobs with major banks and big or small companies. Statistics uses elementary probability theory but has its specific problems related to dealing with large or small data sets obtained from sampling.

The basic concept is indeed random sampling. More often than not, we don't know a certain characteristic of a large set of entities called population. As this characteristic can take on different values for different elements of the population, it is a random variable whose probability distribution depends on some unknown parameters, like its mean value and its standard deviation, that have to be estimated from a random sample. If such a characteristic has its possible values normally distributed, for instance, then this probability distribution essentially depends on two unknown parameters, namely the mean value μ and the standard deviation σ of that characteristic for the entire population, called the population mean value and the population standard deviation, respectively. These two population parameters are unknown and unaccessible to us because the entire population cannot be examined in the majority of real cases. What we can do, however, is to take a random sample, ideally of large size n, from the respective population, to measure the value of that characteristic for each entity from the sample, and calculate the mean value $\overline{x}$ and the standard deviation s of the values thus obtained, called the sample mean and the sample standard deviation, respectively. Using these values, we have to estimate the mean value of the characteristic for the entire population.

In order to be cautious, the estimation is given not as a number but as a confidence interval, centered at the sample mean $\overline{x}$, such that we can say that we are only 95% sure, or 99% sure, depending on the significance level 0.05, or 0.01, respectively, chosen by us, that the true value of the mean value of that characteristic for the entire population is somewhere between a lower bound and an upper bound. The two bounds of the confidence interval essentially depend on the sample mean and the sample standard deviation. In fact the difference between the upper bound and the lower bound, which gives the length of the respective confidence interval, is proportional to the so-called standard error of the mean, which is the ratio between the sample standard deviation s and the square root of the sample size $\sqrt{n}$.

As you can see, the main objective in statistics is to draw general conclusions about a very large, even infinite population, using the results from a finite random sample obtained by the statistician."

–"You mentioned before the mean and standard deviation of a random variable. If a sample is a set of observed or measured numbers, how do we calculate the sample mean and the sample standard deviation? Is this similar to what you explained when you talked about Buffon's needle?"

–"Yes, it is. In fact the computation is very simple and, often, even simple pocket calculators have two keys for getting them directly. Thus, if the observed or measured values are the real numbers $x_1, \ldots, x_n$, where n is the sample size, then the sample mean is just the average, $\overline{x} = (x_1 + \ldots + x_n)/n$, and the sample standard deviation s is the positive square root of the sample variance whose simple expression is $s^2 = [(x_1 - \overline{x})^2 + \ldots + (x_n - \overline{x})^2]/(n-1)$. These formulas are indeed the same as those mentioned when I talked about simulation."

–"It seems that the larger the sample size, the better the approximation. But what does a random sample really mean?"

–"As we want to draw conclusions about a very large population based on a small subset of selected elements of the population, our conclusions could be wrong if we don't give equal chances to all elements of the population to be selected in the sample. The sample is good if it is representative for the population we are sampling from.

Let us say that we want to estimate the mean height of the male students in a certain university. Then, it would be unwise to measure only the height of some members of the basketball team of the respective university. The sample mean and sample standard deviation thus obtained would induce a very biased confidence interval for the mean height of the population of all male students from that university. Thus, in a representative sample we try to select all sorts of students, randomly chosen. Measuring the height of the male students at the cafeteria of the university at lunch time would be a better way of getting a random sample.

Thus, as you have said, we would like to have a very large sample but this is not always possible. One famous statistician, William Sealy Gosset (1876-1937), for instance, worked all his life as a brewer and statistician for Arthur Guiness Sons & Company in Dublin. He had to analyze the quality of the beer produced there but couldn't take a large sample because the analysis had to be performed fast in order to eventually bring corrections to the production process going on. Therefore, he had to study what happens when the sample size n is small, let's say, smaller than 20.

Let us assume that we have a population whose characteristic we are interested in is normally distributed with the population mean μ and population variance σ^2. If a sample of size n is given, the sample mean is a number, $\overline{x}$. If all samples of size n are taken, mentally, into account, then the sample mean takes on different values, for different samples of size n, and, therefore, it may be viewed as being a random variable $\overline{X}$. Gosset showed that the standardized sample mean $t = (\overline{X} - \mu)/(\sigma/\sqrt{n})$ has a new kind of probability distribution, similar to the normal probability distribution but still different, essentially depending on the sample size n. This new probability distribution was called by him the

'Student' distribution, also known in literature as t-distribution, with $n-1$ degrees of freedom, and not Gosset's distribution, as it should have been called, because he preferred to remain anonymous, an example of modesty very rare among the scientists whose ego reaches sometimes catastrophic proportions. When the population variance is known or is replaced by the sample variance s^2, using the 'Student' distribution we can obtain a $100(1-\alpha)\%$ confidence interval for the population mean μ, as an interval of the form: $(\bar{x} - t_{\alpha/2,n-1}\, s/\sqrt{n}, \bar{x} + t_{\alpha/2,n-1}\, s/\sqrt{n})$, where the critical point $t_{\alpha/2,n-1}$, easily available from tables which may be found in practically every textbook in statistics, is the positive real value for which the probability that $t > t_{\alpha/2,n-1}$ is equal to the small number $\alpha/2$. The standard value of α is 0.05."

–"You have mentioned the name Guiness. Has it something to do with the 'Guiness Book' of strange world records which is printed every year?"

–"As a matter-of-fact it has. As far as I know, taking into account that in Ireland, and not only there, it is raining very often and people are spending a lot of time in pubs, drinking beer and telling funny stories, one of the members of Guiness family, or company, had the idea of putting together a collection of the most extraordinary and striking facts. This is how the *Guiness Book of Records* was born. It is constantly updated because people do all sorts of strange things, all over the globe, all the time."

–"I read in newspapers that, these days, some people do very strange and eccentric things indeed, like spending a certain number of days on the top of a pole, or preparing the longest sausage ever made, for instance, just for being mentioned in the *Guiness Book of Records*. But I am sorry that I have interrupted you. Please, continue."

–"It is all right. So, we start from a random sample. A small sample or a large sample is anyway only a small subset of the population itself and statistics uses methods for drawing general conclusions about the entire population from the partial measurements and computations obtained by analyzing only the elements selected in the sample. I find this very nice and deeply human. We have a limited time, limited resources, and limited data to rely on and still want to draw general conclusions. But we have to be cautious in our estimations and, therefore, we express our predictions in terms of intervals, not sharp numbers, and we assign to these prediction intervals different levels of significance.

In fact, statistics doesn't build only confidence intervals, in what is being called estimation theory, but also tests hypotheses. A so called 'null hypothesis' makes such and such assumption about the value of an unknown parameter of a certain probability distribution of a characteristic of a population, or about the independence or the degree of dependence of two random variables, for instance. This null hypothesis is being tested against the 'alternative hypothesis' stating that what the null hypothesis says is not true. A certain sample function, called the test statistic, is introduced. For one sample of size n, where n is the number of elements, or observations, in the sample, like 12, 30, or 125, for instance, the value calculated for this test statistic is a well-defined real number. If all possible samples of size n are taken, mentally of course, into account, this test statistic takes different possible values and is a random variable whose probability distribution is known if the respective null hypothesis is assumed to be true.

Therefore, under the null hypothesis, there is a very probable interval of possible values of the test statistic and a complementary set for which there is a very small probability for the possible values of the test statistic to belong to. This last set of small probability is called the critical region of the test. When a random sample is available and the corresponding value of the test statistic falls into the critical region, having a small probability α, such a thing can happen either because the null hypothesis is true but the sample wasn't representative, but the probability of such a sampling accident is small, namely α, or because the null hypothesis is false and therefore the alternative hypothesis is true. Therefore, if the value of the test statistics, calculated from the sample available, falls into the critical region, then the statistician rejects the null hypothesis and, in doing this, the probability of making an error, which means to wrongly reject a true hypothesis, is equal to the number α, which has been chosen to be a very small positive number, like 0.05, for instance. If the value of the test statistics calculated from the sample available doesn't fall into the critical region, which means that this calculated value doesn't belong to the critical region, then the statistician doesn't reject the respective null hypothesis.

Testing hypothesis becomes a kind of subtle probabilistic logic, known as statistical inference. Again, it is nice and human to recognize that you could reject a true hypothesis but, by choosing the critical region of the test you want to keep the probability of making such an error very small. How many judges do talk openly and sincerely about the possibility of wrongly condemning an innocent person?"

–"Can you give a simple example of testing hypotheses in statistics I could understand?"

–"Yes, I can give a simple example but perhaps, this is the right moment to illustrate first the difference between taking a random sample in statistics and generating a random sample in simulation. I have already mentioned this difference before but an example will help understanding this better.

In simulation, if I want to get a representative random sample of any size, say 200, containing the outcomes of the probabilistic experiment 'tossing a fair coin' which has two possible outcomes, 'head' (or H) and 'tail' (or T), with probability 0.5 for each, it is enough to use random numbers R, from a table of random numbers uniformly distributed in the unit interval $[0, 1]$, and assign the outcome H if the corresponding random number R is smaller than or equal to 0.5, and the outcome T if the corresponding random number R is larger than 0.5. Therefore, in simulation, the probability distribution we want to take a sample from is known and, using random numbers, we can generate a representative sample, of any size we want, containing outcomes whose occurrence probabilities are those given beforehand.

In statistics, just the opposite happens. Assume that we have a coin and I don't know whether or not it is fair. If I toss this coin 200 times, then I get a sample of size 200 containing the outcomes H and T. Calculating the absolute frequencies of H and T in the sample, which means counting how many Hs and Ts we have in the sample, and dividing them by 200, we obtain their relative frequencies p and q, respectively. These relative frequencies form the sample probability distribution (p, q) of the outcomes H and T, respectively. We want to test now the so-called null hypothesis that 'the coin is fair', which is equivalent to $p = 0.5$, against the alternative hypothesis that 'the coin is not fair', which is equivalent to $p \neq 0.5$. For doing this, we may use the chi-square goodness-of-fit test introduced by Karl Pearson, one of the great English statisticians. This test uses an ingenious function, or statistic how it is also known, which measures how far a sampling probability distribution is from a given, theoretical probability distribution.

In our context, the theoretical probability distribution is the uniform distribution $(0.5, 0.5)$ assigned to the outcomes H and T. Pearson's chi-square statistic is $\chi^2 = 200[(p - 0.5)^2/0.5 + (q - 0.5)^2]/0.5]$. It is a weighted Euclidean distance. For our sample, the corresponding χ^2 is a positive number. If, however, all possible random samples of size 200 are taken into account, which can be imagined only mentally, in what is called, using a German adjective, a 'gedanken' experiment, then χ^2 takes on different positive values whose probability distribution is known and there are tables for its cumulative distribution function.

A perfect match between the sample probability distribution (p, q) and the theoretical probability distribution $(0.5, 0.5)$ would imply the value $\chi^2 = 0$, but this doesn't happen, in general. We expect, however, to have a small value for χ^2 if the null hypothesis is true and a larger value if the alternative hypothesis is true. Choosing a small positive value, say $\alpha = 0.05$, we can find from tables a so-called critical point, or critical value, $\chi^2_{1,0.05}$, corresponding to one degree of freedom and the significance level $\alpha = 0.05$, such that if the value of χ^2, calculated from the sample, is larger than the critical value $\chi^2_{1,0.05}$, we reject the null hypothesis with the significance level 0.05. If the value of χ^2, calculated from the sample is smaller than the critical value $\chi^2_{1,0.05}$, then we don't reject the null hypothesis. The critical point $\chi^2_{1,0.05}$ is chosen such that if the null hypothesis is true, the probability of the critical region $\chi^2 > \chi^2_{1,0.05}$ is equal to 0.05. The critical point used in the test depends not only on the significance level α, chosen by us, but also on the number of degrees of freedom which is equal to the number of components of the theoretical probability distribution minus one. In this example, the theoretical probability distribution has two components and, therefore, the number of degrees of freedom is $2 - 1 = 1$,

The logic behind this statistic test is very clear. If the null hypothesis is not true, we can expect a sample value of χ^2 in the critical region. If the null hypothesis is true, we can expect a sample value of χ^2 smaller than the critical value $\chi^2_{1,0.05}$, therefore a value outside the critical region. If, however, the null hypothesis is true but the sample value of χ^2 falls into the critical region, then the probability of such a thing to happen is very small, namely $\alpha = 0.05$. In this way, the probability of taking a wrong decision, rejecting a true null hypothesis, is kept very small."

–"What other names than Gosset's are famous in statistics?"

–"Several. With their fondness for empiric, it is not surprising that the most remarkable statisticians from the old generation were Englishmen, even if I don't like to classify mathematicians by their nationality. Mathematics is essentially international and perhaps the only common language of all human beings today.

But, going back to famous statisticians, I have to start with Sir Francis Galton (1822-1911), a first cousin of Charles Darwin, who introduced the so-called 'correlation', as a measure of the amount of dependence between two random variables. For two random variables, X and Y, the so called joint probability density describes the probability distribution of the pairs of possible values (x, y) of the two random variables, taken together. For each random variable, its deviation from the mean is obtained by subtracting the mean value of that random variable from each of its possible values, namely $X - E(X)$. The mean value with respect to the joint probability distribution of the product of the deviations from their mean values of the two random variables, namely $E([X - E(X)][Y - E(Y)])$, is a number called the covariance between these two random variables and is denoted by $C(X, Y)$. If the covariance between two random variables is divided by the product of their standard deviations, which means $C(X, Y)/\sqrt{V(X)V(Y)}$, we obtain the correlation coefficient $\rho(X, Y)$ between the two random variables. This is a real number between -1 and $+1$.

A positive correlation coefficient means that the respective random variables are dependent and have the same type of variation, which means that when one of them increases or decreases, the other one does the same. A negative correlation coefficient means that the respective random variables are dependent and have opposite types of variation, which means that when one of them increases or decreases, the other one does the opposite, decreasing or increasing, respectively. When the correlation coefficient is equal to zero, the two random variables are not correlated. Two independent random variables are noncorrelated. The converse sentence is true if the two random variables are normally distributed.

Measuring the amount of dependence between two random variables was a great step forward because, in this universe, according to the general connection and interdependence, so much emphasized by the ancient Greek philosophers, everything is correlated. We can say, without any exaggeration that, indeed, if somebody moves his finger on the earth, something changes on the moon. I see you smiling but, in fact, absolute independence doesn't exist. It comes into play only when, practically, we ignore weak dependencies, like that between the movement of our finger and its effect on what happens on the moon. This general connection and complexification is beautiful in Theilard de Chardin vision of a future with very strong dependence between all human beings, when everybody would be aware and would care about everybody else.

Galton was also fascinated with the normal probability distribution. He tried to show how many things could be explained by using it. There is even a very simple device with which we can illustrate a case when the normal probability distribution effectively shows up. The so called Galton's sieve consists of a vertical, rectangular wooden plaque on which a regular network of nails are half-knocked into. From a narrow orifice above, some tiny identical balls are introduced into the network. The little balls fall down, due to the force of gravity, experiencing chaotic deviations in different directions due to randomly hitting some nails of the network. When many such tiny balls are introduced through the top orifice, in spite of the unpredictable zigzag trajectory followed by each ball, the set of all balls, taken together, is displayed according to the bell-shaped curve of the normal probability distribution. We have here a random behaviour of the individual balls but a stable probability distribution shown by the ensemble of all balls.

Another major contributor to the progress of the modern statistics was Karl Pearson (1857-1936), who introduced, among other things, the very clever measure of how different a probability distribution is from another probability distribution taken as reference. A variant of this measure was already mentioned in the example with testing hypotheses about whether or not a certain coin is fair. Karl Pearson's chi-square, or chi-squared how it is also called, is a generalization of the Euclidean distance between multi-dimensional vectors, more exactly, a weighted Euclidean distance. It is a sum of the squared differences between the components of the two distributions divided by the respective component of the reference probability distribution. Thus, if $p = (p_1, \ldots, p_m)$ is a reference probability distribution and $q = (q_1, \ldots, q_m)$ is another probability distribution, Pearson's chi-square indicator, showing how different q is from p, is $\chi^2(q, p) = \sum_k (q_k - p_k)^2 / p_k$.

The test statistic $\chi^2 = n\chi^2(q, p)$ is used for testing null hypotheses about whether or not a sampling probability distribution q differs from a given theoretical probability distribution p, where n is the sample size. This technique is known as the goodness-of-fit test. A little earlier, we discussed its application to testing hypotheses about whether or not a certain coin was fair.

Karl Pearson was very much involved in teaching but still found time to publish more than 500 papers, articles, and books. Asked about his impressive productivity, he explained that he never answered a telephone call and didn't attend any committee meeting.

Finally, another big name is Sir Ronald Fisher (1890-1962), who introduced the analysis of variance and the discriminant function. He also coined terms which have become standard, like statistic, for a quantity computed from a population, and variance. He took a job at the Rothamsted Experimental Station, located not far from London, perhaps the oldest agricultural research station, where he studied the effects of fertilizers on crop grow. He remained there for 14 years, which offered him first hand access to experimental data and a great freedom to pursue his own ideas.

More often than not, the variation of a certain quantity is produced by the action of several independent causes. Thus, three sources of variation were affecting yield: weather, deterioration of the soil, and weeds. Ronald Fisher developed analysis of variance to assess the contribution of each of these factors to changes in mean yield. The variance produced by all the causes, simultaneously, is the sum of the values of the variance produced by each cause separately. Several portions of the total variance are assigned to their appropriate causes or groups of causes. The analysis of variance is based on examining the ratio of two estimates of variance, as an instrument of measuring how much one variance is greater than the other. Fisher studied the probability distribution of the ratio of two estimates of variance, called F-distribution in his honour, which allows to formulate tests of significance for the ratio of two estimates of variance.

Finally, discriminant analysis is a technique for classifying objects into distinct groups on the basis of their measurements on a number of variables. Fisher studied a data set of measurements on three species of iris, collected in your country Canada, and showed that four kinds of measurements from each iris flower are sufficient to put it in one of the three distinct classes.

Ronald Fisher also had several books and many papers published, among which a popular book entitled *Statistical Methods for Research Workers.*"

–"From what you have said, it seems to me that probability theory and statistics have practical applications like playing games of chance, or trying to estimate the mean height of students from a university using observations made in a small or large sample of students, for instance. But are there probabilities in the way the laws of nature do work? Well, I cannot quite express myself in a clear way, but what I am asking is: does nature behave according to probability theory or was the concept of probability only invented by some mathematicians?"

–"The nature of probability is a philosophical topic. It may be subjective, as a way of coping with our ignorance by approximating, somehow vaguely, what we cannot know precisely, like predicting what happens with every molecule of a gas, for instance. Or, it may be objective, reflecting how causality, universal connection, and interdependence work in this world, as quantum mechanics, who introduced an unavoidable unpredictability and randomness in its microscopic models, seems to suggest. When this last viewpoint is correct, then we resign ourselves to see what happens on average, in which case our strictly deterministic models of reality refer to the level of mean values. Therefore, the dilemma is: are the probabilistic models only approximations of a strictly deterministic nature, or are the strictly deterministic models only approximations of a nature essentially probabilistic? Scientists are split about this. It has been said several times, in different publications, that Albert Einstein, who never accepted that the universe could be governed by chance, believed that 'God doesn't play dice'. Other people said just the opposite."

–"What do you think?"

–"I am not Einstein but only an ordinary human being and, therefore, I don't know the subtleties about how nature really is and functions. I would be tempted to say that God does play dice, which would explain also why there is wrong and not only good in this world, but he has eternity on his side, allowing him to perform long run probabilistic experiments during which everything becomes simpler and more stable. What I know is that the strictly deterministic models seem to work at a larger scale, whereas the probabilistic models seem to be proper for describing what happens at a smaller scale. Certainly, we can cope with the omnipresent uncertainty only by using probabilistic models of reality, and the only stability we can rely upon is at the level of mean values. Long ago, a Belgian statistician, Adolphe Quetelet (1786-1874), insisted that nature attempts to preserve the 'type', or the average. I do believe that nature seems to preserve mean values, which would explain the global stability, but allows random fluctuations, which would explain local instability."

INFORMATION THEORY

–"Except probability theory and statistics, you mentioned information theory among the courses taught by you. What is this?"

–"The first domain I became interested in, immediately after graduation, was just information theory. I shall never regret this because it is a fascinating topic. Information theory deals basically with how to measure uncertainty and how to develop a mathematical model of a communication system in which messages, generated by an information source, are perturbed by random noise through a communication channel, and have to be recovered at the reception. I was more interested in the management and measuring of uncertainty and less in communication theory. Before, the entities measured quantitatively, like length, area, volume, velocity, acceleration, temperature, and pressure, to mention only some of them, were accessible to our senses or to our instruments. Information theory has come up with ambitious formulas for measuring the amount of uncertainty contained by a probabilistic experiment, a notion so vague and, however, so omnipresent.

Historically, we have to go back to the second half of the nineteenth century, when Ludwig Boltzmann, an Austrian physicist, revitalized the old atomic theory of matter. Studying the chaotic behaviour of the molecules of a gas, he put the basis of statistical mechanics in order to give a probabilistic microscopic justification to the laws of thermodynamics, empirically formulated at the macroscopic level of reality. Due to many collisions between the numerous molecules, it is practically impossible to study with certainty the motion of each molecule of the gas. Instead, we have to resign ourselves to a probabilistic description. Thus, instead of asking which is the precise state of a system of molecules of a gas, we are happy to know at least which is the probability that the state of the system of molecules of the gas belongs to a given set of possible states. On this line of thought, among many other things, Boltzmann had the idea of introducing a strange function, called the *H*-function, which was simply a multiple integral giving the mean value of the logarithm of the density of a probability distribution. He claimed that this function measured somehow the amount of uncertainty on the possible states of the system of molecules."

– "How did he get such an idea?"

– "There are several ways of getting new ideas in mathematics, or to create something new, in general. The simplest way is by generalizing. A certain result, known beforehand, is proved to be true under more general assumptions, or is proved to be a particular case of a more general result of the same kind. Very often, the first original contribution of somebody is entitled 'A generalization of some inequality, lemma, or theorem'.

A more subtle original contribution refers to discovering an unknown kind of result, never got before, very often obtained by entering a smaller world, where unexpected things and facts can occur. It is like discovering a new cave, never touched by human feet, with unbelievably coloured stalactites and stalagmites. An example of this kind is offered by the discovery of the binary field. If instead of all positive integers we take only the binary set $\{0, 1\}$, consisting of the numbers 0, 1, and we define the addition, or sum, by 0+0=0, 0+1=1, 1+0=1, 1+1=0, and the multiplication, or product, by $0 \times 0 = 0$, $0 \times 1 = 0$, $1 \times 0 = 0$, $1 \times 1 = 1$, this binary world is self-contained and has unique properties. First of all, it accommodates the classic logic, taking the logical values to be 1 for 'true' and 0 for 'false'. The negation of 0, denoted by $\bar{0}$, is 1 and the negation of 1, denoted by $\bar{1}$, is 0. The arithmetic operations $+$ and $\times$ correspond to the logical operations 'or' and 'and', respectively. More than that, for any pair of numbers from $\{0, 1\}$, not necessarily different, their minimum is equal to their product, namely $\min\{k, \ell\} = k \times \ell$, and their maximum is equal to their sum minus their product, namely $\max\{k, \ell\} = (k + \ell) - (k \times \ell)$, whatever values 0 or 1 are assigned to k and ℓ. It is a close world where classic logic and arithmetic coexist harmoniously and where the optimization is reduced to arithmetic operations. This explains why the modern computers use the binary system and why a compiler translates any list of words and symbols into binary sequences of 1s and 0s, assembling what is called a machine language that can be understood and operated upon by the computer. In coding theory, detecting an error in a certain position doesn't mean that we know how to correct it. If binary 0-1 sequences, however, are associated with messages to be transmitted through noisy communication channels, detecting an error is enough because its correction simply means to change the corresponding received symbol from 0 to 1 or from 1 to 0, respectively.

Finally, another way of getting original results in mathematics is by analogy. It is possible to detect analogies between theorems, between proofs, and some exceptional mathematicians can discover even analogies between different theories. Somebody notices similarities between two different domains of mathematics. Once a 'dictionary' is established, showing the correspondence between the main terms of the two domains, there are real chances to solve problems from one of these domains by borrowing techniques from the other domain. Large parts of modern mathematics, like set theory, functional analysis, topology, and category theory, have been built up by analogy."

ENTROPY

–"You are talking about different ways of discovering new results in general. But how does somebody get a certain new idea at a certain time of his life?"

–"I don't know. Apparently, Isaac Newton said that he had got the formula of the gravitational attraction by continuously thinking about it for a couple of years. Definitely, thinking a lot on an open problem is a must. But, sometimes, it is a good strategy to stop dealing with it and switch to something different for a period of time. Later, resuming the old problem, it is possible to look at it from a different angle and, for not very clear reasons, even solve it.

It is said that everything experienced by us is registered somehow in our conscious or unconscious memory where the storage is not static, such that new connections may be formed among different facts, impressions, and thoughts residing there. The French mathematician Jacques Hadamard wrote a very interesting little book on the discovery in mathematics, stressing the existence of an intermediary level, the subconscious, between the conscious and unconscious levels. Sometimes, new ideas and the so called intuition of new facts are flicking at the subconscious level, a confusing state between dream and reality, whereas the deep unconscious level remains unaccessible to us and is out of our control.

Going back to Boltzmann, I think that he introduced his probabilistic entropy by intuition. Anyway, it brought him only headaches. First, during his times, many influential physicists were not willing to accept the atomic structure of matter advocated by Boltzmann. Second, his entropy, or H-function, proved to have the strange property that, for a closed physical system, it evolves only in the direction of an increased uncertainty on the set of possible states of the system, result known as the famous H-theorem. It proved to justify mathematically the second law of thermodynamics. Extrapolating this result to the whole universe, considered to be a closed system, the H-theorem implies an evolution towards a uniform distribution of temperature, pressure, and density on the possible states, resulting, in long run, in the impossibility of any transfer of heat from warm regions to colder ones, which means the thermal death of the universe. It is possible to get local organization, as the humans and even animals do, but this is achieved at the cost of overall increase of global entropy. Nobody knows the real causes why Ludwig Boltzmann committed suicide, but it seems reasonable to assume that the intense criticism of his scientific results played a part in his premature death."

SHANNON

−"If I understand it right, Boltzmann was a physicist. How does information fit into the picture?"

−"This brings us to Claude Elwood Shannon, an amazing American mathematician and engineer, who had a lot of new ideas. Born in 1916, his heroes were Edison, Newton, Darwin, Einstein, and von Neumann. In his Master's thesis, he applied Boolean algebra to the switching electric circuits, allowing an elegant and rigorous way of coping with the complexity of such sophisticated systems. In dealing with switching circuits, he noticed that 'open' or 'closed' are like 'yes' or 'no'. Two things in series are described by the operator 'and' from logic, whereas two things joined in parallel are described by the logical operator 'or'.

He worked at the Massachusetts Institute of Technology, at Bell Telephone Laboratories in New York City, and at the Institute for Advanced Study in Princeton. All three are famous for important mathematical research done by some brilliant people there. He is the creator of information theory. He wrote an important paper on the secret systems, remained classified for a long period of time, giving evaluations of the amount of ciphered text that has to be received in order to recover the original message. Around 1950, he was among the first who worked on programming a computer for playing chess.

Shannon was also interested in all sorts of new computerized machines. He even designed a devise for beating roulette in Las Vegas, by almost instantly predicting where the spinning ball was likely to come to rest. There is no serious indication that such a devise was really successful. Later in life, however, he was interested in the stock market, optimal investment strategies, and the maximization of utility function by proper choice and adjustment of a portfolio. After making some good personal investments, he was asked whether his stock market success was based on mathematics. 'Oh, yes. Mathematics and some good friends,' was his answer. Towards the end of his life, after doing so much, he still declared, in a rare interview, that: 'I have spent lots of time on totally useless things.' He died in 2001.

But let me go back to information theory and the mathematical concept of entropy. Claude Shannon took the finite discrete analog of Boltzmann's H-function from statistical mechanics and, in a seminal paper, simply titled *A mathematical theory of communication*, published in 1948 in a scientific journal of the telephone company Bell, which became one of the most cited mathematical papers ever, proved that it is an excellent measure for the amount of uncertainty contained by any finite probability space.

More precisely, if we have a probabilistic experiment which has a finite number n of distinct, possible outcomes, and their occurrence probabilities are $p_1, \ldots, p_n$, respectively, then, the entropy of the corresponding probability distribution is: $H = -p_1 \log p_1 - \ldots - p_n \log p_n$, where the logarithm is either the natural logarithm ln, or the logarithm in base 10, or base 2, in which cases the corresponding entropy is measured in digits and bits, respectively. We obtain this way a nonnegative number which measures the amount of uncertainty we have about the outcome of the probabilistic experiment before performing the experiment.

It may be proved, in a relatively elementary way, that this is a very good measure for how much uncertainty is contained by a probabilistic experiment. In fact, it is the unique measure of the amount of uncertainty, up to a multiplicative positive constant, which satisfies a couple of conditions that are in agreement with our intuition about what uncertainty is. In particular, the entropy of a trivial experiment that has only one possible outcome is equal to zero. On the contrary, the entropy of a probabilistic experiment whose possible outcomes are equally likely is maximum and equal to the logarithm of the number of possible outcomes.

Shannon switched from uncertainty to information by noticing that information is just removed uncertainty. Before performing the probabilistic experiment, Shannon's entropy measures the amount of prior uncertainty about what particular outcome is going to occur. After performing the probabilistic experiment, Shannon's entropy measures the amount of information received by removing the prior uncertainty.

As an engineer working for the telephone Bell company, Shannon applied his entropy to the communication systems, consisting of an information source, generating messages formed with signals belonging to an initial alphabet, a noisy channel, where the transmitted messages are randomly distorted by perturbations, and the receiver, where the perturbed messages arrive. In order to counteract the destructive effect of the noise in the communication channels, the solution is to codify the initial messages. Instead of transmitting directly the initial messages, we make them longer, transforming each word written with symbols of the initial alphabet into a longer and better structured code word first, such that in spite of the noise on the communication channel, which continues to alter the transmitted messages, the receiver can still get the original message by decoding the received message. Shannon proved the existence of coding procedures that make the information transmission reliable. In all this approach, probabilistic entropy plays the central role. Coding theory added some algebraic procedures for encoding the initial messages, introducing enough order induced by algebraic structures to counteract the destructive effect of random perturbation occurring during transmission. Like a regular pattern whose partially and locally destroyed portions could be recovered due to the regular symmetry of the pattern itself.

Besides the importance of making the communication systems more reliable by coping with the chaotic noise, information theory dramatically extended its domain of applications due to the fact that, for the first time, uncertainty, an entity so abstract and evasive, has been measured quantitatively.

Shannon's paper had an amazing impact. It is said that it has been one of the most cited scientific papers ever. It is also said that even Shannon became worried by the utilization of his entropy in too many areas. Reality is that entropy proved not only to be an excellent measure for the amount of uncertainty contained by a probability distribution but also induced a surprising measure for the amount of interdependence among the randomly behaving components of an arbitrary system. And there are systems with random behaviour everywhere, namely in engineering, biology, economics, or society.

There are many different definitions about what a system really means in different domains and areas. In spite of such a diversity, however, all specialists agree that a system represents something more than the union of its components. A car is something more than the union of its wheels, doors, windows, electric circuits, gas tank, and engine. It is not so difficult to prove that the difference between the sum of the entropies of the components of the system, taken separately, and the entropy of all the components of the system, taken together, measures the amount of interdependence among the components making up the respective system. This was very well explained by Satosi Watanabe in a very unorthodox book, full of new ideas, entitled *Knowing and Guessing*, published in 1969.

Summarizing, Shannon's entropy, inspired by Boltzmann's known *H*-function from his statistical description for the behaviour of the molecules of a gas, measures the amount of uncertainty contained by any probabilistic experiment, whereas the sum of the entropies of the parts minus the entropy of the whole provides a measure of the amount of interdependence among these parts making up the whole.

This was a major step forward in mathematical modeling. As I already said, before, we could measure length, areas, volumes, or concrete entities accessible to our instruments, like temperature, pressure, energy, etc. Now, we dare to measure such apparently abstract entities as uncertainty and interdependence."

–"Why is this entropy function so important?"

–"I don't know. We can write down hundreds and hundreds of functions depending on the components of a discrete probability distribution or on the density of a continuous probability distribution. We can study their properties. Some of them could even be interesting, but the tremendous majority of them are not really important. Isaac Newton once said that he felt himself as being a child playing on the seashore and looking for a beautiful shell or pebble while the great ocean of truth remained unknown in front of him. Taking into account how much Newton did in science, I don't really believe that he meant what he said. Anyway, what I do believe is that the probabilistic entropy, discovered by Boltzmann but generalized and polished by Shannon, is a genuine jewel that allows us to decipher at least a little from the ocean of truth poetically mentioned by Newton.

To illustrate what amazing properties entropy has, I have to mention the so called principle of maximum entropy. This is a special case of what is called variational principle which, generally, involves a maximization or minimization of a function or functional, subject to some constraints. A function depends on one or several variables and assigns a number to every set of values of such variables from a given domain of definition. A functional depends on one or several functions and assigns a number to each set of such functions from a certain class of functions which forms the domain of definition of the respective functional. The constraints define the so-called feasible space. When a function is optimized, we are looking for those values of the variables, from the domain of definition, for which the respective function reaches its optimum value. When a functional is optimized, we are looking for those functions, from the domain of definition, for which the respective functional reaches its optimum value.

In the discrete case, the entropy is a function of the components $p_1, p_2, \ldots$ of a discrete probability distribution, namely $H = -\sum_i p_i \ln p_i$, similar to the formula mentioned before when we dealt with the entropy of a finite discrete probability distribution. In the continuous case, the entropy is a functional of the probability density $f(x)$ of a continuous probability distribution on a certain domain D. The continuous entropy is a generalization of the discrete entropy and is equal to minus the integral of the product between the probability density $f(x)$ and its natural logarithm on the domain of definition D, namely: $H = -\int_D f(x) \ln f(x)\, dx$. This is a multiple integral, if the domain D of the respective probability distribution is a set from a multidimensional Euclidean space. In the one-dimensional space, the domain D is almost always a line segment, the positive half-real line, or the entire real line. If the probability distribution, discrete or continuous, is given, then we may calculate its entropy, reflecting the amount of uncertainty contained by that probability distribution. For instance, if we roll a fair dice, each possible outcome has the occurrence probability equal to 1/6 and the corresponding entropy is: $H = -(6)(1/6)\ln(1/6) = \ln 6 = 1.79176$.

Often, however, the probability distribution is not known and the only information available is given by a known mean value of a random variable defined on the set of possible outcomes. As there are infinitely many probability distributions compatible with the constraint represented by the given mean value, the problem is how to choose the best one? According to the principle of maximum entropy, from the set of all possible probability distributions subject to the given mean value of a certain random variable, we select the one which maximizes the entropy. In this way, we choose the probability distribution which is the most uncertain or, equivalently, the most unbiased one, compatible with the given mean of the respective random variable. For instance, if the random variable is the energy of a system that has a discrete set of possible values $x_1, x_2, \ldots$ and the only data available is the mean, or average, energy of the system, $\overline{E} = \sum_i x_i\, p_i$, then the probability distribution on the set of possible values of the energy obtained by applying the principle of maximum entropy is the famous canonical distribution $p_i = (1/\Phi(\beta))\exp(-\beta x_i)$, $(i = 1, 2, \ldots)$, where β is the unique solution of the equation $\Phi'(\beta) + \overline{E}\Phi(\beta) = 0$, where $\Phi(\beta) = \sum_i\exp(-\beta x_i)$, and $\Phi'(\beta)$ is the derivative of the function $\Phi(\beta)$ with respect to the variable β. This probability distribution plays a central role in the statistical mechanics founded by Josiah Willard Gibbs (1839-1903).

Going back to the principle of maximum entropy, its solution, when we know only the mean μ and standard deviation σ of a continuous random variable, is just the normal distribution $N(\mu, \sigma^2)$, whose probability density function is $f(x) = (\sigma\sqrt{2\pi})^{-1}\exp(-(x - \mu)^2/2\sigma^2)$. This explains now why the so-called normal distribution is normal indeed or, more explicitly, why this distribution has proved to be so useful in so many applications of statistical inference that it has been called normal. From the infinite set of probability distributions compatible with a given mean value and a given standard deviation, the symmetric, bell-shaped, normal distribution is the best; it is the most uncertain, therefore nondiscriminatory and unbiased, probability distribution on the real line subject to the two constraints represented by the given mean and standard deviation.

And the list of similar surprising results is very long. To give another example, the solution of the principle of maximum entropy when the only constraint is a given mean value μ of a nonnegative random variable is the exponential distribution, whose probability density function is $f(x) = (1/\mu)\exp(-x/\mu)$, which has also played a central role in so many applications, notably in queueing theory and in reliability theory.

The funny thing is that, very long ago, in the first quarter of the 19th century, Pierre Simon Marquis de Laplace, in his treatise on probability theory, we talked about earlier, mentioned the so called 'principle of insufficient reason', according to which, if we have no reason to discriminate between the possible outcomes of a probabilistic experiment, the fair attitude is to take them as being equally likely. Laplace's principle is in agreement with common sense to such an extent that we are using it in everyday life without even being aware of it. Indeed, when we refer to tossing a coin, we don't repeat this experiment hundreds and hundreds of times or check whether or not its two possible outcomes, 'head' and 'tail', have equal probabilities. As we think that we have no reason to discriminate between these two outcomes, we take them as being equally likely, applying in fact Laplace's principle even if, very rigorously speaking, no coin on the market is 100% fair. Obviously, Laplace's principle of insufficient reason is the simplest case of the principle of maximum entropy because the uniform probability distribution maximizes the entropy when we have no constraints at all. Common sense or our intuition, however, couldn't help us guess which is the most unbiased probability distribution when we know the mean value of a random variable, for instance. Maximizing entropy, subject to that constraint, gives us the solution, mathematically, and by solving an optimization problem we get Gibbs's canonical distribution, in the discrete case, and the overwhelmingly important exponential distribution, in the continuous case."

–"Who discovered this mathematical principle of maximum entropy?"

–"John von Neumann vaguely talked about it in an appendix of his typed lecture notes on quantum mechanics. It is also said that he advised Claude Shannon to call his new measure of uncertainty entropy, for two reasons: 'First, it is similar to Boltzmann's continuous entropy that had already been used in statistical mechanics; Second, every time you use the mysterious name entropy, you win any argument.' But the one who formulated the principle of maximum entropy clearly, as an effective tool for constructing the most uncertain probability distribution subject to constraints represented by mean values of random variables, was Edwin Jaynes, in a paper published in 1957. I have to confess that when I read his paper I was so impressed that I was almost about to fall down; luckily, I was sitting at that time."

–"Wow, your students must like information theory. How many have been enrolled in such a course?"

–"In fact, I haven't taught information theory in the last 20 years. The departments of mathematics say that engineers should teach it. The engineering departments say that it is too mathematical and therefore mathematicians ought to teach it. And so on. Lately, I have taught only operations research courses."

OPERATIONS RESEARCH

–"Does this mean linear programming, you have talked about earlier?"

–"Not really, operations research may be divided in two big parts and, normally, there is a distinct full course dealing with each part.

The first part deals with strictly deterministic models, like linear programming, which means to optimize a linear function (maximize the linear profit or minimize the linear cost), subject to linear inequality constraints that describe limits for resources available or for production levels. Nothing is left to chance. As I mentioned yesterday, the general results are applied to solving transportation and network problems, like finding the minimum cost strategy for shipping commodities from a set of sources to a set of destinations, and to the analysis of networks, for finding either the minimum path from a source to a destination in a network of possible routes involving different lengths, or the maximum flow of commodities that can be sent from a source to a destination using the maximum capacity of the different connections between the initial source and the final destination passing through the intermediary nodes of a network. Basically, this first part requires only knowledge of linear algebra, more exactly, how to deal with systems of linear equations and how to manipulate matrices.

The second part deals with probabilistic models in operations research whose chapters are game theory, decision theory, simulation, reliability, and queueing theory. For dealing with these topics, the students are supposed to have basic knowledge in multivariate calculus, probability theory, and statistics. I always try to minimize the amount of prerequisites and to refresh their memory about some important concepts and results supposed to be known from previous courses. Generally, as one of my old professors told us, you learn something which is important and you forget it. Being important, you will get into it several other times and, in this repeated process of learning and forgetting, you will end up finally knowing it."

GAME THEORY

—"You already explained something about what simulation is. But is it possible to use mathematics for playing games?"

—"Yes and no. It depends on what kind of games you are referring to. The so called two-person zero-sum games have been completely solved mathematically. In such a game there are two players, called player I and player II, competing against each other. When one player wins a certain amount, the opponent loses the same amount. Each player has a finite set of so called pure strategies. The two sets could be different or identical. A pure strategy could be an action or a series of actions. A variant of the game consists of a pair of pure strategies, chosen independently by the two players. To give a two person zero-sum game means to give the sets of pure strategies of the two players and a payoff matrix of one player, let's say player I. This matrix, or tableau, contains the payoff for player I corresponding to each variant of the game. The rows correspond to the pure strategies of player I and the columns refer to the pure strategies of player II. Thus, the entry in row 3 and column 5 represents the payoff for player I if he plays his third pure strategy and player II plays his fifth pure strategy. The payoff matrix of player II is obtained from that of player I, changing the sign of each entry, because when one player wins, which means that his payoff is positive, then the opponent loses the same amount, which means that his payoff is the same number but with the sign minus in front of it.

As the outcome of the game depends on both players, each player will try to maximize the minimum payoff the opponent can inflict on him. If we look only at the payoff matrix of player I but have both players in mind, then player I will try to maximize the minimum payoff imposed by player II and player II will try to minimize the maximum payoff player I will try to get. We use to say that player I is looking for his 'maximin' strategy and player II is looking for his 'minimax' strategy.

Some two-person zero-sum games have a so-called equilibrium point. This happens if in the payoff matrix of player I there is an entry which is the largest in its column and the smallest in its row. The corresponding pure strategies, namely the row and the column where the equilibrium point lays, are the optimum strategies of the two players, namely the maximin strategy for player I and the minimax strategy for player II. The corresponding entry in the payoff matrix of player I is the optimum payoff for player I; changing its sign, we get the optimum payoff of player II. For such a game, if each player uses his optimum strategy, maximin strategy for player I and minimax strategy for player II, then the result of the game is fully predictable. Thus, if the game has an equilibrium point, then the maximin and minimax strategies are the optimum strategies of player I and player II, respectively. If one player, unilaterally, gives up his optimum strategy, he cannot do better but can do worse. Finally, if both players use nonoptimum strategies, the result of the game is unpredictable."

–"Can you give an example of such a game?"

John took his microscopic notebook from one of his many pockets and sketched for me an example of payoff matrix of player I. It was funny to see that such a simple tableau of integers could describe what happens in the confrontation between two players. John showed a lot

		I			
		1	2	3	min
	1	−3	6	−2	−3
II	2	2	2	$\boxed{1}$	$\boxed{1}$
	3	5	−4	−2	−4
	max	5	6	$\boxed{1}$	

Figure 5: An example of a payoff matrix of player I.

of patience in explaining me how to look at the rows and columns of his tableau, saying:

–"Here is a simple example. If both players have three pure strategies, labelled by 1, 2, 3, and the payoff matrix for player I has the entries −3, 6, −2 in the first row, 2, 2, 1 in the second row and 5, −4, −2 in the third row, the game has an equilibrium point in the second row and third column. Therefore, the second pure strategy is optimum for player I and the third pure strategy is optimum for player II. The optimum payoff for player I is 1 and the optimum payoff for player II is −1."

–"It seems strange that the best solution for player II is to lose."

–"Not really. First, it doesn't mean that player I has to win always. It does happen in this particular game. Second, if player I plays his optimum strategy, which is the second pure strategy, but player II refuses to play his optimum strategy, choosing his first or second pure strategy, he can do only worse, losing 2 instead of only 1."

–"This means that the two-person zero-sum games may be solved easily looking for equilibrium points."

–"Unfortunately, not every two-person zero-sum game has an equilibrium point and, therefore, not every such game has optimum solutions for the two players in terms of pure strategies. In a game without equilibrium point every player can take advantage of any information about the opponent's way of acting. Consequently, in order to prevent my opponent from learning something about my way of playing the game, the solution is to play randomly. But how? We arrive to the so-called mixed, or random strategies. A random strategy of a player is a probability distribution on the set of his possible pure strategies, representing the probabilities of playing his possible pure strategies. Thus, if player I has a number r of possible pure strategies, a mixed strategy for him is a probability distribution $\xi = (\xi_1, \ldots, \xi_r)$, where ξ_1 means the probability that player I plays his pure strategy 1, for instance. Similarly, if player II has a number s of possible pure strategies, a mixed strategy for him is a probability distribution $\eta = (\eta_1, \ldots, \eta_s)$, where η_1 means the probability that player II plays his pure strategy 1, for instance. Even if each player has a finite number of possible pure strategies, there are infinitely many mixed strategies possible for each player.

To each pair of mixed strategies (ξ, η) of the two players, we may assign the mean payoff of player I, or expected payoff of player I, which is the mean value of the payoff matrix of player I with respect to the product of the respective probability distributions represented by the two given mixed strategies, namely $U(\xi, \eta) = \sum_i \sum_j u_{ij}\, \xi_i\, \eta_j$, where u_{ij} is the entry from row i and column j of the payoff matrix of player I, representing the payoff of player I if he plays his pure strategy labelled i and player II plays his pure strategy labelled j. If u_{ij} is positive, then player I gets this amount from player II; if u_{ij} is negative, then player I has to pay this amount to player II. Changing the sign, we get the mean, or expected payoff of player II, $-U(\xi, \eta)$, corresponding to the two given mixed strategies (ξ, η) of the two players.

We are dealing now with mixed strategies instead of pure strategies and mean payoffs instead of the original payoffs. Again, each player will try to maximize the minimum expected payoff the opponent can inflict on him. But this time, the beauty is that every two-person zero-sum game has an equilibrium point and, therefore, each player has an optimum mixed strategy. If the optimum mixed strategy is degenerate, which means that it has one component equal to one and all the other components equal to zero, than the optimum mixed strategy is a pure strategy."

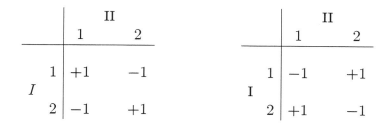

Figure 6: Payoff matrices for John and Mary, respectively.

–"Could you give an example of two-person zero-sum game whose optimum strategy is a mixed strategy?"

–"The simplest example I can give is the so-called 'two-finger mora game'. Don't ask me what 'mora' means, because I don't know. Anyway, John is player I and Mary player II. Each of them shows, independently and simultaneously, one finger or two fingers. If the numbers match, John wins \$1 from Mary. If the numbers don't match, then Mary wins \$1 from John. Showing one finger or showing two fingers are the two pure strategies for both players. The payoff matrix for John has the entries 1, −1 in the first row and −1, 1 in the second row. The payoff matrix for Mary is obtained by changing the signs, which means −1, 1 in the first row and 1, −1 in the second row.

As simple as it is, this game has no equilibrium point for pure strategies but has an equilibrium point for the mixed strategies. The game being symmetric, both John and Mary have the same optimum mixed strategy, namely, the uniform probability distribution (1/2, 1/2). This mean that, practically, each of them has to toss a fair coin and show one finger if the outcome of this probabilistic experiment is 'head' and show two fingers if the outcome is 'tail', creating maximum uncertainty to the opponent about the specific way of playing the game. The optimum expected payoff proves to be 0 for both players, which means that this game is a fair game.

In general, the theory of two-person zero-sum games is completely done, in the sense that there are rigorous proofs for its theoretical results and methods for effectively solving such games. Solving a game means to find the optimum mixed strategies and the optimum expected payoff of the two players. Practically, any such game may be reduced to a primal and dual linear programs for which there are many computer packages available to solve them. There are also algorithms that allow us to approximate the optimum solution very fast."

−"This means that any game may be solved today."

−"Oh, no. Very often, the textbooks and our lectures insist only on what can be solved and what is already known. Very few mention open problems, what is not known.Or, just such open problems could be a motivation and a real challenge for young brains to focus on them and try to solve them, with chances of having new concepts, tools, and even theories newly created. Young people have fresh minds and fewer prejudices induced by reading too much old stuff. The paradox is that sometimes, reading too much in our field of interest, we become not only more informed but we are also influenced about how to look at things from the angle of those who have already worked in that domain. Erudition cannot be identified to creation. Sometimes it is just its opposite. This is why a great contributor to the development of a certain chapter in mathematics could be ignorant about what is happening in other fields of mathematics. I remember one of my professors, already well-known for his work in algebraic topology, a very specialized branch of modern mathematics, who, surprisingly, asked to be assigned to teach an elementary course on classical differential geometry, saying that this would force him to finally learn something about what that meant.

But, going back to game theory, there is no comprehensive and satisfactory study of two-person non-zero sum games. This is regrettable because in many games from real life, there is not only an opposition between the objectives of the two players but also a common interest. Thus, going to the market, I want to buy with less money and the vendor wants to sell with more money, but we both want to reach an agreement. Therefore, negotiations are needed before reaching a final settlement. There is a mathematical theory of negotiations but it is far from the perfection of the theory of two-person zero-sum games, where

	II	
	Talk	Don't talk
Talk	$(-5, -5)$	$(0, -20)$
Don't talk	$(-20, 0)$	$(-1, -1)$

I

Figure 7: Payoff matrices for Prisoner's Dilemma.

the interests of the players are opposite and the win of one player means the loss of the other player, by the same amount.

The so-called 'prisoner's dilemma', for instance, is a good example that shows how many new facts could come up in a non-zero game. One version of it goes on in the following way. During a night, a murder is committed in a dark park. Two suspects are arrested on the spot. Each has a gun with a missing bullet, identical with that found in the victim's body. There is no witness available. The suspects are taken to the police station and put in separate cells. They have one night to think about how to behave on the next day when they will face the judge, separately, knowing that each one can either 'talk', which means 'I am not guilty, the other one did it', or 'don't talk', which means 'keep your mouth shut'. They are also informed that if one 'talks' and the other one 'doesn't talk', then the talking prisoner gets free and the other one gets 20 years in jail because his silence is taken as being an admission of guilt. Also, if both 'talk', then it is not clear whose bullet killed the victim and, consequently, each of them gets five years in jail, whereas if both 'don't talk', then the judge considers that there isn't enough evidence and each prisoner gets one year in jail because they don't have a gun permit. How should the prisoner act on the next day in front of the judge?"

–"Let me think about it, myself. If I am one of the prisoners, God forbid, then let me see what I could do, taking all possibilities into account about what the other fellow can do. If I 'talk' then I either get five years or I get free. If I 'don't talk', then I could get only one year but also 20 years in jail. I cannot take such a huge risk and, obviously, I have to 'talk'."

–"Perfect. You reached the right decision and, as the game is symmetric, the other prisoner will reach the same rational decision and, as a result, on the next day each prisoner will 'talk', resulting in five years in jail for each of them."

–"Right. Why is this a dilemma?"

–"For two reasons. First, if the two prisoners were put in the same cell, they could analyze together the situation and would arrive at the obvious conclusion that by keeping their mouths shut in front of the judge, on the next day, would result in only one year in jail for each of them. If (talk, talk) is the most rational individual solution, (don't talk, don't talk) is the better collective solution of the game. Yes, but such a better solution for both is based on dialogue, fair play, and trust. Think what happens if, on the next day, when facing the judge separately, one prisoner keeps his promise and doesn't talk, whereas the other one talks, mainly when the temptation of double-crossing is so high. Second, it is a paradox because if the prisoners are two brutes, unable to think or speak, who on the next day, in front of the judge, just sit there saying nothing, they achieve a better solution than two rational prisoners who logically analyze the different alternatives deciding to 'talk' on the next day."

–"Back in Toronto, I will tell my best friend Stephen about this dilemma. He likes all sorts of puzzles and paradoxes. He is also addicted to playing card games."

–"I have to add that not every game of chance may be treated as being a two-person zero-sum game. The game of poker, for instance, doesn't fall into this category. In fact, in this game of chance a player has a very limited possibility of acting by himself. He doesn't play according to a mixed strategy chosen by himself. He has no power on the initial hand of cards and the only freedom he has is about which of his cards to be replaced by new ones. Uncertainty is not created by him. It is created by the random distribution of cards. Also, he can only guess what kind of cards his opponents have. Psychology plays an important role too and bluffing is a part of the poker game but has never been incorporated in any serious mathematical game theory I am aware of."

–"There are also more than two players involved. I played poker myself, several times, with three friends of mine, but we played for mini-candies instead of money."

–"Right. In fact there are some results in the study of the n-person games. Coalitions play an important role there. A coalition is a subset of the set of players. The members of a coalition are supposed to act together, as a team. To give such an n-person game means to give its characteristic function which assigns a number to each possible coalition, reflecting the value of this coalition. There are two main problems. The first problem is how to reward equitably the players. The second problem, perhaps the most important one, is to calculate the value of each player. The so-called Shapley value of a player is obtained by summing up the contributions of this player to increasing the value of each coalition he could join in, multiplied by the probability of having the respective coalition formed."

VON NEUMANN

–"Who created the mathematical game theory?"

–"When we talked about the birth of probability theory, I mentioned the dialogue between Blaise Pascal and Pierre de Fermat about games of chance. Much later, Ernst Zermelo, at the beginning of the 20th century, and Émile Borel, about 20 years later, published important papers, trying to build a mathematical model for games. But 1928 was an important year, when John von Neumann proved the famous minimax theorem which states that every two-person zero-sum game has an equilibrium point in terms of mixed strategies. Later, in 1944, John von Neumann, a mathematician, and Oskar Morgenstern, an economist, published a seminal book, entitled *Game Theory and*

Economic Behaviour, which marked the moment when game theory became a distinct mathematical discipline. From the title of the book you can see that the domain of the game theory evolved beyond the original games of chance. Game theory is the first branch of applied mathematics where rational human beings are essential components of the mathematical model itself."

– "Is von Neumann still alive?"

– "No, he died relatively young, when he was about 53 or 54 years old, if I remember well. He was one of the greatest mathematicians of the 20th century.

He was born in Budapest, in 1903. There, he was the favorite student of László Rátz, who taught mathematics in the Lutheran Gymnasium, where many known scientists, including the Nobel laureate theoretical physicist Eugene Wigner, graduated. This is a good example of how an excellent high school teacher could influence some generations of future scholars. Later, von Neumann studied in Berlin and Zürich but moved to the United States in the 30s. He belonged to the brilliant group of scientists gathered in Los Alamos to work on the Manhattan Project of building the first atomic bomb during the World War II. He was actively involved in the construction of the first big computer there. He was also a member of the prestigious Institute of Advanced Studies in Princeton.

Very versatile, he had contributions not only in game theory but also in functional analysis, operator theory, automata theory, and wrote an early book about the mathematical formalism of quantum mechanics. In Los Alamos, he collaborated with Stan Ulam on applications of simulation. According to George Dantzig, one of the contributors to the early development of linear programming, one day he gave a ride to von Neumann, who was going to the train station in Los Alamos for commuting to Princeton. During a 15-minute ride, he tried to explain to von Neumann about what linear programming was all about. John von Neumann instantly realized the connection between a two-person zero-sum game, involving two players with opposite interests, and the pair of primal and dual linear programs involving opposite objectives, namely a maximization of the profit and a minimization of the cost, respectively.

It is said that he had one of the fastest brains among the mathematicians. It is also said that he was a reckless driver and a 'bon vivant' who enjoyed Mexican food. He used to say that in order to do original work in mathematics you have to be below 30 years old, but eventually, as he became older, gradually extended the upper age bound for creativity in mathematics to 35, 40, 45, 50, etc. Without being too religious, as far as I know, he told his mother that perhaps God exists because more things can be better explained if there exists a God than if there is no God."

−"When you listed the chapters of your operations research course you mentioned decision theory. According to what you have just explained, it seems that a player has also to make decisions about how to play the game for winning. Isn't this decision theory too?"

DECISION THEORY

−"Decision theory is an extension of game theory. We have the decision maker, who has a set of possible actions to choose from, confronting nature, which may be in one of several possible states. A number is assigned to each pair consisting of an action and a state of nature, representing the loss for the decision maker corresponding to the respective pair. A negative loss is a gain. Here, nature is understood in abstract sense; it could be anything which, along with the actions of the decision maker, could affect the corresponding loss for the decision maker. We may look at the decision maker as being the first player, engaged in a game against nature. In terms of the loss matrix, the maximin strategy of player I becomes his minimax strategy, because maximizing the minimum gain allowed by nature is equivalent to minimizing the maximum loss inflicted by nature.

Indeed, if $\ell(a, \theta)$ is the loss of the decision maker when he takes the action a and nature is in state θ, according to the minimax strategy, the decision maker will try to minimize the maximum loss inflicted by nature, which mathematically may be written as: $\min_a \max_\theta \ell(a, \theta)$.

Taking a decision making based on the minimax criterion, well justified in a two-person zero-sum game, is not always the best one in general decision theory because nature is not necessarily a malevolent opponent. Consequently, other criteria are also needed. Hurwicz's criterion, for instance, suggests taking an action that minimizes a balance between what happens when nature is acting against us and what happens when nature is acting in our favour. Thus, if a positive number α, between 0 and 1, is taken as an index of optimism, Hurwicz's criterion tells us to choose an action that minimizes the balance between what happens when nature is acting in our favour and what happens when nature is acting against us, mediated by the index of optimism α. Mathematically, the criterion says: $\min_a \{\alpha \min_\theta \ell(a,\theta) + (1-\alpha) \max_\theta \ell(a,\theta)\}$. For a perfect balance between the two extreme positions nature could be in, we take, $\alpha = 1/2 = 0.5$.

When besides the loss matrix $[\ell(a,\theta)]$ we also know a prior probability distribution $[P(\theta)]$ on the set of possible states of nature, another decision criterion chooses the action which minimizes the expected loss, namely $\min_a L_0(a)$, denoted by L_0, where $L_0(a) = \sum_\theta \ell(a,\theta)P(\theta)$. The number L_0 is called the prior expected loss.

More interesting is the case when we have to decide first whether or not to make use of the outcome of an auxiliary experiment which gives indirect information about the states of nature. In calculating the value of the auxiliary experiment and the optimum action corresponding to every possible outcome of the auxiliary experiment, we can use the celebrated Bayes's formula. It allows us to calculate the posterior probability distribution of the states of nature, conditioned by the outcomes of the auxiliary experiment, known also as the retrodiction matrix, from the prior probability distribution of the states of nature and the probability distribution of the outcomes of the auxiliary experiment conditioned by the states of nature, known also as the prediction matrix. The prediction matrix is generally available from past experience. More often than not, if the state of nature is known, then the probability distribution of the possible outcomes is accessible to us. To give an example, if a certain disease is known, the probability distribution of the possible symptoms is known. Much more difficult is to get the probability distribution of the possible diseases when a certain symptom is known. Bayes's formula does just this.

The formula is very simple, more exactly, the posterior probability $P(\theta \mid x)$ of a possible state of nature θ, conditioned by a certain outcome

x of the auxiliary experiment is equal to the probability $P(x \mid \theta)$ of the respective outcome x conditioned by the given state of nature θ, multiplied by the prior probability $P(\theta)$ of that state of nature θ, and divided by the probability $P(x)$ of the respective outcome x of the auxiliary experiment, where $P(x) = \sum_\theta P(x \mid \theta)P(\theta)$.

Bayes's formula involves a simple arithmetic, namely $P(\theta \mid x) = P(x \mid \theta)P(\theta)/P(x)$, but its significance is much deeper because it allows us to reevaluate the probability distribution of causes, which are possible states of nature in our context, given new evidence, which here is provided by the possible outcomes of the auxiliary experiment. Let me denote by $a^*(x)$ the optimum action of the decision maker if the outcome of the auxiliary experiment is x. The minimum expected loss for the decision maker, given the outcome x of the auxiliary experiment, is $L_p(a^*(x)) = \min_a L_p(a, x)$, where the expected loss corresponding to action a and outcome x is $L_p(a, x) = \sum_\theta [\ell(a, \theta) + c(x)]P(\theta \mid x)$, and $c(x)$ is the cost of the auxiliary experiment when the outcome of the auxiliary experiment is x. Taking the average $L_p = \sum_x L_p(a^*(x))P(x)$ with respect to all possible outcomes x of the auxiliary experiment, we get the so-called posterior expected loss L_p. The value of the auxiliary experiment, denoted by V, is the difference between the prior expected loss and posterior expected loss, namely $V = L_0 - L_p$.

All these elementary computations are made before performing the auxiliary experiment. If the value V of the auxiliary experiment is strictly positive, we decide to perform the auxiliary experiment. Only one of the possible outcomes, say x^*, will occur. In such a case the optimum action of the decision maker will be $a^*(x^*)$ and the corresponding expected loss will be $L_p(a^*(x^*))$. If the value of the auxiliary experiment V is negative or zero, we decide not to perform the auxiliary experiment and we go for decision without experimentation, applying Hurwicz's criterion, for instance."

–"It is surprising that problems from decision theory may be solved using such a simple kind of mathematics, I could use myself, but can you give me a simple and intuitive example where this formalism can be applied?"

–"Let me think. Perhaps the simplest example, but not banal nevertheless, would be the following one. Ewing family has just bought a new piece of land in a region rich in oil. The lands in the region may be classified in four categories. These categories are the possible states of nature. Thus, θ_1: 'very rich well', which means that it provides on average 500 000-barrel oil; θ_2: 'rich well', providing on average 200 000-barrel oil; θ_3: 'poor well', providing on average 50 000-barrel oil; θ_4: 'dry well'. Taking into account what happened with other lands in the region, where drilling was performed, 10%, 15%, 25%, and 50% of them proved to be 'very rich', 'rich', 'poor', and 'dry', respectively. This gives the prior probability distribution on the set of possible states of nature.

The possible actions open to Ewing family are: a_1: 'drill for oil', knowing that the profit per barrel is \$1.50 and the cost of drilling is, let's say \$100 000 for a producing well and \$75 000 for a dry well; a_2: 'unconditionally lease the land to an independent driller for a fixed amount of money, let's say \$45 000; a_3: 'conditionally lease the land to in independent driller with a profit of \$0.50 per barrel if the well proves to be very rich or rich, and nothing if the well proves to be poor or dry.

From these data values, we can calculate the loss function in an elementary way. The loss $\ell(a_i, \theta_j)$ corresponding to the action a_i and state of nature θ_j is the corresponding cost of drilling minus the corresponding profit. For instance, $\ell(a_1, \theta_1) = 100000 - (500000)(1.5) = -650000$. By a similar computation we get $\ell(a_1, \theta_2) = -200000$, $\ell(a_1, \theta_3) = 25000$, $\ell(a_1, \theta_4) = 75000$, whereas, for action a_2 we get: $\ell(a_2, \theta_j) = -45000$, for $(j = 1, 2, 3, 4)$, and, finally, for action a_3, we have: $\ell(a_3, \theta_1) = -250000$, $\ell(a_3, \theta_2) = -100000$, and $\ell(a_3, \theta_j) = 0$, for $(j = 3, 4)$.

The auxiliary experiment, provided by a certain company, consists of taking seismic records. Such a seismic record doesn't tell us whether or not there is oil but describes what kind of geological structure is underground, as an indirect indicator of the presence of oil. The possible outcomes are: x_1: 'very favourable geological structure'; x_2: 'favourable geological structure'; x_3: 'relatively unfavourable geological structure'; x_4: 'unfavourable geological structure'. The cost of the auxiliary experiment is \$12 000, whatever the outcome is.

The company specialized in taking seismic records makes available the results obtained from its past experience. Thus, out of 12 cases when the well proved to be very rich after drilling, 7 times the seismic records taken before drilling showed a very favourable geological structure, 4 times showed a favourable geological structure, and once showed a relatively unfavourable geological structure. Thus, $P(x_i \mid \theta_1)$ had the values $7/12$, $4/12$, $1/12$, $0/12$ for $i = 1, 2, 3, 4$, respectively. Similarly, $P(x_i \mid \theta_2)$ had the values $9/16$, $3/16$, $2/16$, $2/16$; $P(x_i \mid \theta_3)$ had the values $11/24$, $6/24$, $3/24$, $4/24$; and $P(x_i \mid \theta_4)$ had the values $9/48$, $13/48$, $15/48$, $11/48$; for $i = 1, 2, 3, 4$, respectively.

Applying Bayes's formula, we calculate the retrodiction matrix and applying the general formalism, which requires a lot of elementary computations, we get that the value of the auxiliary experiment is positive, in fact it is quite large, namely $V = 14\ 734$, and a_1, 'drill for oil', is the optimum action for Ewing family if the outcome of the auxiliary experiment is x_1 or x_2, whereas a_2, 'unconditionally lease the land to an independent driller', is the optimum action if the outcome is x_3 or x_4. This example was given by Hillier and Liebermann."

−"This is not an easy example and seems to be a very serious application. Who was Bayes?"

−"Thomas Bayes, born in 1702, was a minister from a small town in England, whose name I cannot remember now, who introduced the formula for calculating the posterior probability distribution in a paper with a romantic title, *An essay towards solving a problem in the doctrine of chances*. He was afraid to publish his paper. After he died, in 1761, a friend of his found the paper among Bayes's manuscripts and sent it to the Royal Society in London. The paper was published in 1763. Bayes's formula was refined by Pierre-Simon Marquis de Laplace in his famous book on probability theory, at the beginning of 19th century, and has become intensively used since then."

−"Why was he afraid to publish a paper that later proved to be so important? This is very weird."

−"How should I know? I am tempted to say that perhaps because he realized that accepting his formula it was like imposing a rule about how to reason. Those specialists who use Bayes's formula for calculating the posterior probability distribution on the set of states of nature conditioned by the outcomes of an auxiliary experiment, from the prior probability distribution of the states of nature and the prediction probability distribution of the outcomes of the auxiliary experiment conditioned by the states of nature, are embracing the so called Bayesian viewpoint.

Today, due to its generality, Bayes's formula is currently used in many applications. Thus, in pattern-recognition, for instance, the states of nature could be possible diseases and the outcomes are possible results of some test performed in a medical laboratory. The prior probability distribution is the relative frequency distribution of the respective diseases and the prediction matrix contains the probability distribution of the results of the tests when the disease is known. From these data, Bayes's formula allows us to calculate the retrodiction matrix, containing the posterior probability distribution of the possible diseases when the result of the test is known.

Another application of Bayes's formula is in criminology, where the possible states of nature are the suspects in a criminal investigation, the prior probability distribution reflects our prior credibility about their culpability – if we have no reason to discriminate among the suspects we start from the prior uniform probability distribution – and the auxiliary experiment consists in looking for evidence. The prediction matrix contains the probability distribution of different kinds of evidence assuming that each of the suspects, one by one, could be the culprit. Bayes's formula allows us to calculate the posterior credibility about the culpability of each suspect if a certain piece of evidence has indeed been found. Maybe Thomas Bayes realized that his formula could be used by judges and didn't want to see anybody sent to jail as the result of its application. Of course, I am joking."

PATTERN-RECOGNITION

–"Do police, the sleuths, or judges apply such mathematical methods in their current jobs?"

–"I don't know about specific cases when they did but what I know is that many lawyers and criminologists have shown a real interest in learning more scientific investigation techniques. This is more important now when, due to more access to powerful computers and as the result of a larger international cooperation between police forces from different countries, there seems to be a large data base assembled about wanted criminals, which is made available.

In general, the application of different mathematical methods and techniques for solving real life problems raises many thorny questions. Obviously, there are many results in mathematics that are rigorously proved but have no applications to anything. Some mathematicians dealing with such 'pure' topics have no interest at all in any kind of application and are dealing with such topics just for their beauty. In fact, we listen to music, play chess, watch sports, see a mystery movie, or read a fiction book not because they would help us in solving practical problems. They simply make our life more enjoyable. Thinking for the sake of thinking is challenging and highly rewarding for us, as individuals.

There are other mathematicians who obtain new results in 'pure' mathematics but they hope that, one day, what they do could prove useful for solving real life problems or could have applications in other sciences.

Finally, there are those who are interested only in applied topics, algorithms, methods, or techniques. They look at mathematics as being a powerful tool. When somebody asked Carl Friedrich Gauss what was his opinion about the last Fermat's theorem, it is said that he answered back that he had many problems of the same kind but had no time to deal with them. He was much more interested in getting a formula for measuring the curvature of a surface or in applying the least squares method for tracing the trajectory of an invisible comet.

Today, society is very anxious to use more advanced mathematics for solving practical problems. The major banks, for instance, hire more highly educated mathematicians for discovering trends and periodicity under the inevitable random fluctuations in the evolution of the stock market. More and more companies need statisticians and system analysts for coping with large data sets about supply and demand, for maximizing the profits, and minimizing the costs. There is room, however, for more mathematical applications to be tested and for more companies to do this.

To give you only one example, there are some very good pattern-recognition algorithms that could be used in medical diagnosis. One such algorithm is the so-called entropic algorithm. It was introduced in 1962, independently, by P.M. Lewis in the United States and L.N. Landa in the former Soviet Union. Remarkably enough, Landa published his paper in a journal of psychology and applied the algorithm to the classification of sentences in the Russian syntax. The entropic algorithm, more refined since 1962, proved to have a much wider domain of applicability. The entities from any field are defined by the values, numerical or qualitative, of some characteristics, by using the operations of classic logic, namely the conjunction 'and', the nonexclusive disjunction 'or', and the negation 'non'. Between some values of some characteristics we can have incompatibility. The problem is to determine which characteristics to check, and in which order, for identifying an unknown entity which, however, does belong to the class of possible entities under consideration. There is a prior probability distribution available on the set of possible entities.

In order to make everything more concrete, think about a class of diseases, as entities, like kidney diseases for instance, a set of different corresponding symptoms or test results, as characteristics, and a frequency distribution of the possible diseases in a certain region or country, as the prior probability distribution. Using the very intuitive boolean algebra and simple rules from probability calculus, the entropic algorithm finds the characteristic which should be observed and measured first in order to remove the maximum uncertainty on the set of available entities. Depending essentially on the value obtained for this 'optimum' characteristic, the algorithm is looking for the next characteristic that removes the maximum amount of uncertainty on those entities still remained possible, and so on, until the entire uncertainty is removed and a final corresponding entity is identified. Strangely enough, in everyday practice the characteristics are considered to be independent and all of them are examined until the respective entity is identified looking into the entire set of values obtained for all the characteristics. The entropic algorithm reveals, however, that the characteristics are practically never independent and finding the next characteristic to be examined essentially depends on the results obtained by measuring the previous, more important, characteristics. The algorithm gives a decision tree, covering all possible scenarios. When we examine one particular case, we follow only one path in this decision tree which ends up with the final entity possible. The funny thing is that it is almost never necessary to examine all the characteristics on every path of the tree. Very often, there are cases when the corresponding path contains very few essential characteristics to be examined for identifying the corresponding entity."

–"You seem to put a lot of passion in talking about this algorithm."

–"It could be so. In fact I found out about the algorithm from a professor of psychology who had come across Landa's paper and couldn't understand it. I was very young at that time and I was asked by one of my PhD supervisors to look into Landa's paper and explain it to the psychologist who happened to be the wife of an important person, namely the ministry of agriculture. She always sent a chauffeur to bring me to their fancy house. I tried my best, but I am afraid that my efforts remained useless to the psychologist lady, otherwise a good specialist in her own field of research, because she had no mathematical background at all. All she did was to write a beautiful poem, entitled *Entropy*, at the end of our meetings, later published in a literary journal. All the profit was mine because this was how I found out about this beautiful algorithm and because, at the end, the husband sent the chauffeur to my flat with a box full with twenty bottles of different brands of superb wine you cannot find in any regular shop.

As a matter-of-fact, for me this entropic pattern-recognition algorithm was the first contact to what is called today artificial intelligence. It tries to do analytically what the human intellect has been doing for a long time, as a result of evolution. It is often said that 'repetition is the mother of learning'. But why are we doing something better and faster after many repetitions? Why could the trial-and-error strategy be successful in the end? Indeed, during the learning process a subject realizes relatively fast that some steps are useless and should not be done. An intelligent subject, however, farther realizes that even among useful steps some are more important than the other ones and, in the end, learns to speed up the recognition process focusing on the optimum steps only. Learning to do things in an optimum way and therefore faster, is an important quality of the human intellect. We cannot explain, or better said, I cannot explain how the brain is doing that. The entropic algorithm of pattern-recognition, using the new measures of absolute uncertainty and conditional uncertainty, tries to reproduce just what the human intellect does. At least a little part of what our brain is capable of doing. It is necessary to implement a kind of learning process in the new generation of computers because in spite of the tremendous increase in speed and memory capacity, the enormous amount of data requires more discrimination between what is relevant and what is not and, among the relevant stuff, between what is more essential and what is less essential."

RELIABILITY

–"How do you have time to teach all this material in one course?"

–"Not everything I have just mentioned belongs to the syllabus of my course. I don't teach about the entropic algorithm of pattern-recognition, for instance. Instead, there are two other chapters included, namely reliability theory and queueing theory.

How reliable is a system is a natural question because there are systems everywhere. A system consists of subsystems joined in series or in parallel. The elementary subsystems of a system are called components. A series system functions properly if and only if each of its components functions properly; it fails to function properly if at least one of its components fails to function properly. A parallel system fails to function properly if and only if all its components fail to function properly; it functions properly if at least one of its components functions properly. Finally, if k is an integer between 1 and n, a k-out-of-n system functions properly if at least k of its n components function properly. Obviously, a parallel system is an 1-out-of-n system, whereas a series system is an n-out-of-n system.

The funny thing is that only two kinds of subsets of components prove to be essential in any system, namely the minimal paths and the minimal cuts. A minimal path is a minimal subset of components whose proper functioning induces the proper functioning of the entire system. A minimal cut is a minimal subset of components whose failure induces the failure of the entire system. I find simply amazing that any system may be viewed as being either a parallel connection of its minimal paths, or a series connection of its minimal cuts. Inside a minimal path the components are joined in series; inside a minimal cut the components are joined in parallel. A system generally has several minimal paths and several minimal cuts. A system could function properly even when some of its components fail. One properly functioning minimal path is enough for the system to function but if one of its minimal cuts fails, the entire system collapses.

Reliability of a system at time t is the probability that the system is still alive, or functions properly, at time t. Different probability distributions for the life-time of the systems are considered and the temporal variation of the instantaneous failure rate plays an important role. The instantaneous failure rate at a given time t is the probability of dying at time t, or, equivalently, the proportion of similar systems that fail to function properly or die at that time t.

One of the main results in reliability theory is that if we know the behaviour of the instantaneous failure rate, then we can determine both the probability distribution of the life-time of the system and the reliability of the system. Thus, if the instantaneous failure rate is constant, then the life-time of the corresponding system is exponentially distributed. If the instantaneous failure rate is a polynomial function of time, then the life-time of the corresponding system is Weibull distributed. These probability distributions allow us to calculate the probability that the respective system will be still alive at a given time or will die before a given time. Obviously, the main applications are in actuarial science and the results of reliability theory are bread and butter for the insurance companies."

QUEUEING THEORY

–"I think that I would like more to do applied mathematics than pure mathematics. For me, it is always important to deal with intuitive and well-motivated problems from real life. I don't think that my brain is suitable for abstract speculations. But you mentioned one more chapter in your operations research course."

–"As far as queueing theory is concerned, it shows how to build probabilistic models for complex systems where customers arrive randomly, at a constant or variable mean rate, they form or join a queue, waiting to be served, the waiting customers are served, at a constant or variable rate, and the served customers leave the system. There are queueing systems everywhere. A customer is generally a person but could also be an item which is manufactured, or a car to be repaired. A server is generally a person, or a group of persons acting as a team, but could also be a machine. Shopping for food, banking, a barber-shop, an airport, a typing pool, an assembly line, are all queueing systems.

What makes this theory interesting and difficult is the fact that there are several kinds of randomness to take into account: the number of arrivals during a certain time-interval is a discrete random variable, the inter-arrival time between consecutive arriving customers is a continuous random variable, and the service time is also a continuous random variable. The only information we can rely on in building a probabilistic model for what is going on inside a queueing system is the mean arrival rate, and the mean service rate. These mean values are either constant or vary in a relatively simple way.

Normally, the queue discipline is FIFO, meaning 'first in first out', but could also be LIFO, meaning 'last in first out', which happens when we use an elevator to move between the different levels of a building, for instance. We can also have a random selection as well as a preferential selection of the waiting customers for service."

–"Like what happens when an armed bank robber asks for money and the teller has nothing to do but serve him first!"

–"Right. The only stability assumed by queueing theory is at the level of the mean arrival rate, which is the expected number of customers arriving per unit time, and at the level of the mean service rate, which is the expected number of customers served per unit time. The mean arrival rate and/or the mean service rate per busy server may be constant or may depend on how many customers are already in the system. For big queueing systems the mean arrival rate and mean service rate per busy server are constant. It happens, however, that sometimes fewer customers are tempted to enter a crowded queueing system. On the other hand, the servers sometimes speed up service when more customers are waiting for service.

The input, represented by arrivals, is connected with the output, represented by service completion, by assuming that 'the rate-in is equal to the rate-out', which means that the mean rate (expected number of occurrences per unit time) at which entering incidents occur is equal to the mean rate at which leaving incidents occur. This is a dynamic equilibrium, at the level of the mean values, between the input and the output. This 'rate-in is equal to rate-out' assumption characterizes a queueing system in a steady-state condition.

Very often, the interarrival time and the service time are exponentially distributed with the parameters determined by the mean arrival rate and mean service rate, respectively. Such models work because, as we know today from information theory, the exponential distribution is the most uncertain, or unbiased, probability distribution of a positive random variable about which we know only its mean value, as it happens in queueing theory, where both the interarrival time and the service time are nonnegative random variables and the only information available is provided by the mean interarrival time $1/\lambda$, where λ is the mean arrival rate, and the mean service time $1/\mu$, where μ is the mean service rate per server, respectively. For such systems we can determine the expected number of customers in line, waiting to be served, the mean number of customers in the system, waiting to be served and being served, the number of arrivals in any given time interval, and the probability of waiting in line or in the system, more than a given time, less than a given time, or in between two arbitrary times."

STEADY-STATE CONDITION

–"Frankly speaking, I don't understand everything you are saying but I like to listen to, hoping that Hadamard, mentioned by you before, was right when he claimed that everything we hear or experience enters our unconscious level and is stored there, with chances to come up sometime later, at the subconscious and conscious levels of our brain, in a clearer and more structured way. Could you, however, be more specific about dynamic equilibrium a system could be in?"

–"Well, let's take a bathtub. If the tap is off and the sink is closed, then this system is in a static equilibrium, regardless whether there is or not a certain amount of water in the bathtub. If there is a certain amount of water in the bathtub and the tap is off but the sink is open, then the system is in a transient state, tending towards static equilibrium which is reached when all water goes out. Contrary, if the sink is closed but the tap is on, then the system is in a transient state also, until the system blows up when the water overflows. If the tap is on and the sink is open then the system is again in a transient state, when the input exceeds the output, tending to a catastrophic state, or when the output exceeds the input, tending to a static equilibrium, but could be in a state of dynamic equilibrium in the special case when the input is equal to the output."

–"This makes sense, indeed. An example always helps."

–"It could help, of course, but it could be misleading either. The example is clear and simple. But it simplifies too much. In fact a steady-state condition, or a dynamic equilibrium, doesn't mean that the input is exactly equal to the output, as the given example would suggest. In fact, a dynamic equilibrium is not rigid and allows random fluctuations at the input and random fluctuations at the output but requires that the average, or mean, input has to be equal to the average, or mean, output. Therefore, a system is in a steady-state condition when the dynamic equilibrium holds at the level of mean values, which is a much much less restrictive assumption. I should be tempted to call it statistical dynamic equilibrium."

–"Is the universe a big system in a steady-state condition?"

–"I don't know. There are people who say that it is. But some other theories claim that the universe, starting from a big-bang is still expanding. These things are often debated even in newspapers not only in specialized scientific journals. There is no clear cut contradiction between these two theories, apparently so opposite. Indeed, some people claim that the part of the universe we belong to, and can be observed by us, is expanding but another part of it, unaccessible to us, is contracting; the entire universe, consisting of the union of the observable part and unobservable part, is still in a statistical dynamic equilibrium. Finally, some other people claim that the universe, as a whole, is indeed expanding but this expansion phase will be followed by a contraction phase and this will alternate for ever, still allowing the universe to be a system in a global steady-state with respect to a much much longer period of time.

The expanding universe has some evidence in its support but opens more troubling questions about what was before the initial violent 'big-bang' beginning of the expansion and what is going to happen in the far future as a result of a continuous expansion. A unidirectional expansion means a one-sided evolution and we could worry about where it could go if the same trend continues indefinitely. On the other hand, a steady-state condition based on a statistical dynamic equilibrium explains in a relatively easier way the permanence of the universe and its dynamic stability. These are hypotheses that generate debates and are often related to belief.

In general, nature attempts to preserve the average. This is why we are still existing. Stability of the mean values. This seems to be all we can still count on because, somehow fortunately, our lives are not very long."

–"This reminds me of the joke about a talk given by an astronomer who, at a certain moment, mentioned the inevitable death of our sun in the distant future. At that point, a very troubled individual rose and, seriously disturbed, asked the speaker: 'Could you repeat please, when will the sun die?' The astronomer answered: 'About 1 000 000 years from now.' Giving a deep sigh of relief, the person who asked the question sat down saying: 'I was afraid that you had said 100 000 years!"'

–"That is a good one. Reality is that we long for stability. We, as a species, rely on stability, even if it manifests itself only at the level of mean values. Even if a particular winter proves to be colder than usual, we know that spring will come, however. There are random fluctuations everywhere but roughly, on average, we can somehow predict what is going to happen."

−"From what you have said lately, it results that the concept of probability seems to be very important. Still, from what you also said before, Newton was perhaps the greatest mathematician ever but he never used probability in his work. Isn't it strange that he felt no need to deal with probabilistic models?"

DETERMINISTIC AND PROBABILISTIC MODELS

−"Isaac Newton is mainly praised for his theory of universal gravity and for the creation of classical mechanics with celestial applications. At the level of big material bodies the strictly deterministic laws of motion are good enough to describe what is happening. When deviations were experimentally observed in the trajectories followed by planets or comets, they proved to be the result of the strictly deterministic interference with other celestial bodies whose presence had been ignored. Calculus and differential equations were just enough to deal with the strictly

deterministic motion of huge or big material bodies. There was no need for probability there.

But even there, some simplified models of reality had to be introduced. Thus, in many problems from classical mechanics dealing with the motion of one or several material bodies, there is a sentence which says something like 'the friction is ignored'. If it is not ignored, then a part of mechanical energy is transformed in heat, sometimes there is even an emission of light, and things become much more complicated, bringing thermodynamics into play, and so on. Often, we ignore some aspects, or consequences, to make the respective problem solvable. If we are excessively picky, we never end the study of the simplest phenomena.

Anyway, when we switch from big bodies to the molecules of a gas, for instance, we cannot follow the trajectory of each molecule and we have to describe the behaviour of the gas only statistically. In such a case, we make use of the concept of probability for describing the evolution of a gas simply because we don't know how to cope with the deterministic behaviour of each of the molecules of the gas and the collisions between them. Well, we could say that for a superhuman, capable of examining and predicting the evolution of each molecule of the gas, probability wouldn't be necessary as it is for us, the normal humans.

But, if we go deeper into the structure of matter, quantum mechanics teaches us that the evolution of the electrons inside the atom may be described only in a probabilistic way. The use of the concept of probability is not a consequence of 'lack of detailed knowledge' but just the only language that can describe the essentially random behaviour of the electrons.

Therefore, we cope with perfect order at the megascopic level, where the celestial bodies evolve, order and disorder at the macroscopic level, where we reside, and random pictures of what could happen at the microscopic level.

At our macroscopic level, the probabilistic models are inevitable for describing what happens. Take the evolution of the stock market. The daily fluctuations have different causes that are not all known and certainly not under our control. Therefore, we can look at the stock market as being a collection of random variables at different instants of time, forming a so called time series or, better, a stochastic process. It is called a process because the respective random variables are not independent but correlated. Beyond the random fluctuations, we try to detect a trend, with, maybe, some kind of periodicity in it, and to predict, in probability, the future evolution of this sequence of random variables.

Not only the time evolution of the stock market may be described by a stochastic process. Long ago, around 1827, if I remember well, the botanist Robert Brown discovered the chaotic motion of the particles of pollen from plants fallen on the surface of a liquid. At the beginning, he believed that such a chaotic motion was specific to some special kinds of fine particles, when in fact it is the amplified result of the collisions between the molecules of the liquid, collisions that become even more evident when the temperature of the liquid is raised. Until he arrived to the right explanation, for a long time he pounded all sorts of substances and, strewing the powder so obtained on the surface of water, tried to see whether the respective particles experienced the same kind of chaotic motion. The legend says that he did the same thing even with the bone of a rare fossil sent to him from overseas by a good friend of his. This so-called Brownian motion may be described by a stochastic process with independent increments, whose dependent random variables are normally distributed with mean zero and standard deviation increasing in time. Such a stochastic process is similar to the movements of a drunk individual who moves randomly around a pole, with sudden and uncontrolled changes of direction, covering a larger area, as the time passes, but still remaining in the close vicinity around the respective pole."

A CAREER IN MATHEMATICS

–"You didn't mention anything about your own research."

–"As perhaps anybody else, when I look back to my original work I realize that some papers were of minor importance and shouldn't have been published. On the other hand, with some of the good papers, I had a difficult time to have them accepted for publication. Several times the reports written by different anonymous referees on the same paper proved to be contradictory, with opposite final recommendations about the publication of the respective manuscript. Generally, I don't mind if a journal is asking to resubmit a revised variant of a paper. This means that it is almost accepted and a second variant, incorporating suggestions made by referees, could be only better than the first variant. When a paper is rejected, however, and this comes after two or three years since its submission, it is really painful and discouraging, especially when the comments sent by referees, if any, are superficial. It does happen and it hurts.

The strangest thing occurred when I sent a very long manuscript to a very good international journal. After a long time, as almost always, I got a blunt rejection from the editor-in-chief, accompanied by a short and ambiguous report of one referee who, obviously, didn't like the paper. To my big surprise, approximately one month later, I got another letter from the same editor-in-chief who informed me that the same paper has been accepted for publication without any revision. I had to rush answering him that this was no longer possible because, after his initial rejection, I had submitted the paper to another journal, where it was eventually published.What bothered me most was that the editor-in-chief didn't find necessary to apologize or at least explain what happened."

–"You mentioned that there are papers you would have preferred not to have been published. A couple of days ago, when I visited the Vincent van Gogh Museum in Amsterdam, along with his beautifully coloured still lifes, portraits, self-portraits, and landscapes, painted in his unique style, using a myriad of small segments of paint, I saw some horrible, gray, and incoherent so-called paintings, from his 'dark' period. I am sure that van Gogh wouldn't be happy to see them displayed there. Going back to you, I am sure that there are some published papers you still like and find important. I think that this happens to everybody who does creative work."

–"Maybe, I don't know. But I am not van Gogh and I didn't create masterpieces in mathematics comparable, even vaguely, to what he did in painting. Trying to be as objective as I can, which is difficult when I have to examine what I did myself, I can only sketch a list of topics I worked on. The order of listing them is irrelevant.

(a) I should mention first the distribution of prime numbers. As I said several times before, it is generally accepted to denote by $\pi(x)$ the number of primes less than or equal to the real number x. As the 'prime number theorem' refers to how this function behaves when x increases indefinitely, I was more concerned to detect some kind of mathematical regularity in the apparently chaotic behaviour of the function $\pi(x)$ for values of x up to 10^{17}. Obviously, many great names tried the same thing along the years. Gauss's elementary function $x/\ln x$ is only a rough approximation of $\pi(x)$. A little better is Adrien-Marie Legendre's variant of it, namely, $x/(\ln x - 1.08366)$. As I told you before, Gauss's logarithmic integral $Li(x)$ is an excellent approximation of $\pi(x)$ and Riemann's function $R(x)$, which is the sum of an infinite series whose terms depend on Gauss's function $Li(x)$ and Möbius's function $\mu(n)$, is even better. Both of them, however, are not elementary functions. I showed first that a maximum entropy curve describes quite well the trend followed by the function $\pi(x)$.

I tried to generalize Gauss's approximation by using a finite sum of logarithmic integrals instead of an infinite series of logarithmic integrals weighted by values of Möbius's function as Riemann did. If $[x]$

denotes the largest integer not exceeding the real number x, like $[5.6] = 5$, for instance, then I took the approximation $\pi(x) \approx \int_2^x f(x, u)\, du$, where the function $f(x, u)$ is piece-wise logarithmic, defined to be equal to $1/([\log_2 x] \ln u)$, if $\ln 2 \leq \ln u \leq \ln x/[\log_2 x]$, and to $1/(k \ln u)$ if $\ln x/(k + 1) < \ln u \leq \ln x/k$, for $k = 1, \ldots, [\log_2 x] - 1$.

After dealing with all sorts of approximations, I was really shocked one early morning, when I got the impression that I have a new formula that gives the exact values of the mysterious function $\pi(x)$. This was the first and last time when the revelation came in that obscure and uncertain intermediary state between sleeping and awakening. I jumped from my bed, took a piece of paper, and I wrote it down. Here it is:

$$\pi(x) = -\sum_{k=1}^{[\log_2 x]} \mu(k) \sum_{n=2}^{[x^{1/k}]} \mu(n)\, \Omega(n)\, [x^{1/k}/n],$$

where $\mu(n)$ is Möbius's function, equal to 0, if n is divisible by a prime square, to 1 if n is a product of an even number of distinct primes, and to -1 if n is a product of an odd number of distinct primes, and where $\Omega(n)$ is the total number of prime factors of the integer n; for instance, as $252 = 2^2 \times 3^2 \times 7$, we have $\Omega(252) = 5$. I spent a lot of time in front of my computer to check this formula for different integer values of x, as far as I could. I published both the piece-wise logarithmic approximation of $\pi(x)$ and the exact formula for it. The paper has been cited in some journals but, till to this day, I don't really know whether it is obvious, whether somebody else got it before, or if there is some hidden pitfall somewhere. Anyway, the whole time spent on $\pi(x)$, gave me a lot of satisfaction to reveal some kind of order which may be detected beyond the apparently chaotic distribution of primes in the set of positive integers. But I am afraid that I have used too many symbols, which is a major sin of arrogant mathematicians.

(b) Avoiding to enter technical details again, I proved the uniqueness of a generalization of Shannon's entropy, $-\sum_i w_i\, p_i \log p_i$, when some qualitative weights $w_1, \ldots, w_n$ are assigned to the possible outcomes of a probabilistic experiment besides their occurrence probabilities $p_1, \ldots, p_n$. I used it in different applications where such weights have to be essentially taken into account.

(c) I proved the optimality of the generalized Landa-Lewis entropic pattern-recognition algorithm I talked about earlier.

(d) When I was very young, I got some results in the statistical mechanics of the systems that don't conserve their energy and I obtained a formula for the temporal evolution of the probability distribution on the possible states of such a system. I also proved that there is no contradiction between microscopic reversibility, which assumes that the time may be reversed in the differential equations that describe the evolution at the microscopic level, and macroscopic irreversibility expressed by the increase of the macroscopic entropy of close systems. I still like the short proof I got for Boltzmann's H-theorem, using tools from information theory.

(e) Much later, I brought as many arguments as I could for showing that the non-relativist quantum mechanics may be based on the optimization principle of minimum mean deviation from statistical equilibrium, using Karl Pearson's χ^2 indicator as measure of the mean deviation and the principle of maximum entropy to describe statistical equilibrium. I liked it because I strongly believe that there are always some optimization principles behind how nature operates. Applications of the mathematical formalism to quantum chemistry showed a good agreement with numerical experimental data. Chemists proved to be receptive to the probabilistic model of the atom I built, keeping Niels Bohr's orbits as mean orbits of the random motion of the electrons around the nucleus. The rigid planetary model suggested by Bohr, long ago, is certainly obsolete, but I was very happy to show that the concordance between the predictions of the probabilistic model of the atom in the ground state, compatible with the mean Bohr's orbits, and experimental results, showed that Niels Bohr was right after all, but only on average.

(f) A stochastic process, or time series, is a family of random variables $\{X(t)\}$, one assigned at each time t. In my PhD thesis I dealt with stochastic processes when time is a random variable itself.

(g) I published a series of papers on fuzzy sets with interdependent elements and a little book on the relative logic, a long time hobby of mine. The implicit motto of this book is that the problem with truth is its many varieties. The relative logic heavily depends on circumstances, time, and context.

(h) Finally, not so long ago, I gave a method for solving linear programs moving inside the feasible space, and not on its frontier as the standard methods do. As I mentioned before, Karmarkar had such an idea before. But I used an essentially different approach, a probabilistic one, following a step-by-step strategy based again on the minimization of Karl Pearson's chi-square indicator and the maximization of Shannon's entropy. I should try to work more on the very promising consequences of such a probabilistic approach, never used before in the strictly deterministic algebraic linear programming, as far as I know.

I think that I have to stop at this point. I cannot find other results worth mentioning in what I did. Perhaps I have already forgot some of my own papers, which is a clear indication that they are not important even for my relatively lower standards.

Reality is that, objectively speaking, all the results just mentioned have had a very little impact. Of course, I could think about me as being not understood, underrated, or just unlucky. By the way, Josiah Willard Gibbs, one of the first great scientists born in America, was an obscure individual, unknown even to his students, and became famous only after his death. His little book on statistical mechanics, a masterpiece, was published in 1902, the last year of his life. I am not even sure that he saw it published. Anyway, its major scientific impact came after his death. It has been reprinted many times since then. When our own research is practically ignored, we can still think about Gibbs and hope, perhaps in vain, that, who knows, maybe one day something from what we did will prove to be useful or even important. But this is an illusory, improbable dream. There are so many results published and, as Paul Erdös said, 'everybody writes, nobody reads anymore.' In fact, some do read but, unfortunately, not my own papers or books."

–"Are you happy about your career?"

–"Approaching the end of it, I would say no. I am not. When I was about eight years old, I read an Oriental story in which a genie asked a young man to choose between becoming famous or getting rich. I thought about it a long time and I decided that, if I had been offered such an alternative, I would have chosen both of them. Looking backwards into my life, I have to admit that I got neither of them. Maybe this was the punishment for greedily choosing both alternatives instead of only one, as required by the genie. Even if I cannot really complain about what fate has given me, there are always regrets about 'it would have been better if I had done this' and 'it would have been better if I hadn't done that'. Even Werner Heisenberg, the brilliant physicist who discovered his matrix version of quantum mechanics when he was only 24 years old and later became a Nobel Prize winner university professor in Germany and the United States, when he was asked whether he would do physics again if he started his career from scratch, he answered: 'No. I would rather do something else, perhaps biology.'

Anyway, I liked and still like doing mathematics and I had a comfortable life due to it. It took me a long time until I realized that it was possible to do mathematics while walking and not only sitting in front of a table using some paper and a pencil. And I have never been bored. There is always a mathematical problem to think about. Professionally, sometimes it was difficult. Teaching a certain course for the first time is very difficult. Doing research is also difficult sometimes. There is too much literature to read and too many mathematical journals to look into. Long long ago, mathematicians exchanged letters to keep informed about new results or open problems. Thus, they could focus on some special topics, think about for a long time, and polish their own results. Remember Pierre de Fermat who had an easy job for living and had enough spare time to do mathematics for his own pleasure. Today, there is too much information available. Too much information is almost as bad and confusing as no information at all. This is a paradox occurring when extremes meet. A lot of time is spent trying to keep pace with what has been already obtained, or to attend conferences for getting an insight into what is being done right now, which is sometimes important because publishing a paper normally takes a couple of years and, consequently, a newly published article already tells something about the past. Fortunately, the mathematicians know how to organize their conferences in nice places and thus, the time and money spent for attending them are not entirely wasted.

Looking into too many books and journals has also two different faces. On one side, you learn about new results and techniques that could help you in your own research. On the other side, your creativity is affected by what you read, becoming more biased and less original. Spending more time on reading and understanding what other people have done leave you with less time and energy for your own original work and ideas. Often, a very original contributor to the progress of mathematics knows less than his collaborators or even his students and is even ignorant about the progress made in other fields of mathematics. But in his or her own very specialized domain of research, he or she has gone deeper than anybody else and leaves durable original fingerprints, often bearing his or her name for ever.

Another drawback is the fact that even in mathematics, unfortunately, subjectively biased evaluations are frequent. In teaching, if many students are taking your optional course, the friends would say: 'Of course, because he is an excellent teacher', while the enemies would promptly notice: 'Of course, because the course is too easy and he gives high marks'. If very few students are taking your course, or many students drop it, the friends would say: 'Of course, because he teaches real stuff and is very demanding', while the enemies would argue: 'Of course, because he is a weak professor and the course is not interesting'.

The same opposite remarks could be made about the value of personal research. The people who decide about the acceptance for publication of a manuscript sent to a journal, or the committees chosen for deciding whether or not to grant money to a certain research project, are unknown to the author of the paper or to the author of the grant application. Some members of the decision body are sincere, and mean well but, inevitably, they have their own ideas about what is valuable and not. Some are correct people, want to do things right but have no time. Many of them belong to several committees or editorial boards and jump from one meeting to another one. When to find time for reading the material they have to decide upon? Finally, there are those strongly biased, and even vicious, who either postpone sending their evaluations or bluntly reject the paper or the proposal without trying to see any merit in it. It is always easier to reject and deny instead of taking responsibilities induced by accepting or favourably recommending something.

I am not talking about stealing ideas or forming gangs or cliques who decide what and who are important in a certain field or control what kind of mathematics should be promoted and published. In a written confession, Edwin Jaynes, the author of a seminal paper on the principle of maximum entropy, later cited several thousands times, bitterly mentioned that he had a lot of difficulties in having it eventually accepted for publication. One of the referees, in particular, was extremely critical and wrote a caustic negative report about the manuscript, asking for its rejection. According to Jaynes, he posted a magnified copy of this negative report on the wall in his office, to show it to young people and prevent them from becoming depressed and discouraged when their manuscripts or projects are rejected by scientific journals or selection committees, respectively.

Even if mathematicians are generally reclusive and focused on their own research, it is not uncommon to have trouble makers or bossy people in a math department, who want to get control on what is going on there, like some bad and corrupt sheriffs in western movies. I have also seen cases when a new academic position is advertised in several journals, to play by the rules of ethics and objectivity, but the job was given to somebody chosen beforehand. Or, even more frequent cases when the selection committee takes hiring decisions exclusively based on the recommendation letters, without even looking into the publications of the candidates. Getting a strong recommendation letter from a big name in the field often proves much more important than what the candidate has produced or really is himself or herself. Affirmative actions, of all sorts, still applied in hiring academic people in many places, were meant to correct real or imaginary past injustices, but they simply make new actual injustices. I sincerely believe that new affirmative actions to counteract present affirmative actions are needed. And if we go on this way, a real fairness will never be achieved. Correcting real, potential, or imaginary past injustices by doing other injustices is never a solution for getting an ideal, injustice-free society.

I don't want to speak either about the immense ego some mathematicians have, believing that only their opinions, theories, and papers are really important. And, strangely enough, they look normal. In spite of all this, I have met many mathematicians of different races, nationalities, and ages for which I have had a tremendous respect and admiration for their professional and human qualities.

Looking back, I remember an old associate professor who had serious hearing difficulties and once remained lecturing without any of his few students, who gradually had sheepishly left the lecture hall. When a colleague of his, opening the door and seeing him talking and writing on the blackboard, stopped him and told him that nobody was there, he calmly answered: 'I know, but I wanted to finish the proof because it is so beautiful.'

I cannot forget also how proud and happy a little man was when he graduated in mathematics a couple of days after his 80th birthday anniversary. After his retirement, he just wanted to study mathematics for the beauty of it. Not many of our regular students have this motivation on their minds. The majority just want a degree for getting a job. It is fully understandable but I still would like to see more young and senior students who just want to study this beautiful science as a pure intellectual adventure.

Talking about regrets, at the same time, I am not proud of all my own decisions, actions, and reactions that occurred along all these years. The tragedy is that you mainly remember what you did wrong or improperly, living a lot of regrets in your conscience. The good deeds cannot cancel or erase the regrettable ones. This somehow reminds me of a Japanese story about a mother who knocked a nail in the door after each bad deed of her son. After a couple of years, when the door was full of nails, the son, full of remorses, changed for the better and asked his mother to remove a nail after each of his good deeds. When the last nail was finally removed, the son said: 'Look, mother! There are no nails left in the door!' 'This is true', his mother replied, 'but the holes have remained.' I find this story to be very sad but, unfortunately, it is very true. The holes and even some nails are still there in our own doors."

After our very long talk, we parted our ways, John to the hotel, to prepare his luggage, and I to my tent, to dispose of my hiking equipment and refresh a little myself. Before leaving, I promised John to meet him later at the bus station, in front of the post office, to say good bye.

When I went back to the camping site, I saw a group of people in a high level of excitement and agitation, near my own tent. When I arrived there, I realized that the family from the neighbouring tent had a problem. The father went crazy, shouting uncontrollably:

–"Mitzi is missing! Mitzi is missing! My God, what am I going to do? What am I going to do? Mitzi is missing! And my wife has fainted!"

I thought that Mitzi should be some cat or a little puppy dog, because there were many around in the camping, but I found out soon that Mitzi was their ten years old daughter. The desperate father, trying to regain his composure, begged me:

– "Please, young man, help us to find her!"

– "There is no reason to panic," I said. "There are no wild animals or strange people around. She should be somewhere here. Maybe she is playing hide-and-seek with some other children."

Frankly, I would have been more worried if Mitzi's little brother, about four years old, had played alone near one of the torrents but, apparently, all mother's care focused on supervising the energetic little boy, leaving more room to breath to Mitzi, who seemed to be more of a quiet and obedient type of girl.

We started our search by looking around, rapidly inspecting some closer tents, but with no positive results. I put my knapsack down and together with Mitzi's father, who spoke an acceptable English with a heavy German accent, asked ourselves what the hell to further do and where to go from here? Then, suddenly, I had a stroke of genius coming over me. I instantly remembered that, one day, I saw Mitzi picking up flowers. A lot of them. I even wanted to tell her to stop picking up so many, but I gave up because I knew from Toronto that it wasn't a good strategy to patronize children these days because you could easily be accused of child molestation by hysterical parents. On the other hand, I remembered from the walk along the semicircle around the camping area, taken with John on the day of my arrival here, that the most blue flowers from the gentian and anemone families in the vicinity were around the marked indicator where the ascent to the Refuge Dolent started. Let's go there first, I said to myself. Confused, Mitzi's father was willing to comply with any suggestion about where to go.

To make the story short, luckily, my hypothesis proved to be correct. When we found her in dense bushes, not far from the derivation to the Refuge, she was talking to some plants. But it took us a longer time to find her than expected. At the end of the successful search, the parents wanted to show their gratitude, inviting me to their tent and insisting to drink from a large bottle containing a strong plum brandy, ceremoniously opened by Mitzi's father. Risking to be rude, I took only a small sip and I ran, as fast as I could, to the post office, hoping that the last bus of the day to Orsières would arrive from Ferret with a slight delay. Unfortunately, I do suspect that it arrived even a little earlier than scheduled. All in all, there was nobody around. I felt a deep, deep sadness inside my heart. I really wanted to tell John good bye and thank him for a wonderful time. Then, I noticed a white wrapped note, with the name Mike on it, pinned on the wooden door of the post office. I took it and opened it. Here is its content:

KV YCU TGCNA PKEG OGGVKPI AQW
CPF VCNMKPI YKVJ AQW. K YKUJ
AQW CNN VJG DGUV. CPF FQ PQV
HQTIGV, VJGTG KU CNYCAU C DNWG
UMA CDQXG VJG FCTM ENQWFU!
Caesar

Very sad about missing the 'Good bye' meeting with John and the last possibility of finding how to keep in touch with him in the future, I slowly went back to the camping site. At the entrance of my tent, another note was waiting for me, carefully stuck in the lock. In plain English, this time, the message was:

I have not forgotten about
your promise! Tomorrow morning
at 8, I will be in front of your tent
to take you with us. See you then.
Good night! Sleep tight!
Francine

EPILOGUE

All this happened seven years ago. In the meantime, I went back to Canada and decided to become a professional mathematician. I got a Bachelor Degree in mathematics from York University in Toronto and a Master's Degree in mathematics from the University of Toronto. Now, I am enrolled in a PhD program in operations research at the Massachusetts Institute of Technology in Cambridge. It is not clear what kind of future is reserved for me, as a mathematician, but I like what I am doing.

I tried hard to find John and resume our dialogue that had such a big impact on me. Now, I could be a relatively competent partner in discussing about mathematics whereas, back then, I rather played the role of stupid Dr. Watson or Captain Hastings as opposed to Sherlock Holmes and Hercule Poirot, respectively, played by John. At least, I made him speak. In the previous pages, I tried to reproduce, as accurately as possible, what he said during our short sejour in the beautiful surroundings of the village La Fouly. As my notes of what he said were briefly written in my tent, in the evening of each day spent together, I was afraid that I made mistakes, due to my lack of knowledge, or I misspelled proper names and mixed up dates. This is why I had to look for corrections into some references, listed at the end of the book. They may be useful to those who want to find much more about the history of mathematics. If, however, there are still mistakes and mathematical inaccuracies left in my pages, I am the only one to be blamed for them.

As I have just said, I tried to find John. I went to the Department of Mathematics at Victoria University in Manchester. Several members of the department spoke very highly on him but nobody really knew where he had gone after taking his retirement. I went even to La Fouly. The mountains, the glaciers, Hotel Edelweiss, and the camping site were still there, unchanged, ignoring the passage of time, but not John. I am tempted to believe that, maybe, he went somewhere in the Pyrenees, met Grothendieck and convinced him both to do mathematics again and that there are so many other good things to eat than the dandelion soup.

Sometimes, I am asking myself whether John really existed or was simply a spirit who descended from the Alps, revealed to me the beauty of mathematics, and went back on the snowy peaks. Strangely enough, he is not in any picture taken by me back then, though I remember catching him in the frame of some of them.

As for Francine, she moved to Toronto with me. Next year, she intends to graduate in fine arts at Boston University. She is desperate about my ignorance in the history of arts, my slow progress in learning Dutch, and my blunt refusal to try oil painting.

Bibliography

[1] Aczel A.D. (1996). *Fermat's Last Theorem.* Delta Book, Dell Publishing, New York.

[2] Albers, D. J. and Alexanderson, G.L. (eds.) (1985). *Mathematical People. Profiles and Interviews.* Contemporary Books, Chicago, New York.

[3] Aleksandrov, A.D., Kolmogorov, A.N., and Lavrentiev, M.A. (eds.) (1999). *Mathematics. Its Content, Methods, and Meaning.* Dover Publications, Inc., Mineola, New York. (The Russian original version was written in 1956).

[4] Bass, T.A. (1999). *The Predictors.* Henry Holt and Company, New York.

[5] Bell, E. T. (1986). *Men of Mathematics.* Simon and Schuster, New York.

[6] Berndt, B. C. and Rankin, R. A. (eds.) (2001). *Ramanujan: Essays and Surveys.* American Mathematical Society, Providence, RI; London Mathematical Society, London.

[7] Bourbaki, N. (1999). *Elements of the History of Mathematics.* Springer Verlag, Berlin-Heidelberg-New York.

[8] Brown, J. R. (1999) *Philosophy of Mathematics.* Routledge, London and New York.

[9] Bühler, W.K. (1981). *Gauss. A Biographical Study.* Springer-Verlag, Berlin, Heidelberg, New York.

343

[10] Campbell, D.M. and Higgins, J.C. (eds.) (1984). *Mathematics. People, Problems, Results.* Volumes I and II, Wadsworth International, Belmont, California.

[11] Casti, J.L. (2001). *Mathematical Mountaintops.* University Press, Oxford.

[12] Casti, J. L. and DePauli, W. (2000). *Gödel. A Life of Logic.* Perseus Publishing, Cambridge, Massachusetts.

[13] Cavaillès, J. (1962). *Philosophie Mathématique.* Hermann, Paris.

[14] Cliff, P. (1993). *The Haute Route Chamonix-Zermatt.* Cordee, Leicester, Great Britain.

[15] Dalmas, A. (1956). *Évariste Galois révolutionnaire et géomètre.* Fasquelle, Paris.

[16] Davis, P.J. and Hersh, R. (1981). *The Mathematical Experience.* Birkhäuser, Boston.

[17] Dieudonné, J. (1992). *Mathematics – The Music of Reason.* Springer-Verlag, Berlin-Heidelberg-New York.

[18] Dunham, W. (1999). *Euler. The Master of Us All.* The Mathematical Association of America, Washington, DC.

[19] Ekeland, I. (1988). *Mathematics and the Unexpected.* The University of Chicago Press, Chicago and London.

[20] Hadamard, J. (1954). *The Psychology of Invention in the Mathematical Field.* Dover Publications, New York.

[21] Hardy, G.H. (1940). *Ramanujan.* Cambridge University Press, Cambridge, UK.

[22] Hardy, G.H. (1967). *A Mathematician's Apology.* Cambridge University Press, Cambridge, U.K.

[23] Hilbert, D. (1971) *Foundations of Geometry.* Open Court Publishing Company, La Salle, Illinois. (Translated from the tenth German edition of Hilbert's *Grundlagen der Geometrie*, published by B.G. Teubner, Stuttgart).

[24] Hillier, F.S. and Lieberman, G.J. (1980). *Introduction to Operations Research.* Third Edition, Holden-Day, Inc., Oakland, California.

[25] Hoffman, P. (1998). *The Man Who Loved Only Numbers. The Story of Paul Erdös and the Search for Mathematical Truth.* Hyperion, New York.

[26] Kac, M. (1987). *Enigmas of Chance. An Autobiography.* University of California Press, Berkeley, Los Angeles, London.

[27] Kline, M. (1980). *Mathematics. The Loss of Certainty.* Oxford University Press, Oxford.

[28] MacHale, D. (1985). *George Boole. His Life and Work.* Boole Press, Dublin.

[29] Macrae, N. (1992). *John von Neumann.* Pantheon Books, New York.

[30] Nagel, E. and Newman, J. R. (1958). *Gödel's Proof.* New York University Press, New York.

[31] Odifredi, P. (2004). *The Mathematical Century.* Princeton University Press, Princeton and Oxford.

[32] Ore, O. (1957). *Niels Henrik Abel. Mathematician Extraordinary.* University of Minnesota Press, Minneapolis.

[33] Pappas, T. (1997). *Mathematical Scandals.* Wide World Publishing/Tetra, San Carlos, California.

[34] Péter, R. (1976). *Playing with Infinity.* Dover Publications, New York.

[35] Peterson, I. (1988). *The Mathematical Tourist. Snapshots of Modern Mathematics.* W.H. Freeman and Company, New York.

[36] Purcaru, I. and Bâscă, O. (1996). *Oameni, Idei, Fapte din Istoria Matematicii.* Editura Economică, Bucureşti.

[37] Reid, C. (1970). *Hilbert.* Springer-Verlag, New York-Heidelberg-Berlin.

[38] Reid, C. (1976). *Courant.* Springer-Verlag, New York-Heidelberg-Berlin.

[39] Reid, C. (1982). *Neyman – From Life.* Springer-Verlag, New York-Heidelberg-Berlin.

[40] Sabbagh, K. (2002). *The Riemann Hypothesis.* Farrar, Straus, and Giroux, New York.

[41] Seife C. (2000). *Zero: The Biography of a Dangerous Idea.* Viking, Penguin Putnam, Inc., New York.

[42] Singh S. (1997). *Fermat's Enigma.* Penguin Books, Toronto, New York.

[43] Steen, L. A. (ed.) (1980). *Mathematics Today.* Vintage Books, New York.

[44] Stewart, I. (1973). *Galois Theory.* Chapman and Hall, London, New York.

[45] Struik, D. J. (1987). *A Concise History of Mathematics.* Dover Publications, Mineola, New York.

[46] Tankard Jr., J. W. (1984). *The Statistical Pioneers.* Schenkman Publishing Company, Cambridge, Massachusetts.

[47] Watanabe, S. (1969). *Knowing and Guessing.* Wiley, New York.

Index